OC

MEDICINE

& HEALTH THROUGH TIME

Ian Dawson
Dale Banham
Peter Smith

HODDER EDUCATION
AN HACHETTE UK COMPANY

The Schools History Project

Set up in 1972 to bring new life to history for students aged 13–16, the Schools History Project continues to play an innovatory role in secondary history education. From the start, SHP aimed to show how good history has an important contribution to make to the education of a young person. It does this by creating courses and materials which both respect the importance of up-to-date, well-researched history and provide enjoyable learning experiences for students.

Since 1978 the Project has been based at Trinity and All Saints University College Leeds. It continues to support, inspire and challenge teachers through the annual conference, regional courses and website: http://www.schoolshistoryproject.org.uk. The Project is also closely involved with government bodies and awarding bodies in the planning of courses for Key Stage 3, GCSE and A level.

Note: The wording and sentence structure of some written sources have been adapted and simplified to make them accessible to all students, while faithfully preserving the sense of the orginal.

Memory map on p. 15, 196 courtesy of Hannah Mitcheson.

Orders: please contact Bookpoint Ltd, 130 Milton Park, Abingdon, Oxon OX14 4SB. Telephone: (44) 01235 827720. Fax: (44) 01235 400454. Lines are open 9.00–5.00, Monday to Saturday, with a 24-hour message answering service. Visit our website at www.hoddereducation.co.uk

First published in 2009 by
Hodder Education,
An Hachette UK Company
338 Euston Road
London NW1 3BH

Impression number 5 4 3 2 1
Year 2012 2011 2010 2009

Cover photo: akg-images
Illustrations by Dylan Gibson, Ian Foulis, Barking Dog, Janek Matysiak, Pat Murray, Peter Lubach, Richard Duszczak, Steve Smith, Tony Randell
Typeset in Palatino Light by Ian Foulis and Mark Walker
Printed and bound in Italy

A catalogue record for this title is available from the British Library

ISBN: 978 0340 985 069

Contents

Photo credits

The publishers would like to thank the following for permission to reproduce copyright material:

p.18 akg-images/ullstein bild; **p.19** (t) Private Collection/Peter Newark American Pictures/The Bridgeman Art Library; (bl) Wellcome Library, London, (br) Werner Forman Archive/Centennial Museum, Vancouver, British Columbia, Canada; **p.22** © Sandro Vannini/Corbis; **p.23** The Art Archive/Graeco-Roman Museum, Alexandria/Nicholas J. Saunders; **p.24** The Art Archive/Dagli Orti; **p.30** © The Trustees of the British Museum; **p.31** (l) © The Trustees of the British Museum, (r) Photograph: Rohrer, DAI Athen, Neg.D-DAI-ATH-Thera 110; **p.32** The Art Archive/National Archaeological Museum Athens/Dagli Orti; **p.33** akg-images/Erich Lessing; **p.34** Wellcome Library, London; **p.35** Museo della Civilta Romana, Rome, Italy/Giraudon/The Bridgeman Art Library; **p.36** The Art Archive/Anagni Cathedral Italy/Dagli Orti (A); **p.37** © Peter Smith; **p.40** The Oxford Archaeological Unit ltd.; **p.53** (t) By permission of the British Library (MS Egerton, f53), (bl) Topfoto/AP, (br) Rischgitz/Hulton Archive/Getty Images; **p.54** (l) Bodleian Library MS Rawlings B124f 197v Oxford, (r) Hulton Archive/Getty Images; **p.55** (t) akg-images, (c) Musee Conde, Chantilly, France/The Bridgeman Art Library; **p.59** geogphotos/Alamy; **p.64** Mary Evans Picture Library; **p.65** The Art Archive/Victoria and Albert Museum London/Eileen Tweedy; **p.67** The Art Archive/Bibliothèque Universitaire de Médecine, Montpellier/Dagli Orti; **p.68** (l) The Art Archive/University Library Prague/Dagli Orti, (r) The Art Archive/Bodleian Library Oxford/The Bodleian Library; **p.69** akg-images/British Library; **p.70** English Heritage Photo Library; **p.71** (l) The Art Archive/Bibliothèque Universitaire de Médecine, Montpellier/Dagli Orti, (r) Wellcome Library, London; **p.73** Trinity College, Cambridge, UK/The Bridgeman Art Library; **p.76** akg-images; **p.80** (l) Wellcome Library, London, (r) www.topfoto.co.uk; **p.81** (l) Fitzwilliam Museum, University of Cambridge, UK/The Bridgeman Art Library, (r) www.topfoto.co.uk; **p.88** Ann Ronan Picture Library/HIP/TopFoto; **p.90** Mary Evans Picture Library; **p.91** TopFoto.co.uk; **p.92** (c) The Art Archive/Marc Charmet, (l) Wellcome Library, London; **p.94** The Art Archive/Musée des Beaux Arts Orléans/Dagli Orti (A); **p.95** The Art Archive/Palazzo del Te Mantua/Dagli Orti (A); **p.96** (t) Wellcome Library, London, (b) © Charles Walker/TopFoto; **p.97** Wellcome Library, London; **p.98** Wellcome Library, London; **p.99** City of London/HIP/TopFoto; **p.110** Wellcome Library, London; **p.115** Wellcome Library, London; **p.116** The Art Archive/Private Collection/Eileen Tweedy; **p.124** (l and r) Paul Nadar/Getty Images, (c) Hulton Archive/Getty Images; **p.125** (l) Ann Ronan Picture Library/HIP/TopFoto, (c all) AP/Press Association, (r) © Bettmann/Corbis; **p.126** Wellcome Library, London; **p.127** Science Museum; **p.129** © Bettmann/Corbis; **p.130** Hulton Archive/Getty Images; **p.131** Hulton Archive/Getty Images; **p.132** (l) Chris Ware/Keystone Features/Getty Images, (r) © Bettmann/Corbis; **p.133** (t both) World History Archive/TopFoto, (b) © Hulton-Deutsch Collection/Corbis; **p.139** Alexander Fleming Laboratory Museum, St Mary's Hospital, London; **p.143** (t) The Art Archive/Science Museum London/Eileen Tweedy, (b) Museum of London/HIP/TopFoto; **p.144** © Punch Limited/TopFoto; **p.146** British Museum, London, UK/The Bridgeman Art Library; **p.147** Punch Limited/Topfoto; **p.151** Hulton Archive/Getty Images; **p.155** (t) Wellcome Library, London, (b) The Granger Collection/TopFoto; **p.156** HIP/TopFoto; **p.158** (tl) Courtesy of Newham Heritage and Archives Service, (tr) © Hulton-Deutsch Collection/Corbis, (c) Popperfoto/Getty Images, (b) Science Museum; **p.160** Wellcome Library, London; **p.162** (both) Mirrorpix; **p.166** Royal College of Surgeons, London, UK/The Bridgeman Art Library; **p.167** The Art Archive/British Museum/Eileen Tweedy; **p.171** Wellcome Library, London; **p.172** © Mary Evans Picture Library; **p.174** Hulton Archive/Getty Images; **p.183** (both) © Peter Smith; **p.184** Hulton Archive/Getty Images; **p.186** (l) Hulton Archive/Getty Images, (r) National Portrait Gallery/Getty Images; **p.188** Greater London Council, UK/The Bridgeman Art Library; **p.202** © Peter Smith.

Every effort has been made to trace all copyright holders, but if any have been inadvertently overlooked the Publishers will be pleased to make the necessary arrangements at the first opportunity.

Key features of Smarter History
Medicine through time

Before you start using this book here is a guide to help you get the most out of it.

Enquiries

The book is structured around a series of Enquiries, each one focussing on a key aspect of your GCSE course. Each Enquiry helps you understand a particular event, person or breakthrough and then links it to the broader history of medicine.

Banners introduce each Enquiry so you know exactly what you are focussing on from the start.

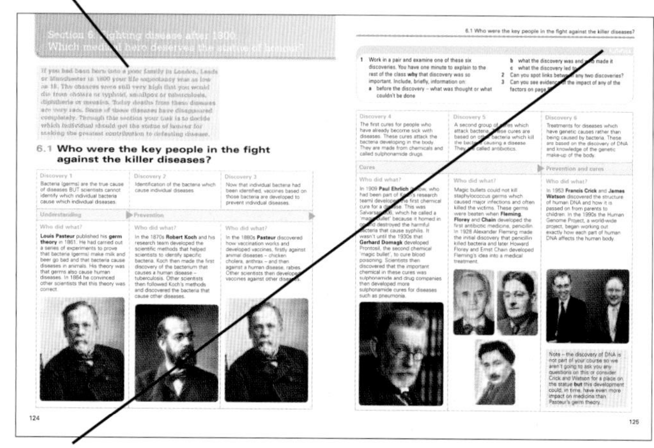

Activities guide you through the material so you build up your knowledge and understanding of the key content of your GCSE course. They also link into the on-going Smarter Revision activities.

Medical Moments in Time

These pages (e.g. pp.12–13) give you an overview of the key features of medicine at five important points in history – AD200, 1347, 1665, 1848 and 1935.

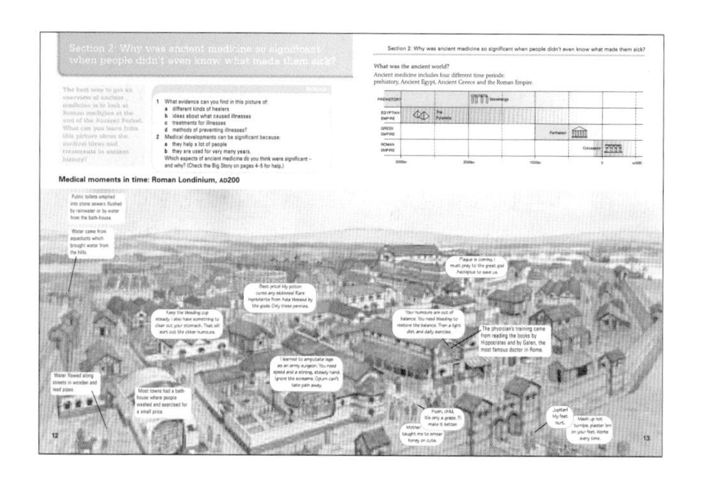

Smarter Revision

These pages help you prepare effectively for your examinations, showing you a variety of ways to build up your knowledge and understanding of the history of medicine. You will be building up your revision material from the very beginning of your course – not waiting until you have completed it. See page 11 for more details on Smarter Revision pages.

Smarter Revision pages give you clear advice on how to use each Smarter Revision strategy.

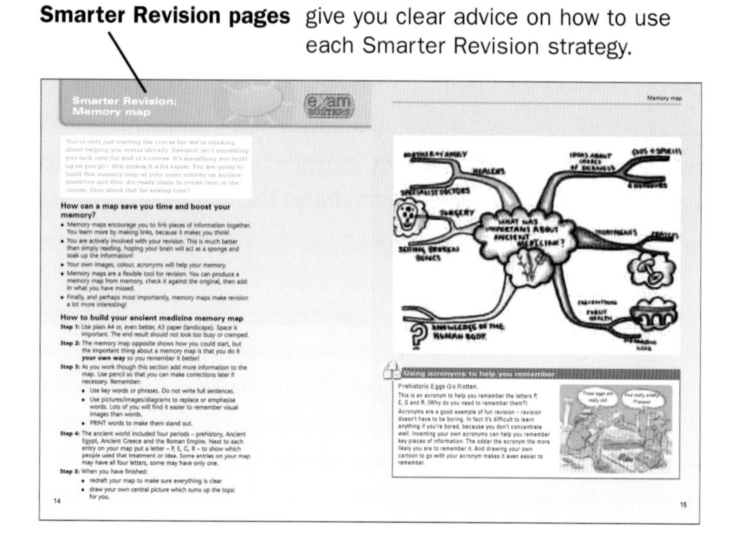

Meet the Examiner

These pages explain how to win high marks in your exams. They show you how to

- answer each type of question in your examinations
- identify exactly what a question is asking
- structure answers and develop the vocabulary to make full use of what you know.

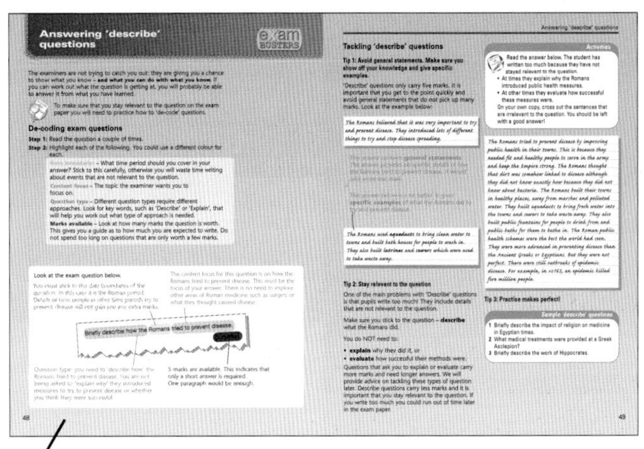

Answering 'describe' questions

exam BUSTERS

The examiners are not trying to catch you out: they are giving you a chance to show what you know – **and what you can do with what you know.** If you can work out what the question is getting at, you will probably be able to answer it from what you have learned.

To make sure that you stay relevant to the question on the exam paper you will need to practice how to 'de-code' questions.

De-coding exam questions

Step 1: Read the question a couple of times.

Step 2: Highlight each of the following. You could use a different colour for each.

Date boundaries – What time period should you cover in your answer? Stick to this carefully, otherwise you will waste time writing about events that are not relevant to the question.

Content focus – The topic the examiner wants you to focus on.

Question type – Different question types require different approaches. Look for key words, such as 'Describe' or 'Explain', that will help you work out what type of approach is needed.

Marks available – Look at how many marks the question is worth. This gives you a guide as to how much you are expected to write. Do not spend too long on questions that are only worth a few marks.

Look at the exam question below.

You must stick to the date boundaries of the question. In this case it is the Roman period. Details of how people in other time periods try to prevent disease will not gain you any extra marks.

The content focus for this question is on how the Romans tried to prevent disease. This must be the focus of your answer. There is no need to explore other areas of Roman medicine such as surgery or what they thought caused disease.

Briefly describe how the Romans tried to prevent disease.

Question type: you need to 'describe how' the Romans tried to prevent disease. You are not being asked to 'explain why' they introduced measures to try to prevent disease or whether you think they were successful.

5 marks are available. This indicates that only a short answer is required. One paragraph would be enough.

48

Answering 'describe' questions

Tackling 'describe' questions

Tip 1: Avoid general statements. Make sure you show off your knowledge and give specific examples.

'Describe' questions only carry five marks. It is important that you get to the point quickly and avoid general statements that do not pick up many marks. Look at the example below:

The Romans believed that it was very important to try and prevent disease. They introduced lots of different things to try and stop disease spreading.

*The Romans used **aqueducts** to bring clean water to towns and built bath houses for people to wash in. They also built **latrines** and **sewers** which were used to take waste away.*

Tip 2: Stay relevant to the question

One of the main problems with 'Describe' questions is that pupils write too much! They include details that are not relevant to the question.

Make sure you stick to the question – **describe** what the Romans did.

You do NOT need to:

- **explain** why they did it, or
- **evaluate** how successful their methods were.

Questions that ask you to explain or evaluate carry more marks and need longer answers. We will provide advice on tackling these types of question later. Describe questions carry less marks and it is important that you stay relevant to the question. If you write too much you could run out of time later in the exam paper.

Activities

Read the answer below. The student has written too much because they have not stayed relevant to the question.

- At times they explain why the Romans introduced public health measures.
- At other times they evaluate how successful these measures were.

On your own copy, cross out the sentences that are irrelevant to the question. You should be left with a good answer!

The Romans tried to prevent disease by improving public health in their towns. This is because they needed fit and healthy people to serve in the army and keep the Empire strong. The Romans thought that dirt was somehow linked to disease although they did not know exactly how because they did not know about bacteria. The Romans built their towns in healthy places, away from marshes and polluted water. They built aqueducts to bring fresh water into the towns and sewers to take waste away. They also built public fountains for people to drink from and public baths for them to bathe in. The Roman public health schemes were the best the world had seen. They were more advanced in preventing disease than the Ancient Greeks or Egyptians. But they were not perfect. There were still outbreaks of epidemic disease. For example, in AD165, an epidemic killed five million people.

Tip 3: Practise makes perfect!

Sample 'describe' questions

1 Briefly describe the impact of religion on medicine in Egyptian times.
2 What medical treatments were provided at a Greek Asclepion?
3 Briefly describe the work of Hippocrates.

49

Sample answers help you identify what makes a good answer.

Dynamic Learning CDs

Dynamic Learning CDs provide an extensive range of supporting resources. They feature:

- Enquiries developing your knowledge and understanding of key topics within each period
- Thematic investigations helping you understand the development of major themes across time
- Exambuster activities helping you revise and prepare effectively for examinations.

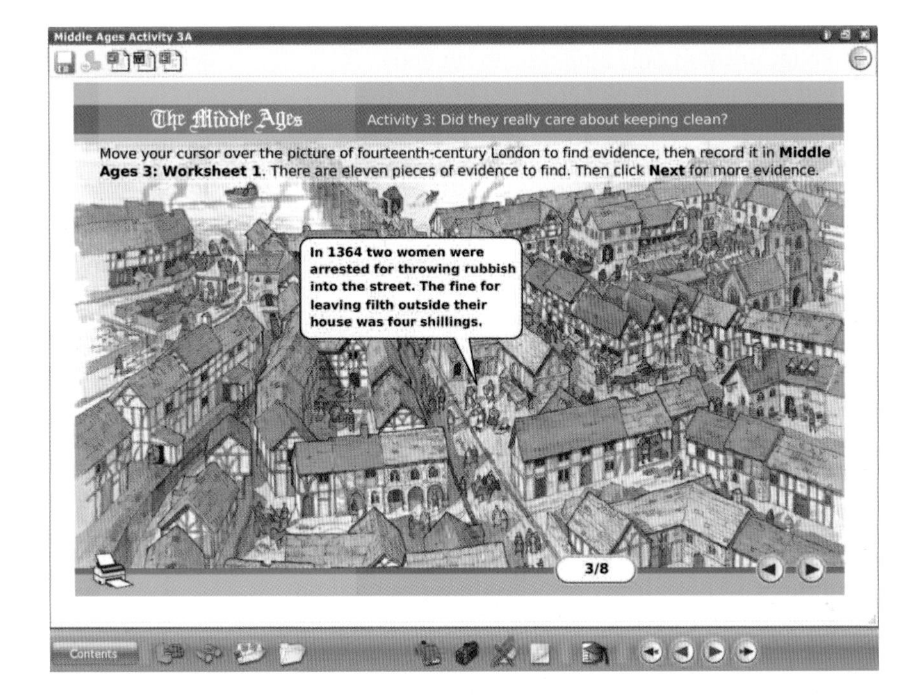

Section 1: The Big Story of medicine and health through time – what do you think happened when?

This section helps you build up an outline picture of the history of medicine in your mind and on paper. We'll start by getting you to think! Which period of history do you think each of the clues comes from?

Activities

The history of medicine can be surprising. Sometimes what seems to be a modern idea turns out to be thousands of years old. Sometimes a treatment we take for granted only began quite recently.
Read clues A–J. Think about what each one tells you about medical ideas or treatments. Then draw your own version of the timeline at the foot of these pages and pencil in each clue heading where you think it belongs on the timeline.

Clue A Treatments – Penicillin, the first antibiotic

'We had an enormous number of wounded with infections, terrible burn cases among the crews of armoured cars. The usual medicines had absolutely no effect. The last thing I tried was penicillin. The first man was a young man called Newton. He had been in bed for six months with fractures of both legs. His sheets were soaked with pus. Normally he would have died in a short time. I gave three injections of penicillin a day and studied the effects under a microscope. The thing seemed like a miracle. In ten days' time the leg was cured and in a month's time the young fellow was back on his feet. I had enough penicillin for ten cases. Nine were complete cures.'

Clue B Treatments – herbal medicine

'Medicine for dimness of the eyes: take the juice of the celandine plant, mix with bumblebees' honey, put in a brass container then warm until it is cooked and apply to the eyes.'

Clue C Explaining disease – the four humours

Hippocrates wrote: 'Man's body contains Four Humours – blood, phlegm, yellow bile and melancholy (black) bile. When all these humours are truly balanced, he feels the most perfect health. Illness occurs when there is too much or too little of one of these Humours or one is entirely thrown out of the body.'

Clue D Explaining disease – God sends diseases

'Terrible is God towards men. He sends plagues of disease and uses them to terrify and torment men and drive out their sins. That is why the realm of England is struck by plagues – because of the sins of the people.'

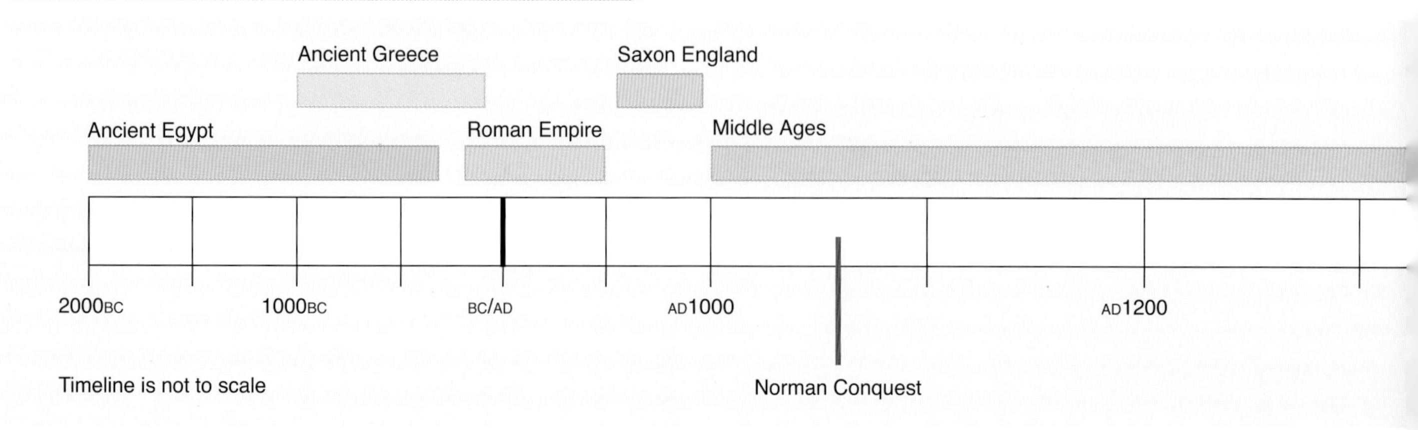

Clue E Public health – the NHS begins

'On the first day of free treatment on the NHS, Mother went and got tested for new glasses. Then she went further down the road to the chiropodist and had her feet done. Then she went back to the doctor's because she'd been having trouble with her ears and the doctor said he would fix her up with a hearing aid.'

Clue F Explaining disease – Pasteur and germ theory

Louis Pasteur, a French scientist, published his 'germ theory' suggesting that bacteria or 'germs' were the true cause of diseases. His germ theory replaced all previous ideas about the causes of disease.

Clue G Treatments – the black cat remedy

'The stye on my right eyelid was still swollen and inflamed very much. It is commonly said that rubbing the eyelid with the tail of a black cat will do it much good so, having a black cat, a little before dinner I tried it and very soon after dinner the swelling on my eyelid was much reduced and almost free of pain.'

Clue H Treatments – wash, exercise, diet

'Every day wash face and eyes with the purest water and clean the teeth using fine peppermint powder. Begin the day with a walk. Long walks before meals clear out the body, prepare it for receiving food and give it more power for digesting.'

Clue I Surgery – without anaesthetics

Robert Liston, a famous London surgeon, once amputated a man's leg in two and a half minutes but worked so fast he accidentally cut off his patient's testicles as well. During another high-speed operation Liston amputated the fingers of his assistant and slashed the coat of a spectator who, fearing he had been stabbed, dropped dead with fright. Both the assistant and the patient then died of infection caught during the operation or on the hospital ward. Liston worked really fast because there were no anaesthetics.

Clue J Public health – fresh water, baths and sewers

Sextus Julius Frontinus wrote: 'There was a great increase in the number of reservoirs, fountains and water-basins. As a result the air is purer. Water is now carried through the city to latrines, baths and houses.'

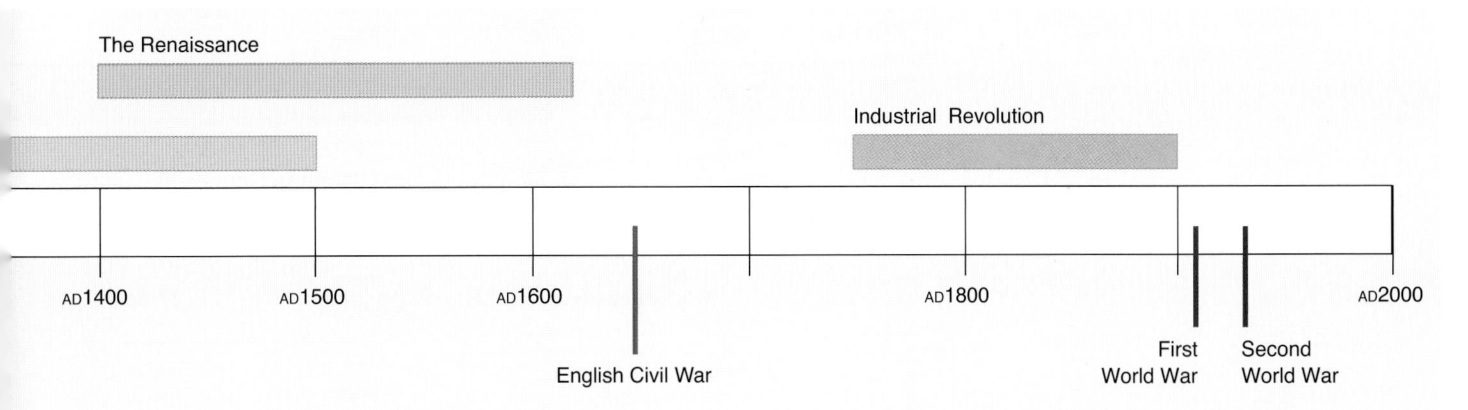

The Big Story of medicine and health through time

Activity

1 Work in a group of three. You have one minute to tell the outline story of medicine. Your story needs to answer the question: 'Why do people today have better health and live longer lives than people in the past?'

Spend ten minutes preparing your story. Include each of these words:

- continuity
- change
- turning point
- progress

2 One of the most important skills in history is asking questions.

a What questions do you want to ask to fill in the gaps in the story?

b Look at the blue and red lines on the graph. What questions do you want to ask about the shapes of these lines?

Information

Life expectancy

These graphs show the life expectancy of men and women throughout history. The life expectancy age is the average age that people lived to.

Until the 1900s around 20 per cent of babies died before their first birthday and this therefore reduced the average life expectancy.

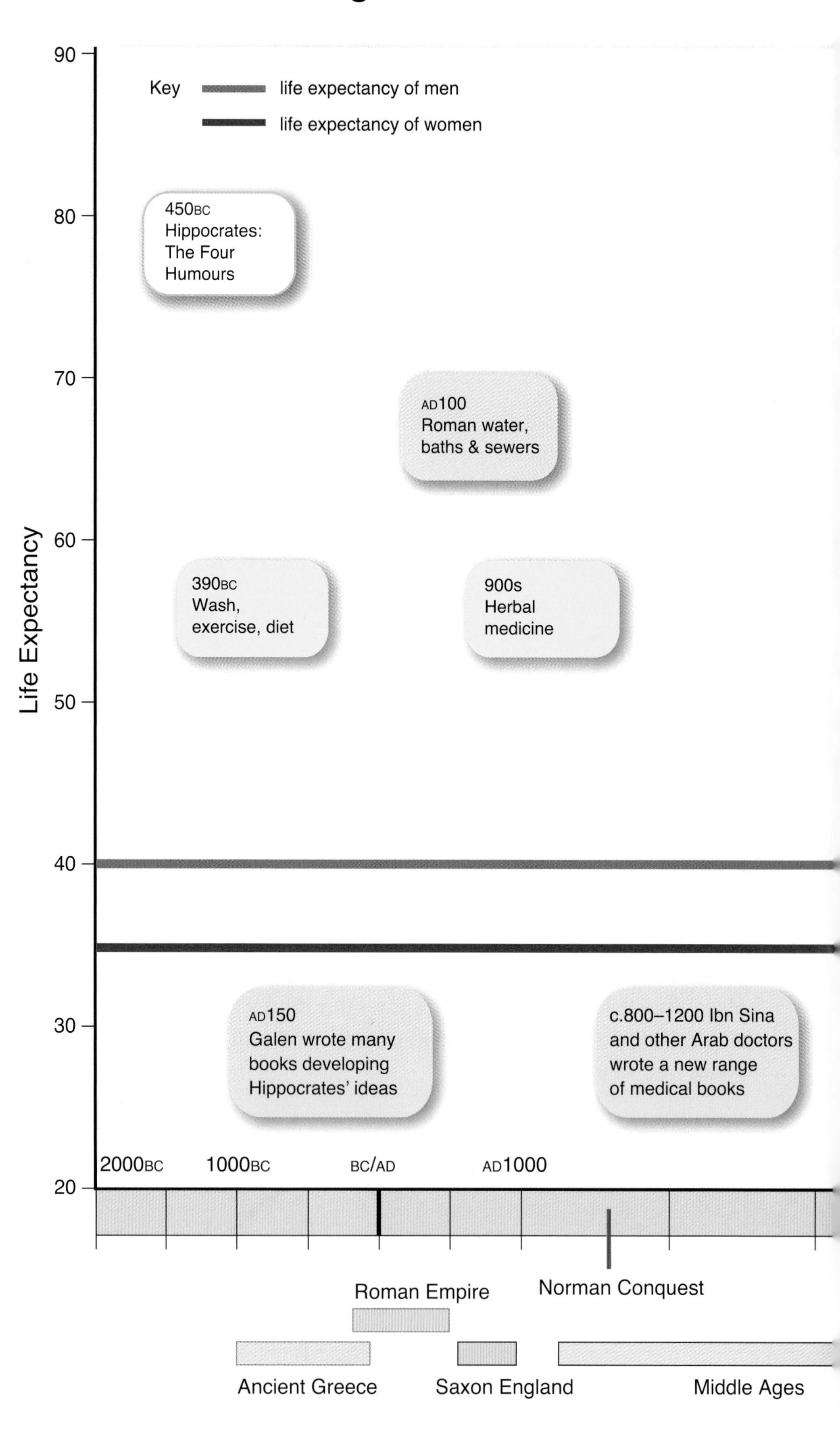

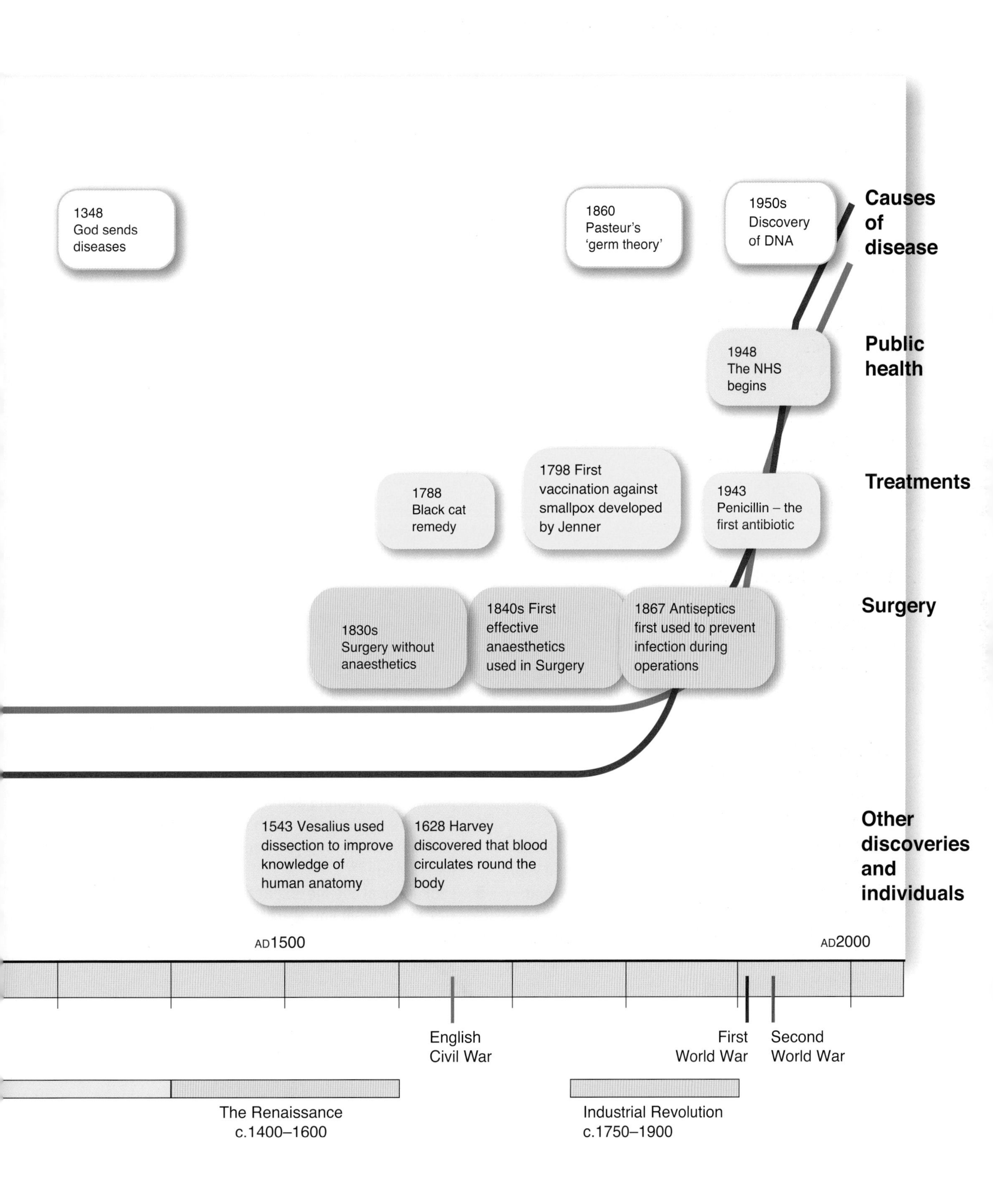
1348
God sends
diseases
1860
Pasteur's
'germ theory'
1950s
Discovery
of DNA
Causes
of
disease
1948
The NHS
begins
Public
health
1788
Black cat
remedy
1798 First
vaccination against
smallpox developed
by Jenner
1943
Penicillin – the
first antibiotic
Treatments
1830s
Surgery without
anaesthetics
1840s First
effective
anaesthetics
used in Surgery
1867 Antiseptics
first used to prevent
infection during
operations
Surgery
1543 Vesalius used
dissection to improve
knowledge of
human anatomy
1628 Harvey
discovered that blood
circulates round the
body
Other
discoveries
and
individuals
AD1500
AD2000
English
Civil War
First
World War
Second
World War
The Renaissance
c.1400–1600
Industrial Revolution
c.1750–1900

Smarter Revision: Living graph

On the last two pages you saw the story of life expectancy right across time – all in one graph. Graphs are really helpful for following the story of medicine across time so it's important to start early – NOW!

Activities

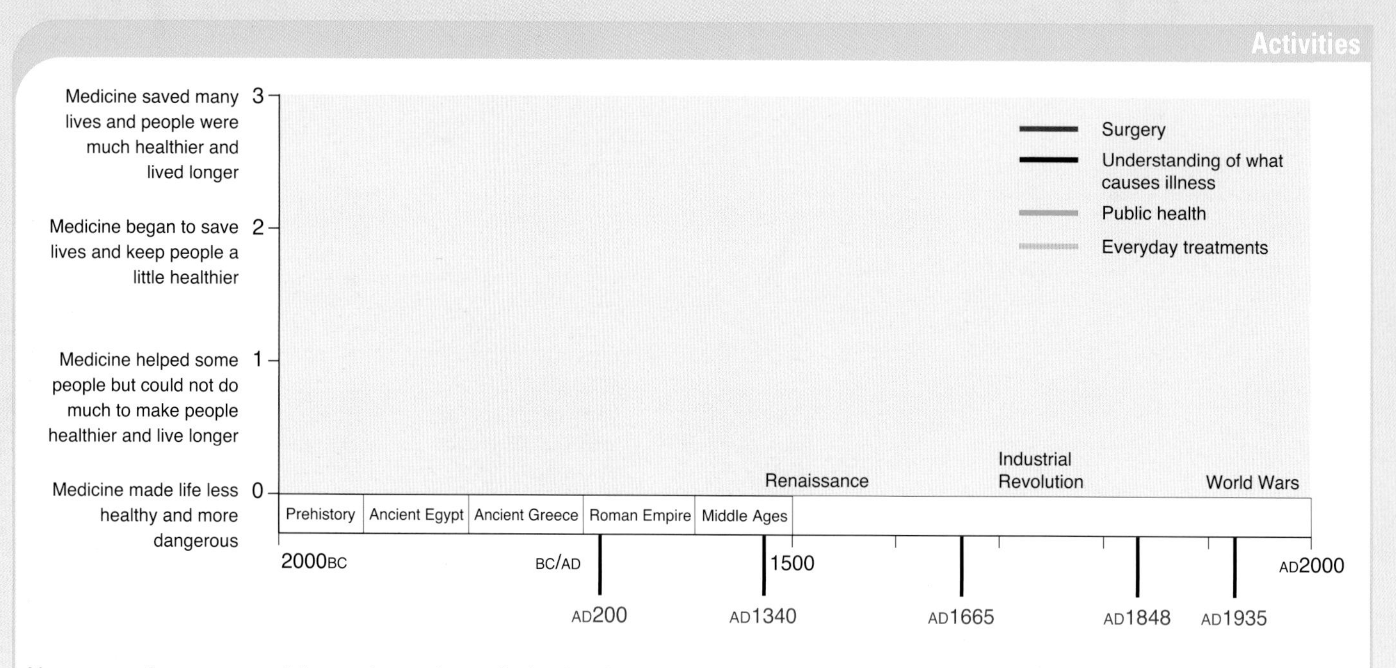

You are going on an evidence hunt through the book to create four lines on your graph.

1 Work in a group of three. Choose one theme:
- **a** Surgery
- **b** Understanding of what causes illnesses
- **c** Public health (how governments try to prevent illnesses)
- **d** Everyday treatments

2 Use the Medical Moments pages 12, 50, 86, 118, 120.
- **a** Pick out from each picture the evidence about your theme. Decide for each date where to place your theme on the graph.
  (For example, if you think surgery in AD200 made life less healthy and more dangerous put a cross at level 0 above AD200.)
- **b** Use sticky notes to list the evidence for your choice of level. Stick these on your graph.

3 When your outline graph is complete you have one minute to explain it aloud to your class. You must include each of these words:
change continuity
progress turning point

4 Compare the lines for each theme. What similarities and differences can you see between the shapes of the four lines?

5 Look back at the life-expectancy graph on pages 4–5. What have you learned from your new graphs that helps to explain the shape of the life-expectancy graph?

Why is this page really important?

To be successful in your examination you need to have an overview of the history of medicine in your mind. You will remember this outline better if you build it up from the beginning, filling in the detail as you go through the course. The best way to build up this outline knowledge is to see it as a graph. You can do this in different ways:

1 Draw the graph on A3 paper and add notes to explain the lines going up or down. Use sticky notes for the Activity opposite when suggesting first ideas. Then copy the notes onto the graph as you feel more certain about the patterns of changes and continuities.

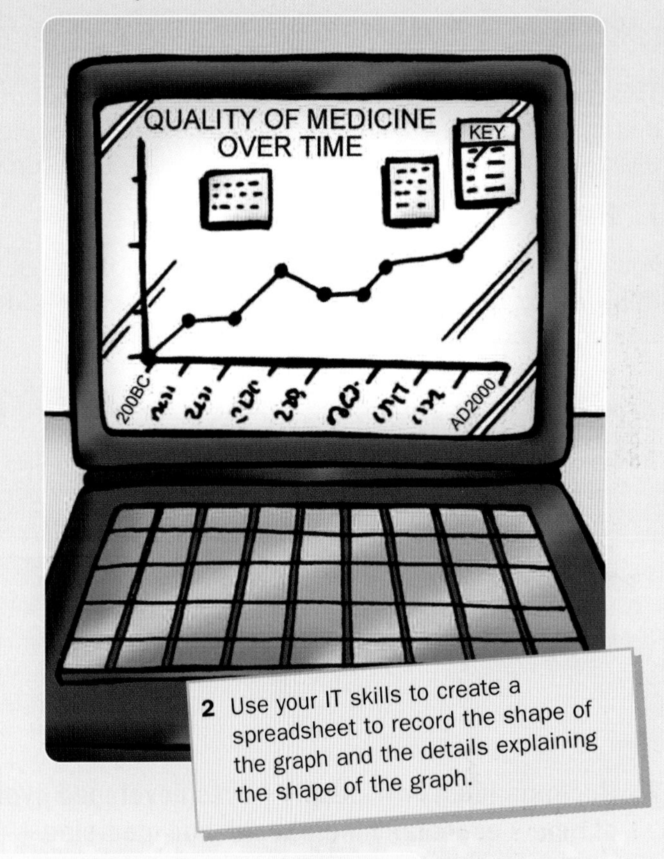

2 Use your IT skills to create a spreadsheet to record the shape of the graph and the details explaining the shape of the graph.

3 Turn the graphs into living graphs with a group of friends. Create a graph on the floor, then choose a theme such as understanding of the causes of disease. Each person is a period in history and you have to decide where on the graph you stand. Then each person has 30 seconds to explain why they are in that place on the graph. Turning your ideas into more precise spoken words and sentences is an effective way of revising. Doing this physically is an excellent way of remembering the patterns of changes and continuities.

Why are you studying the History of Medicine?

Your course will stretch back over 4000 years, all the way to prehistoric times. Why are we going so far back? Why are you studying the history of medicine? Pages 8–11 help you understand how your History course links together and where the history of medicine fits in.

This course isn't trying to turn you into doctors. It's aiming to help you get better at history and enjoy finding out about the people who lived in the past. Here are three things that you are going to become a lot better at.

1 Having a sense of chronology

You will increase your knowledge of some of the most important events in history, understand better how they fit together and why each period was important.

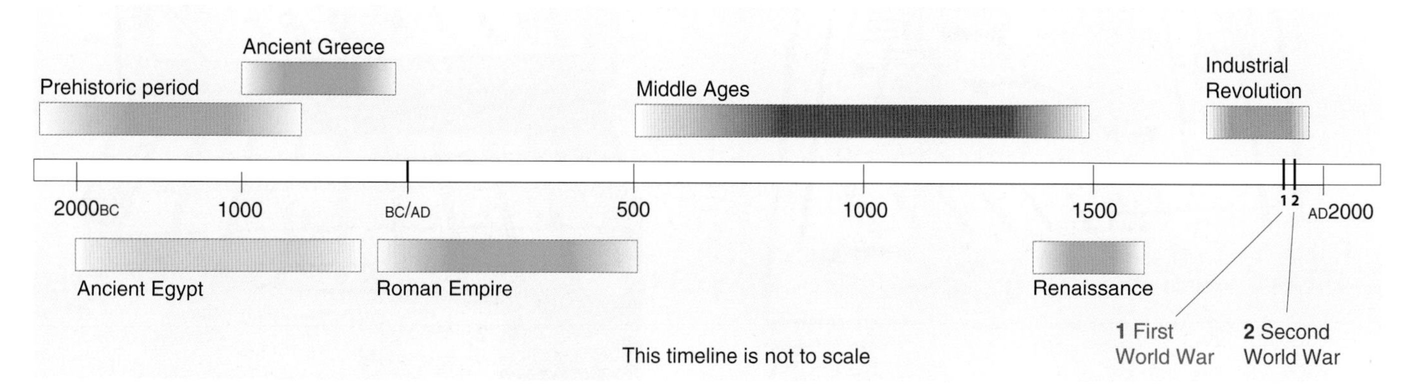

2 Understanding how people's lives developed over this long period of time – especially their health and medicine

Your core question is 'why are we healthier and why do we live longer lives than people in the past?' but by the end of the course you will be able to answer this question and many more!

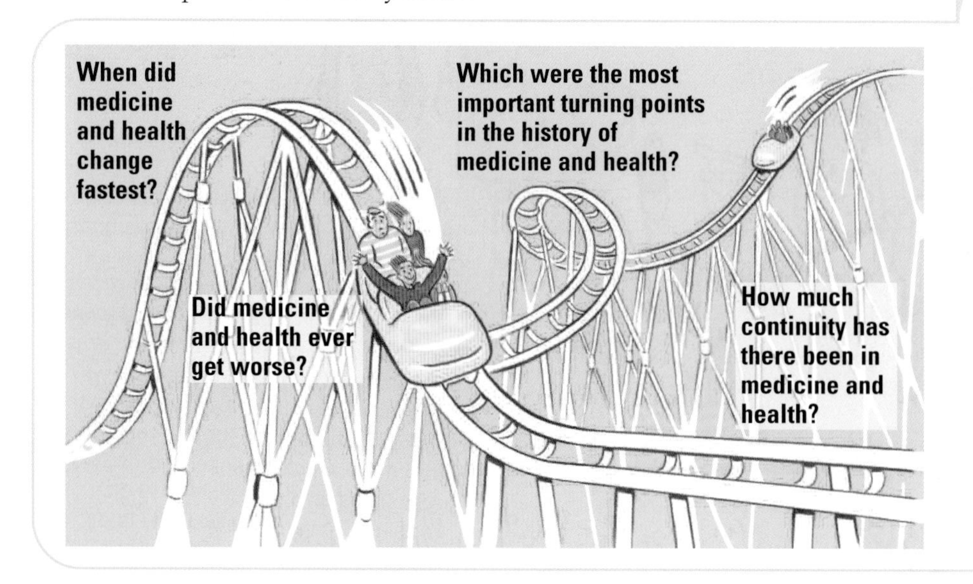

Activities

1. Think back to your KS3 History and what you learned about different periods.
   a. Do you think the Middle Ages was a time of many improvements in medicine?
   b. How might the Industrial Revolution have affected people's health?
   c. When do you think changes in medicine have been fastest?
2. Now use your answers to question 1 to suggest answers to the questions on the rollercoaster.

3 Explaining why changes happened – and why they didn't happen

You are going to describe the continuities and changes in medicine and why they happened. The people shown below will help you a lot with your explanations. They are the reasons, the factors, which explain the changes and continuities in medicine.

Activities

3 Can you suggest how any of the factors shown in the cartoon below improved medicine and so helped to save lives?

4 How might any of the factors have hindered (stopped or slowed down) the development of medicine?

(Don't worry if you can't suggest any ideas right now. You will be able to give really good answers at the end of the course.)

How does your GCSE History course all fit together?

Your GCSE History course is special.
Here are three good reasons why.

Reason 1: different types, topics and periods

Your course may look like a random set of topics, but it's not like that at all. This course was designed to let you investigate different types, topics and periods of history. This is much more varied and interesting than sticking to just one period throughout your course.

Reason 2: concepts and processes

It's not just just about topics such as the history of medicine. It is developing your ability to use all the concepts and processes you used in KS3. The people, topics and periods we study can change but we always use the same concepts and processes to study that content.

Interpretations
Diversity
Sources and evidence
Chronological understanding
Significance
Cause and consequence
Enquiry
Change and continuity

Reason 3: understand events today

Finally, it will help you see how an understanding and knowledge of history helps us better understand events today. It's really satisfying to understand how past events and people have led to the items you see in the news – and knowing that events are complicated stops us leaping to simple conclusions.

HISTORICAL SOURCE INVESTIGATION
This unit tests your skills in using sources in the context of a topic from the Development Study.

DEVELOPMENT STUDY
An investigation of a topic over a long span of time, showing the value of understanding the long term patterns in the topic and reasons for its changes and continuities.

DEPTH STUDY
This investigation of a short period of time allows you to understand the ideas and attitudes of a period and contrasts with the much longer Development Study.

HISTORY AROUND US
An investigation of a historical site in your locality which lets you use different kinds of sources and contrasts with the national and international history in the other units.

OR

MODERN WORLD STUDY
An exploration of an issue or event in the news, investigating its history so that you can understand its complexities and why there are different views on it.

Activities

1. Which topics are you studying and where do they fit into this diagram?
2. Can you suggest how any part of your History course helps you understand the world today?

What are the best ways to prepare for your GCSE exams?

Good revision and planning will help you do well at GCSE. We will help you with the two important features below.

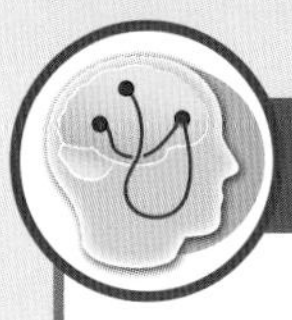

smarter revision

The Smarter Revision Toolkit

The toolkit helps you prepare your revision notes thoroughly and intelligently. Each tool helps you with a different aspect of your revision.

SMARTER REVISION TOOLKIT

Factors Chart - helps you record how difficult factors affected the development of Medicine. See page 45.

Concept Map - helps you to link factors to improve your explanation. See page 102.

Living Graph - helps you see the pattern of change and continuity in each medical theme. See page 7.

Using a digital camera to help revision - find out more on page 37.

Memory Map - helps you remember the key medical developments in each period. See page 4.

Role of Individual chart - helps you record the impact of key people. See page 27.

meet the examiner

These pages will:

- advise you how to write good answers and how to avoid writing bad answers
- show you sample answers and ask you to mark and improve them
- set you sample questions to improve your skills at writing good answers.

They will also explain how to answer the main types of exam questions, e.g.:

- Briefly describe ______
- Why did they make more progress than ______?
- How did ______ affect the development of medicine over time?
- How useful is this source for ______ ?
- Using the sources and your own knowledge ______
- And more!

Section 2: Why was ancient medicine so significant when people didn't even know what made them sick?

The best way to get an overview of ancient medicine is to look at Roman medicine at the end of the Ancient Period. What can you learn from this picture about the medical ideas and treatments in ancient history?

Activities

1. What evidence can you find in this picture of:
   a different kinds of healers
   b ideas about what caused illnesses
   c treatments for illnesses
   d methods of preventing illnesses?
2. Medical developments can be significant because:
   a they help a lot of people
   b they are used for very many years.
   Which aspects of ancient medicine do you think were significant – and why? (Check the Big Story on pages 4–5 for help.)

Medical moments in time: Roman Londinium, AD200

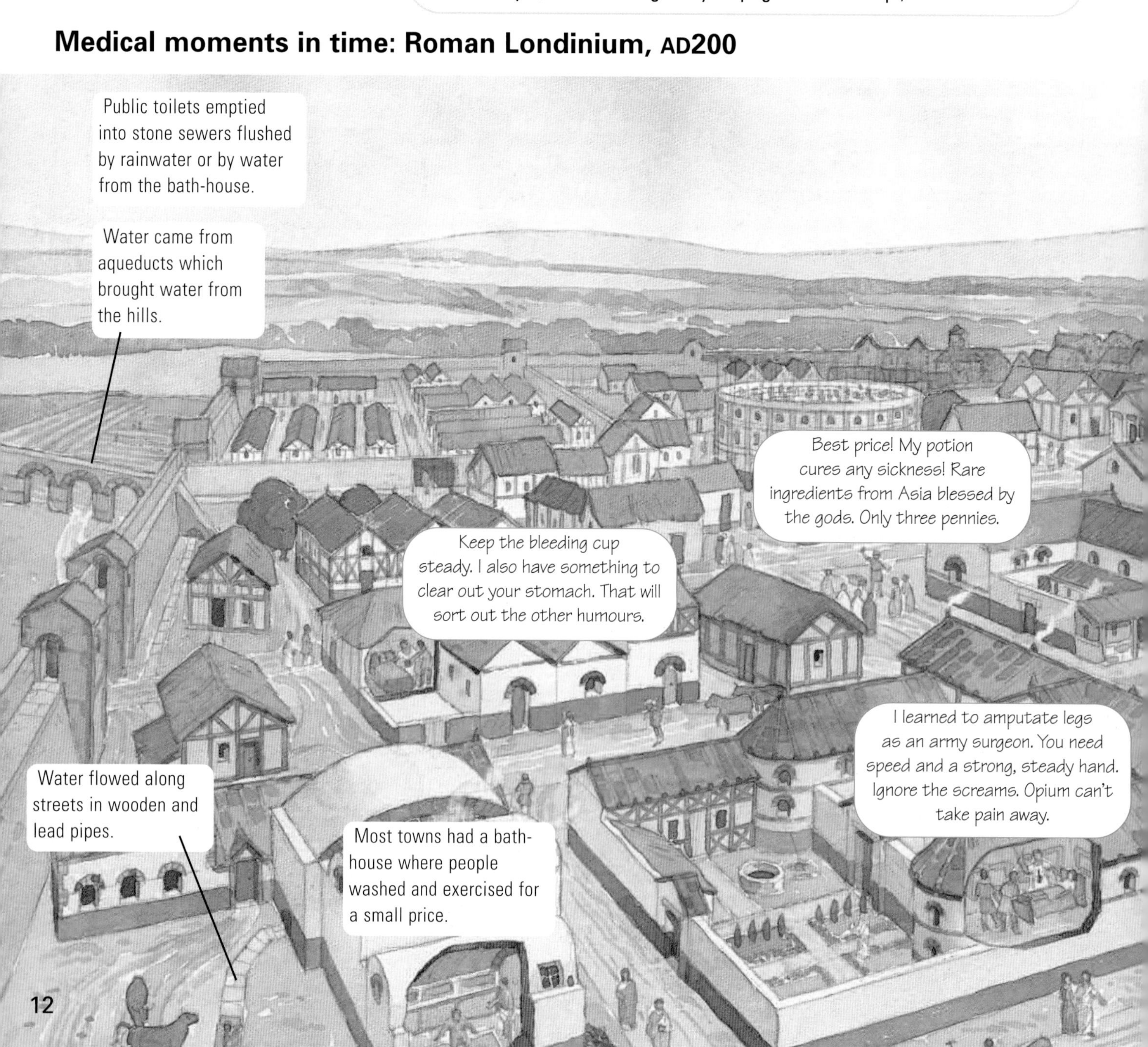

Public toilets emptied into stone sewers flushed by rainwater or by water from the bath-house.
Water came from aqueducts which brought water from the hills.
Best price! My potion cures any sickness! Rare ingredients from Asia blessed by the gods. Only three pennies.
Keep the bleeding cup steady. I also have something to clear out your stomach. That will sort out the other humours.
I learned to amputate legs as an army surgeon. You need speed and a strong, steady hand. Ignore the screams. Opium can't take pain away.
Water flowed along streets in wooden and lead pipes.
Most towns had a bath-house where people washed and exercised for a small price.

What was the ancient world?

Ancient medicine includes four different time periods: prehistory, Ancient Egypt, Ancient Greece and the Roman Empire.

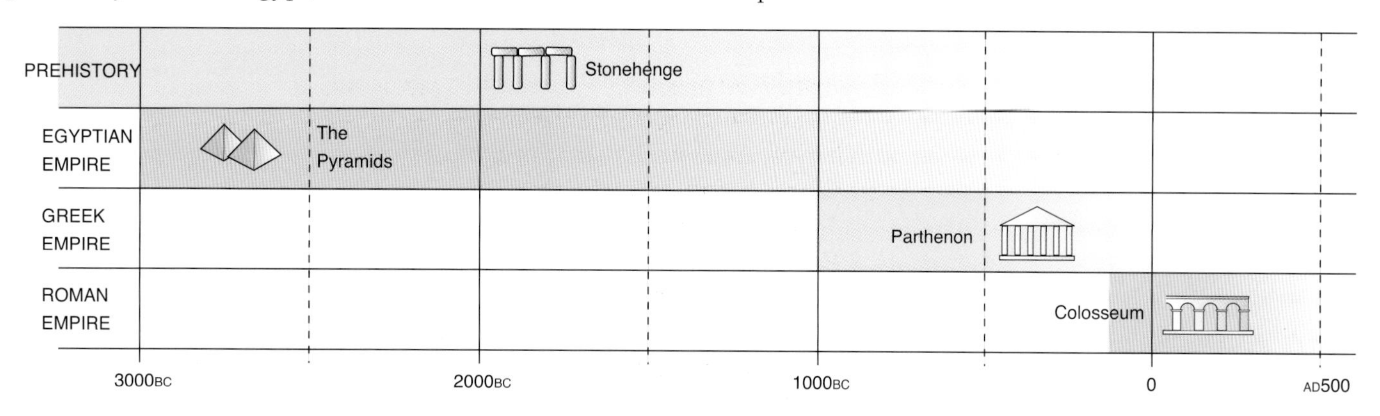

Smarter Revision: Memory map

You're only just starting the course but we're thinking about helping you revise already. Revision isn't something you tack onto the end of a course. It's something you build up as you go – that makes it a lot easier. You are going to build this memory map as your main activity on ancient medicine and then it's ready made to revise later in the course. How about that for saving time?

How can a map save you time and boost your memory?

- Memory maps encourage you to link pieces of information together. You learn more by making links, because it makes you think!
- You are actively involved with your revision. This is much better than simply reading, hoping your brain will act as a sponge and soak up the information!
- Your own images, colour, acronyms will help your memory.
- Memory maps are a flexible tool for revision. You can produce a memory map from memory, check it against the original, then add in what you have missed.
- Finally, and perhaps most importantly, memory maps make revision a lot more interesting!

How to build your ancient medicine memory map

Step 1: Use plain A4 or, even better, A3 paper (landscape). Space is important. The end result should not look too busy or cramped.

Step 2: The memory map opposite shows how you could start, but the important thing about a memory map is that you do it **your own way** so you remember it better!

Step 3: As you work though this section add more information to the map. Use pencil so that you can make corrections later if necessary. Remember:

- Use key words or phrases. Do not write full sentences.
- Use pictures/images/diagrams to replace or emphasise words. Lots of you will find it easier to remember visual images than words.
- PRINT words to make them stand out.

Step 4: The ancient world included four periods – prehistory, Ancient Egypt, Ancient Greece and the Roman Empire. Next to each entry on your map put a letter – P, E, G, R – to show which people used that treatment or idea. Some entries on your map may have all four letters, some may have only one.

Step 5: When you have finished:

- redraft your map to make sure everything is clear
- draw your own central picture which sums up the topic for you.

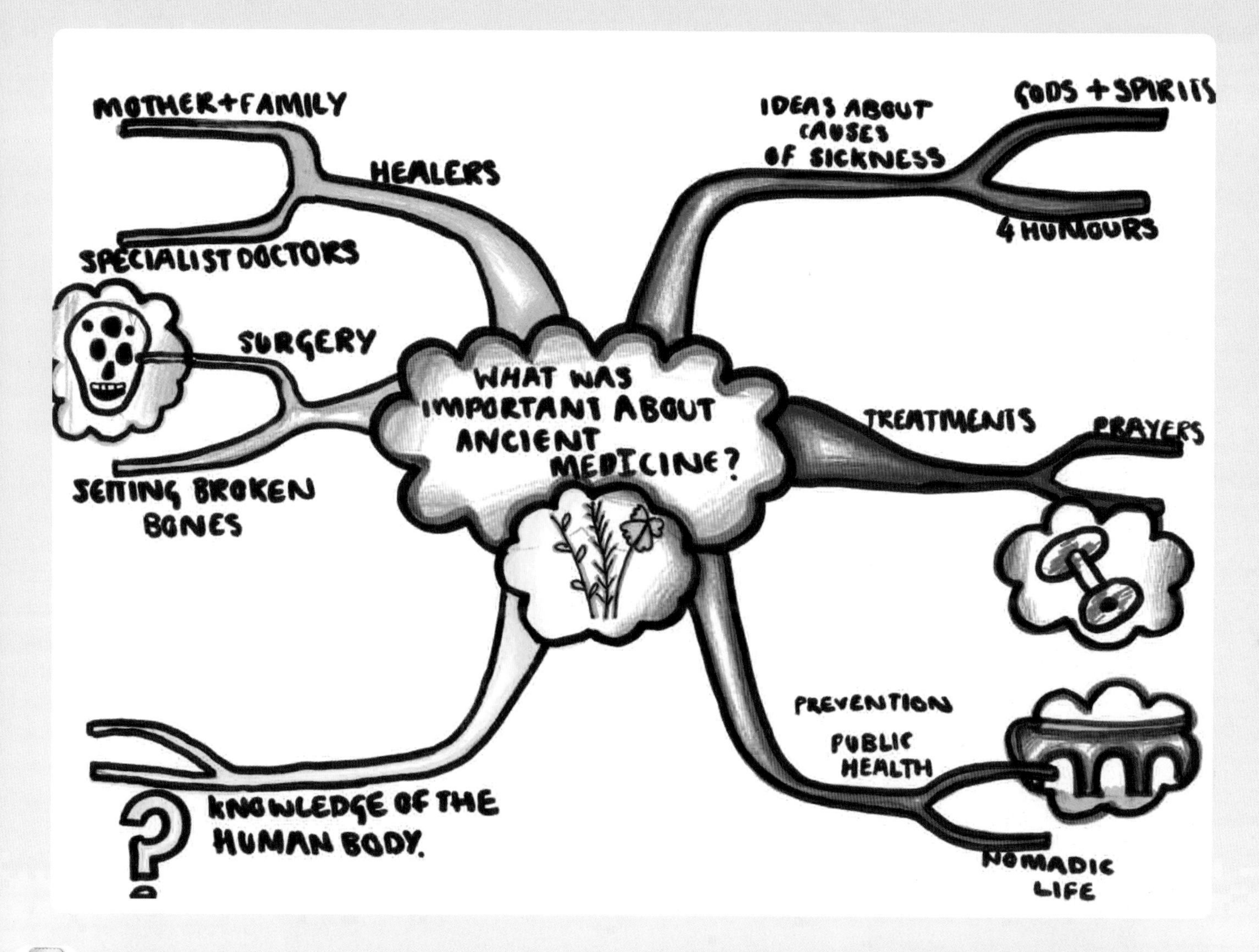

Using acronyms to help you remember

Prehistoric **E**ggs **G**o **R**otten.

This is an acronym to help you remember the letters P, E, G and R. (Why do you need to remember them?)

Acronyms are a good example of fun revision – revision doesn't have to be boring. In fact it's difficult to learn anything if you're bored, because you don't concentrate well. Inventing your own acronyms can help you remember key pieces of information. The odder the acronym the more likely you are to remember it. And drawing your own cartoon to go with your acronym makes it even easier to remember.

2.1 What kinds of medicine were prehistoric peoples good at – and not so good at?

Now let's go back to the beginning of ancient medicine, right back to the Prehistoric Period. In prehistoric times people lived in two different ways, as shown on these pages. What can you work out from the pictures and information about prehistoric medicine?

Activities

Use both reconstruction drawings. What can you learn about:

- **a** the kinds of health problems people suffered from
- **b** their ideas about what caused illnesses and injuries
- **c** the treatments they used
- **d** who treated the sick?

Hunter-gatherers (life expectancy around 19–25)

Until about 10,000BC people lived by hunting animals and gathering fruits and nuts as they travelled. They were nomads, living 'on the move'.

He is wearing a charm round his neck to ward off evil spirits who cause illnesses. It was given to him by the group's medicine man.
Keeping on the move avoids some diseases. There are no polluted water supplies or piles of human excrement to attract disease-carrying insects because people do not stay in one place long enough.
He will die. They could not stop his severe bleeding.
She has been sick for days and is too weak to walk. Her family will cook her a good meal but then they will leave her to die. They need to keep up with the herds for food.
He has a gash on his hand from the attack. It will be covered with mud and bound with strips of tree bark. A chant will be sung to keep away evil spirits but open wounds can lead to gangrene, which rapidly kills the victim. Hunters could also catch diseases (e.g. anthrax, rabies) from animal skins or bites.

Information

What does prehistoric mean?

The word 'prehistory' means 'before writing'. Therefore the Prehistoric Period was the time before writing began, so 'prehistory' means different times in different places. For example, the Ancient Egyptians developed writing c. 3000BC and so that is when the Prehistoric Period ended in Egypt. In Britain, the Prehistoric Period lasted three thousand years longer, until the Romans brought writing when they conquered Britain in AD43. Peoples such as the aboriginals of Australia or the Azande in Sudan, Africa, did not develop writing until the nineteenth century so their Prehistoric Periods lasted until the nineteenth century.

Farmers (life expectancy around 20–27)

Around 10,000BC people developed a different lifestyle, settling in one place and farming the land, growing crops and keeping herds of animals. This drawing shows prehistoric farmers 5000 years ago.

Farmers suffered fewer injuries and accidents than hunters but lots of hard physical work meant men and women suffered from painful joints and bones. Animals also polluted water supplies.
The man has cut his hand on the flint knife and it is red and painful. He has smeared the cut with healing herbs but he thinks that an evil spirit has got into his body through the cut. In ten days' time his jaw will lock together. The medicine man will drill a hole in his skull to release the evil spirit but it won't work and the man will die.
The woman feels sick and tired all the time. The medicine man puts charms on her forehead and says prayers to the gods but she is not getting better. She will die in a few weeks' time.
The boy broke his ankle last year. His father covered it in mud and leaves until the mud set hard. The break healed but the boy still walks with a limp.
The girl has a sore throat. This is a common illness and her mother has a good remedy that she learned from her own mother. She gives the girl a drink made from herbs and honey and she soon feels better.

Explaining and treating illnesses – the natural and the supernatural

Activities

1. Work in a small group. Explain to the rest of the class how prehistoric people would have treated someone with one of these problems:
   - **a** a broken arm
   - **b** a pain in the stomach
   - **c** a headache that won't go away

   Include details about the healer, the kind of treatment and what you think caused the problem.
2. Memory map: use the information on pages 16–19 to add to the memory map you began on page 14.
3. Look back to pages 12–13. Which aspects of Roman medicine had been first developed thousands of years earlier in the Prehistoric Period?
4. Why aren't we completely certain about the details of prehistoric medicine?

Illnesses and injuries that had NATURAL causes

Examples

Accidents, hunting or war wounds, hunger, ailments such as fever.

Who would you go to for help?

Family, probably the women who had learned remedies from their own mothers.

Source 1

▲ A tea-tree plant.

How did they treat wounds and illnesses?

Common remedies were made from herbs, plants, minerals and animal parts. Although prehistoric people did not understand why, some cures worked because the ingredients included chemicals which acted as antiseptics to combat infection or as anaesthetics.

Cuts and wounds were also helped by the use of plants. Aboriginals covered cuts with sphagnum moss, which is now an ingredient in hospital dressings and field dressings in war zones. Broken bones and cuts were covered with mud, clay or animal fat and then bound up with feathers, animal skin or tree bark.

A cure developed by the aboriginals of Australia was based on tea-tree leaves. People with colds and coughs breathed in the vapour from crushed tea-tree leaves boiled in water. People with fevers bathed in tea-tree liquid. Today tea-tree oil is used to treat colds and other ailments and as an antiseptic. American Indians used the bark of the cherry tree, which contains chemicals that reduce coughing.

Fevers, pain and lung complaints were treated with steam. Sweat lodges were used all over North America. In 1805 a European explorer became so crippled with back pain that he could not ride or walk but after using a steam lodge and drinking a local herbal tea he was able to walk freely for the first time in four months.

These natural and supernatural methods were not two different systems but all part of one overall system of medicine.

Natural

Information

How do we know about prehistoric medicine?

There are no written records of prehistoric medicine but there are two important sources of evidence which tell us a lot.

1. Archaeological evidence from skeletons tell us about simple surgery or about the height of people and the age at which they died.
2. Peoples who continued to live in the same ways as their ancestors. Hunter-gatherers and farmers in Australia, Africa and America did not need to change their ways of life because they were well-suited to their environments and produced plentiful supplies of food.

Illnesses and injuries that had SUPERNATURAL causes

Examples

Anything caused by gods, the spirits of the dead, enemies, witches, for example, the aboriginal belief that illness could be caused by an enemy who made evil spirits enter the victim's body by using a pointing bone and chanting a curse. The bone could also cause illness by taking someone's spirit out of their body.

Who would you go to for help?

The medicine man who had been trained to communicate with the gods and spirits. The training of North American medicine men (as in Source 2) took several years of constant work.

How did they treat wounds and illnesses?

Medicine men gave people charms to protect them from evils spirits but if this didn't work they used a range of methods, including the same kinds of herbal remedies and practical remedies as other people. However, medicine men also used special prayers and chants, and some were skilled in surgery such as trephining. The skull shown in Source 4 had been cut open, probably to let out evil spirits that were causing pain.

Source 2

▲ A medicine man c. 1834 from the Mandan tribe, which lived in North America.

Source 3

▲ A bone used as an amulet (a charm worn as protection against evil spirits).

Source 4

▲ Trephined skulls have been found all over the world. On many the bone grew back, showing that the patient lived after the operation.

Medicine men used herbs; mothers used chants and charms.
There were strong connections between the two approaches.

Supernatural

2.2 Did the Egyptians develop any important new medical ideas?

Now it's time to find out about medicine in Ancient Egypt, the land of pyramids and Pharaohs. What can you learn from the picture below?

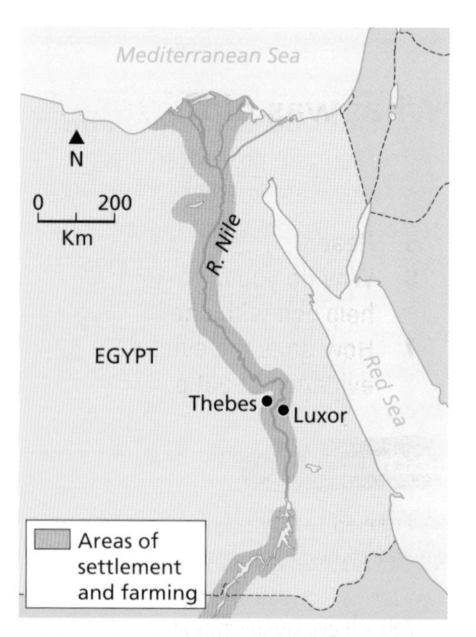

Activity

Look carefully at the details in the picture below.

1. What evidence can you see of similarities with prehistoric medicine?
2. What evidence can you see of differences from prehistoric medicine?
3. What evidence can you see of
   a religion **b** communications **c** technology?
4. How might each factor have affected medicine in Egypt?

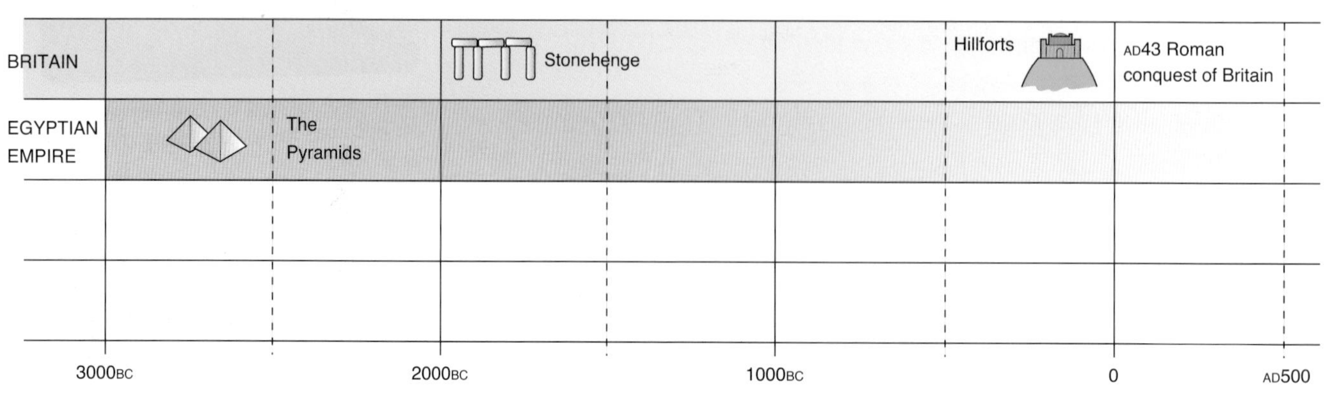

What was old? What was new?

Activities

5 Read Sources 1–3. How are they similar to prehistoric treatments?

6 Why do you think each of them continued to be used? (Source 4 will help you with one of the remedies.)

7 How does the evidence about Egyptian medicine differ from the evidence about prehistoric medicine?

Source 1

From an Egyptian medical document dating from between 1900 and 1500BC:

'I have made a charm for my child which will protect him against you, oh evil spirits! This charm is made from evil smelling herbs and from garlic which is harmful to you; from honey which is sweet for men and horrible for spirits, from a fishtail and a rag and a backbone of a perch.'

Source 2

A cure for a diseased eye from the Ebers Papyrus from c.1500BC:'To clear up the pus: honey, balm from Mecca and gum ammoniac.To treat its discharge: red ochre, malachite, honey.' [Gum ammoniac is the resin from the Dorena ammoniac plant.]

Source 3

How to treat a broken nose – instructions from a papyrus dating from c.1600BC. The document contains descriptions of the diagnosis and treatment of 48 surgical cases.

EXAMINATION

If you examine a man whose nose is disfigured, part of it being squashed in, while the other part is swollen and both nostrils are bleeding.

DIAGNOSIS

Then you should say 'You have a broken nose and I can treat this ailment.'

TREATMENT

You should clean his nose with two plugs of linen and then insert two plugs soaked in grease into his nostrils. You should make him rest until the swelling has gone down. Bandage his nose with stiff rolls of linen and treat him with lint every day until he recovers.

Source 4

Scientists have analysed and tested some Ancient Egyptian remedies. Honey was used in 30 per cent of remedies recorded in one document. Malachite was another common ingredient. Malachite is a kind of stone that contains copper. It was also used by American Indians as a medicine.

Malachite is mentioned in 39 of the treatments in this papyrus. It was used for treating eye operations and open wounds.
Let's test it to see if it actually works.
The tests are clear. Malachite does stop bacteria from growing in wounds.
So these old Egyptian remedies really did help wounds to heal!

How about honey? That was the most common ingredient they used. Does that work too?
Yes, honey stops bacteria from growing so it would help to heal an infected wound.

Why did Egyptian medicine change?

One important skill that helps you learn more effectively is skim-reading. You read quickly to get an overall idea of what the key points are on a page. Then you go back and read more carefully, picking out the detail that supports those key points. Pages 22–25 help you develop your skim-reading skills with a game of Egyptian Bingo!

Activities

1. Organise yourselves into pairs. Each pair has to skim-read pages 23–25 looking for examples of how the factors shown on the Bingo card on the right affected Egyptian medicine.
2. The winners are the first pair to find one example of each factor in one of the rows. As soon as you have completed a row, shout out 'Pyramid' and ask your teacher to check that your examples are correct.
3. When you have finished turn to page 25 and complete the more detailed activity.

Information

The importance of writing

The Egyptians were one of the first peoples to develop writing and they also learned to make a kind of paper from a plant called papyrus.

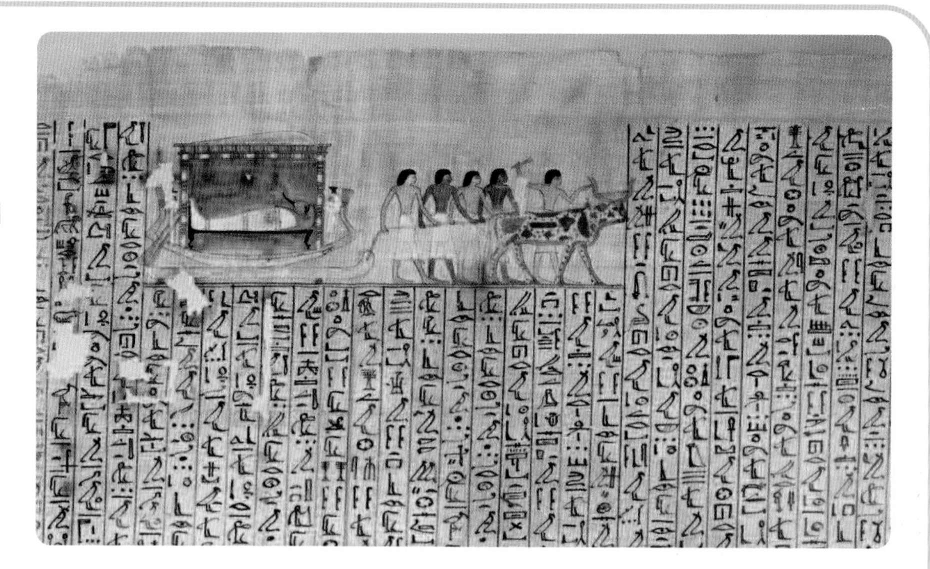

On papyrus Egyptian doctors recorded their medical cases, detailing symptoms, how to examine a patient and treatments. This is why we know a lot more about Egyptian medicine than about prehistoric medicine.

Writing was also important because doctors could pass on their knowledge more easily to new generations of Egyptian doctors. Unfortunately, the two different kinds of Egyptian writing – hieroglyphs and hieratic writing – were not understood by people from other countries who had their own kinds of writing so doctors from other countries, such as Greece, did not learn much about Egyptian medicine.

1 Specialist doctors

Egyptian doctors were a mixture of doctor and priest. They were carefully trained, studying the medical papyri recording cases and treatments. Some were general doctors, a little like our GPs, treating soldiers or labourers on huge building projects. However, some doctors were specialists. The Pharaoh's physician Ir-en-akhty, for example, specialised in eye diseases and problems in the stomach and rectum. One thing they all had in common was using a variety of treatments – herbal remedies, simple surgery, charms, prayers and chants.

Specialist doctors developed because the Pharaoh and his lords were very rich and could afford to spend money employing their own doctors – and so the doctors themselves were wealthy enough to spend their time improving their medical knowledge by studying the medical papyri and discussing cases.

▲ This hieroglyph says swnw (pronounced sewnew) meaning physician. It consists of a man, a pot of medicine and a lancet (knife). Sometimes the physician was drawn leaning on a stick to show he was experienced and well-respected.

Specialists

2 Knowledge of the body

Doctors knew about many parts of the body's anatomy – the heart, lungs, liver and brain and about veins, arteries, muscles and many bones – although they often did not know exactly what each part did. For example, they did not know that the heart pumps blood around the body.

They did not learn about the body by dissection (the careful cutting and analysis of dead bodies) because their religion said that the body was needed in the after-life. The most likely method was by examining wounded soldiers or workers injured on building projects. They may have learned about anatomy from embalming, the process of removing and preserving the body's organs after death. However, at times in Egyptian history embalmers were regarded as 'unclean' and were cut off from contact with other people so they could not have passed on knowledge of the body. On the other hand, doctors were also sometimes embalmers and there is a record of an embalmer who was the grandfather of a doctor. So embalming may have increased knowledge of anatomy but we cannot be certain about this.

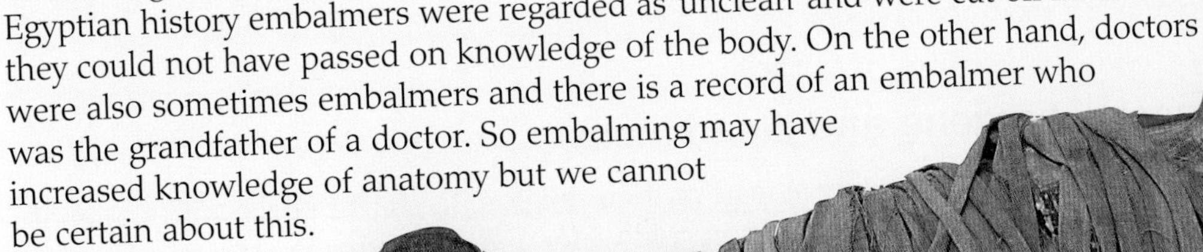

The Body

Causes of illness

3 Ideas about the causes of illness

Egyptians continued to believe that illnesses were caused by the gods and evil spirits but they also developed a new natural theory. This theory said that illness was caused when the channels in the body became blocked. This idea came from farming. Egypt was rich because of its farming, a vital part of Egyptian life. People made sure their crops got plenty of water by digging irrigation channels from the river Nile to their fields. If those channels kept running then the crops grew well but, if the irrigation channels became blocked, the crops did not get enough water and died.

Egyptian doctors thought that crops and people had a lot in common. People stayed healthy so long as blood, air and water flowed through the channels around the body, but if the channels became blocked people fell sick. For example, undigested food rotting in the bowels could cause blockages in the channels and so make people ill.

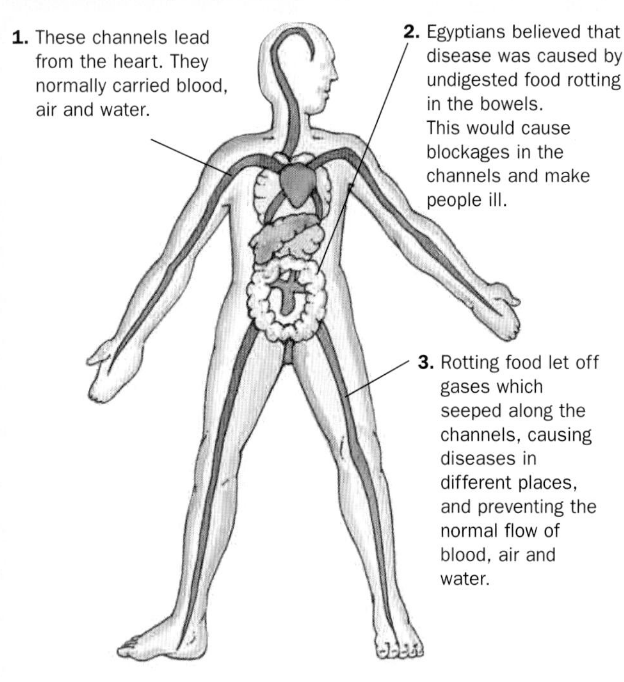

1. These channels lead from the heart. They normally carried blood, air and water.
2. Egyptians believed that disease was caused by undigested food rotting in the bowels. This would cause blockages in the channels and make people ill.
3. Rotting food let off gases which seeped along the channels, causing diseases in different places, and preventing the normal flow of blood, air and water.

▲ A statue of Sekhmet, the lion-headed goddess of war and plagues. Egyptians believed she could cause and cure plagues of disease. Each medical specialisation had its own god. For example, Dauw was the god of eye diseases, Taweret the goddess of childbirth. Gods protected individual parts of the body: for example, Isis protected the liver and Neith the heart.

Hygiene

4 Preventing illness – hygiene and cleanliness

Egyptians took great care to keep clean, probably as part of their religion, to stay at peace with the gods and spirits. People washed twice a day and every night in cold water and before meals. They used soda, scented oil and ointments as soap. Egyptian ladies shaved their bodies with bronze razors and used eye make-up that included powdered emerald-green copper ore, which may well have helped reduce eye-infections, although that was probably not why they wore it!

Excavations by archaeologists tell us that richer homes contained a room for washing and bathing but they did not have plumbing to bring water in and out. People bathed by having a servant pour water over them from a jug. The waste water ran away through a hole in the wall, draining into a sunken vase in the floor or into stone drains in the street.

Toilets for the poor consisted of a wooden stool with a hole cut in it, above a cup half-filled with sand. Richer families had a limestone seat over a bowl standing in a pit. Whatever kind of toilet they had, they all had to be emptied by hand. Keeping clean was up to each individual. The Pharaoh and his government did not do anything to protect the people from illnesses.

5 Everyday treatments

Treatments

Doctors, priests and mothers used treatments made from herbs, plants, minerals and animal parts. Most ingredients, such as honey, were local but others were brought by traders from abroad. Cinnamon and pepper came from India and China, and malachite from North Africa.

Doctors developed new treatments to unblock blocked channels. These included bleeding the patients (taking blood out of their veins) or making the patients vomit or empty their bowels.

Doctors also carried out simple surgery on the outside of the body, such as cutting out swellings or sewing up wounds. They also carried out trephining, cutting holes in the skull, to ease pain or swellings. Doctors had stronger, sharper bronze surgical instruments thanks to improved metal-working skills. Egyptian metalworkers had honed their skills by making weapons and embalming tools, fine jewellery and tools for builders.

Activities

Your skim-reading identified the factors affecting Egyptian medicine. Now build your detailed knowledge.

1. Working in your pair, copy the table below and complete one of the rows of the table as follows.
   - a Summarise each development in column A. Write a sentence or two describing the development below each heading.
   - b Complete columns B and C.
   - c Assess how great a change each development was. Make sure you explain the reasons for your decision.
2. Between you the class should now have completed the whole table. As a whole class, decide:
   - a which factor did most to help the development of Egyptian medicine
   - b which factor did most to hinder the development of Egyptian medicine.
3. Memory map: use the information on pages 20–25 to add to the memory map you began on page 14.

Science, technology and art

Individuals
Teamwork
War
Attitudes (conservatism, enquiry)
Chance
Religion
Communications
Lifestyle
Government

A. What were the developments?	B. Which factors helped this development take place?	C. Did any factors hinder this development?	D. How great a change? 4 = huge; 1 = small;
1. Specialist doctors			
2. Knowledge of the body			
3. Ideas about the causes of illness			
4. Methods of preventing illness			
5. Everyday treatments			

2.3 Did the Greek doctor Hippocrates completely change medicine?

In the Big Story section you discovered that the Greek doctor Hippocrates was one of the most important people in the history of medicine. Doctors were still following his ideas 2000 years after he died. It's easy to think that someone so important changed medicine completely – but did he?

What was special about the Greeks?

Like the Egyptians, many Greeks became rich from farming and trade while the hard work in the fields and towns was done by slaves and the poor. This allowed the wealthy classes to spend their time being educated. Most continued to believe that the gods controlled everything but a small number of educated Greeks became interested in finding more logical, natural explanations for all kinds of aspects of the world around them. One example was Anaximander, who argued that thunder was not the sound of the god Zeus being angry but was a natural event, caused by air being trapped in a cloud and bursting out with great force. Men like Socrates, Plato and Aristotle became famous philosophers (meaning 'lovers of knowledge'), investigating mathematics, science, astronomy, politics and other subjects.

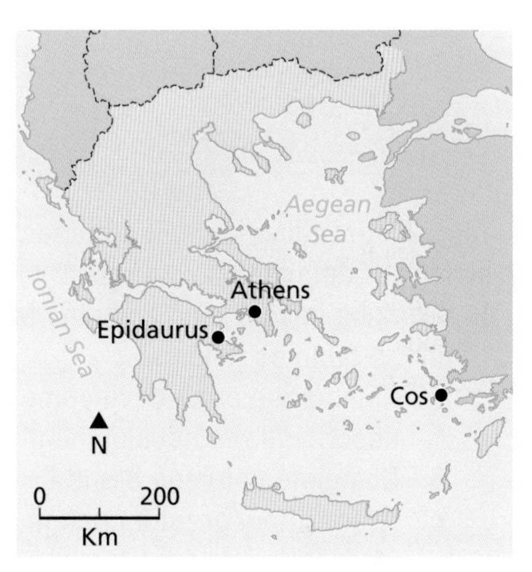

▲ The Greek Empire

Activities

1. Why were the Greeks likely to have new ideas about medicine?
2. Do you expect all their ideas about medicine to change?
3. The chart opposite helps you investigate Hippocrates. We have begun to fill it in for you but your task is to copy the chart and complete the rest. Take pages 28–31 in turn and answer the questions there, then return to this chart and add in what you have discovered **in pencil**.
4. When you have completed your draft, look over the chart and finalise your thoughts. Add small drawings or use colours to pick out the most important developments.

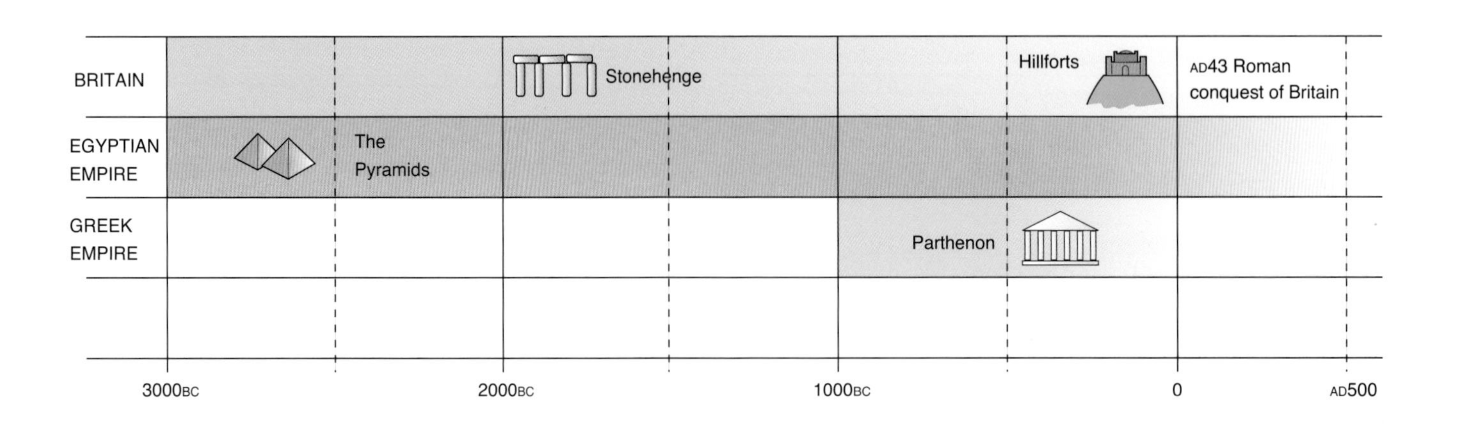

Smarter Revision: 'Role of the individual' chart

During your course you will need to record the achievements of a number of key individuals – Hippocrates, Galen, Vesalius, Pasteur and others. It will be much easier to work out why each person was important (and, later, to revise their achievements) if you use the same kind of chart for each of them. That way you will be able to recall the pattern of the chart in your mind if you need it in an examination.

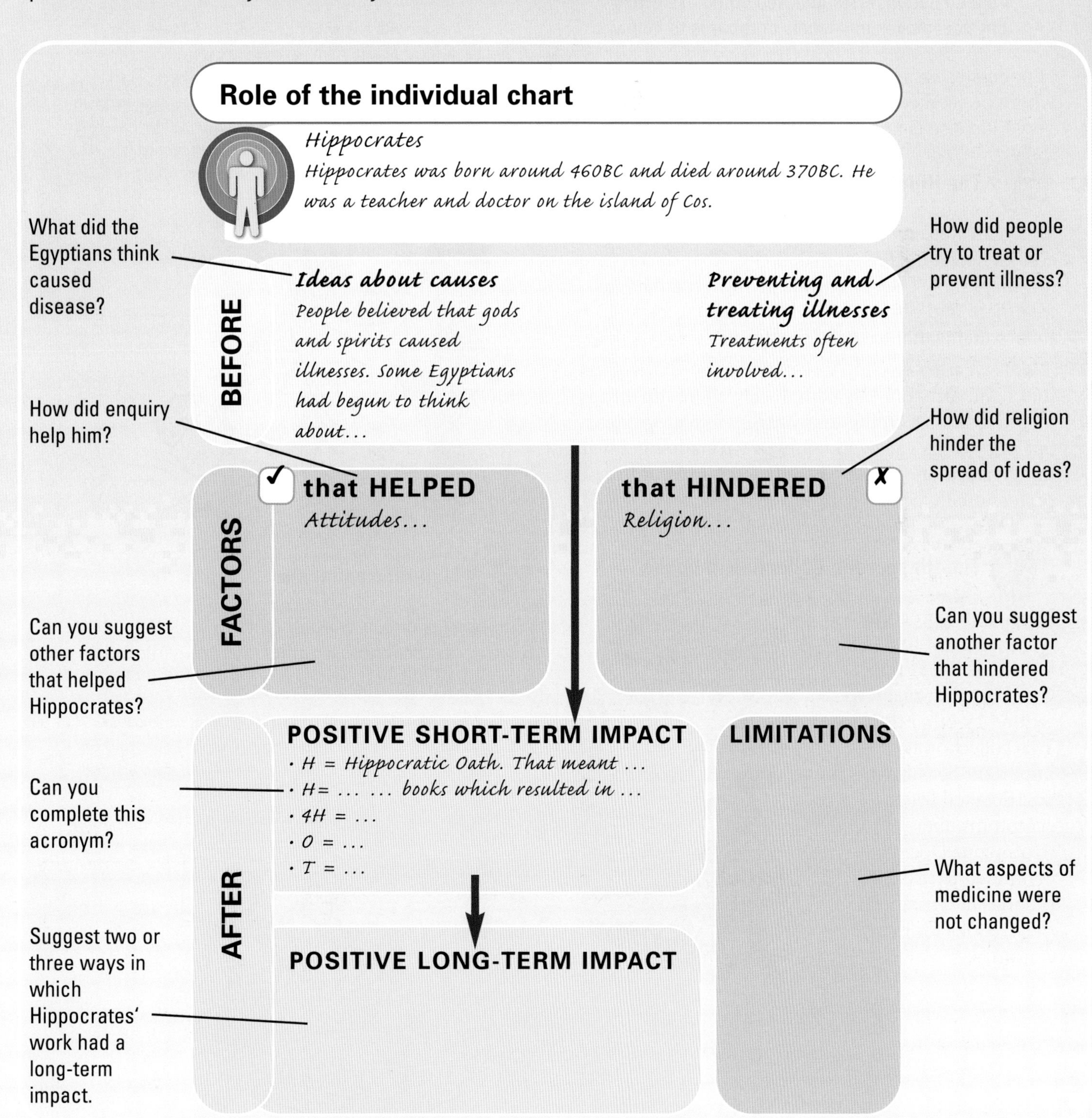

Role of the individual chart
Hippocrates
Hippocrates was born around 460BC and died around 370BC. He was a teacher and doctor on the island of Cos.
What did the Egyptians think caused disease?
BEFORE
Ideas about causes
People believed that gods and spirits caused illnesses. Some Egyptians had begun to think about...
Preventing and treating illnesses
Treatments often involved...
How did people try to treat or prevent illness?
How did enquiry help him?
How did religion hinder the spread of ideas?
FACTORS
that HELPED
Attitudes...
that HINDERED
Religion...
Can you suggest other factors that helped Hippocrates?
Can you suggest another factor that hindered Hippocrates?
AFTER
POSITIVE SHORT-TERM IMPACT
• H = Hippocratic Oath. That meant ...
• H= ... ... books which resulted in ...
• 4H = ...
• O = ...
• T = ...
Can you complete this acronym?
LIMITATIONS
What aspects of medicine were not changed?
POSITIVE LONG-TERM IMPACT
Suggest two or three ways in which Hippocrates' work had a long-term impact.

What did Hippocrates do that was so important?

Activities

1. 'Role of the individual' chart: use pages 28–29 to fill in the 'Impact' boxes on your chart (see page 27).
2. Work in a small group and devise a way of explaining the Theory of Four Humours to people who do not understand it. You could use props, physical movement, labels or tabards to help you.

Hippocrates was born c.460BC on the island of Cos where he worked as a doctor and teacher of doctors. Very little else is known about him. He died c.370BC.

The Hippocratic Oath

This oath was created by Hippocrates to give people confidence in doctors. It makes clear that doctors are not magicians. They have to keep high standards of treatment and behaviour and work for the benefit of their patients, not to make themselves wealthy.

'I will swear by Apollo, Asclepius and by all the gods that I will carry out this oath. I will use treatment to help the sick according to my ability and judgement but never with a view to injury or wrongdoing. I will not give poison to anybody. Whatever I see or hear professionally will be kept secret.'

The Hippocratic Collection of books

Hippocrates probably wrote some of the books known as the Hippocratic Collection but many were written by other doctors. This collection is important because it is the first detailed list of symptoms and treatments. Doctors continued to use the theories and methods in these books for many centuries.

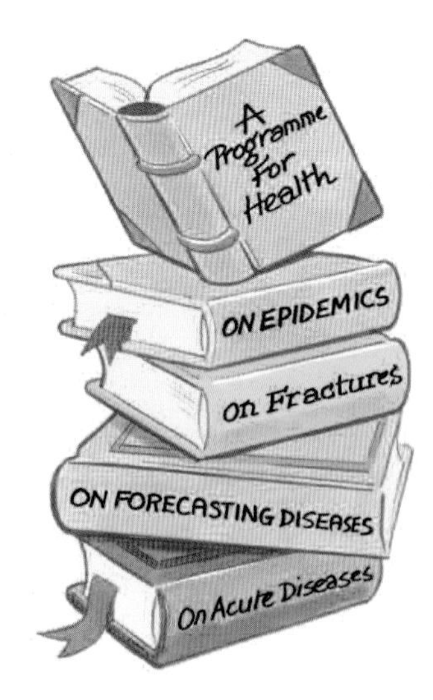

Observing and recording

Hippocrates showed that it was very important to observe and record carefully the symptoms and development of diseases. This had two advantages. Doctors were more likely to choose the right cure if they took care to find the cause of the problem. These notes could then be used to help with diagnosis and treatment of future patients.

First look at the patient's face. The following are bad signs – a sharp, pointed nose, hollow eyes, dry skin on the forehead, strange face colour such as green, black, red or lead coloured. If the face is like this at the beginning of the illness, the doctor must ask the patient if he has lost sleep or had diarrhoea, or not eaten. Then record how his condition changes each day.

Natural treatments

Hippocrates encouraged doctors to look for natural treatments for illnesses rather than praying to the gods for help.

We must use natural treatments because illnesses have natural causes. For example, many illnesses can be treated by rest and a change in diet. Then, when you feel stronger, take regular exercise. If this does not work then we can bleed or purge you to remove excess humours.

4H The causes of disease

The body contains four humours or liquids: blood, phlegm, yellow bile and black bile. When we are healthy these four humours are perfectly balanced in our bodies but we fall sick when they become unbalanced and we have too much or too little of one humour.
Look at how our bodies naturally try to get rid of excess humours.

When we observe patients carefully we see that the humours are linked to the four seasons of the year.
My nose keeps running and I can't stop sneezing.
These cold, moist symptoms are typical of winter that is a cold, moist season. This is when illnesses are caused by too much phlegm, and this man's body is trying to get rid of excess phlegm.

Here is another example. In spring, a hot, moist season, patients often have too much blood so they have nosebleeds or suffer from dysentery, getting rid of excess blood when they go to the toilet.

How much of Greek medicine was really changed by Hippocrates?

Activities

1. Which aspects of Hippocrates' work do Sources 1–3 each tell you about? Use pages 28–29 and your 'role of the individual' chart to help you.
2. There are five statements below about Greek medicine. Use pages 30–33 to decide which statements are correct and which are incorrect.
   - **a** List the correct ones and explain which evidence supports each correct statement.
   - **b** Re-write the incorrect statements so that they are correct and include evidence to show why your version is correct.
     - **i** Greek doctors were not very interested in surgery although they made some improvements, especially in wartime.
     - **ii** People continued to use herbal remedies.
     - **iii** People stopped believing that gods caused diseases.
     - **iv** Greek cities took great care to protect people's health.
     - **v** Greek doctors made some new discoveries about anatomy.
3. 'Greek medicine was a mixture of natural and supernatural methods, just like prehistoric and Egyptian medicine.' Which evidence would you use to prove this statement is correct?

Source 1

Case notes from *On Epidemics*, a book in the Hippocratic collection:

At Larisa, a bald man suddenly had a pain in the right thigh. Of the treatments, none helped.

Day 1: Sharp burning fever, he did not tremble, but the pains persisted.

Day 2: The pains in the thigh abated, but the fever was worse. He became restless and did not sleep; his extremities were cold. He passed a lot of urine but this was not of the favourable kind.

Day 3: The pain in the thigh stopped. His mind was deranged, with disturbance and much tossing about.

Day 4: Near midday, he died.

Greek healers

If you lived in a Greek city and had a little money to spare you could have a choice of healers. A holy man or magician could sell you a prayer or a charm to save you from ill-health or you could see a physician, one of the followers of Hippocrates. These physicians usually trained for several years as apprentices to another doctor, often their father or uncle. They would have studied the books in the Hippocratic Collection. However, women were the only healers most people saw. Wives and mothers used remedies passed down through families, often using herbal cures. Experienced older women were also called in as midwives.

Source 2

▲ A bleeding cup from a set of Greek medical instruments. The warm cup was placed over a small cut and, as the cup cooled, it caused blood to flow out and fill the cup.

Source 3

From *A Programme for Health*, a book in the Hippocratic Collection:

In winter, people should eat as much as possible and drink as little as possible – unwatered wine, bread, roast meat and few vegetables. This will keep the body hot and dry. In summer they should drink more and eat less – watered wine, barley cakes and boiled meat so that the body will stay cold and moist. Walking should be fast in winter and slow in summer.

Source 4

An extract from Homer's *The Iliad*, the story of the Greek war against the Trojans:

'My lord,' said the wounded man, 'I want you to cut out this arrow from my thigh, wash off the blood with warm water and spread soothing ointment on the wound. Men say you have some excellent remedies.'

Source 5

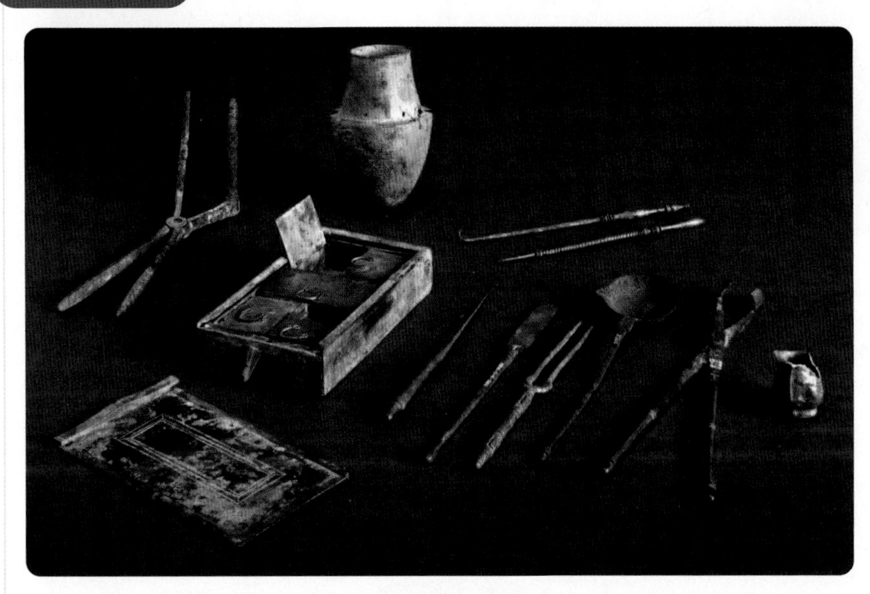

▲ A set of surgical instruments. Greek surgeons were good at setting broken bones and could amputate limbs, although they did not have effective anaesthetics. They learned how to drain the lungs of people who had pneumonia, but very few operations were done inside the body. Greek doctors were much more interested in understanding the causes of illness and in remedies based on the four humours than in surgery – probably because it was so dangerous.

Source 6

▲ A public lavatory in the Greek city of Thera. Running water under the seats took the waste away. However, public lavatories were rare. City governments left people to keep clean and prevent illnesses in their own ways. The rich could afford their own baths and lavatories but most people lived in small dirty houses with only basins to wash in. The streets were filthy but the city governments did not organise any cleaning.

Source 7

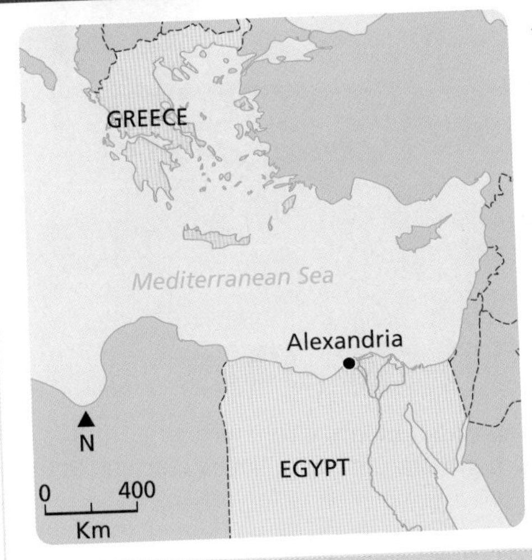

Around 330BC Alexander the Great conquered Egypt and made it part of the Greek Empire. He founded the city of Alexandria and made it the capital of Egypt. At Alexandria, the Greeks built a university and library that collected medical books from India, China and Mesopotamia as well as those by Hippocrates and other Greek writers. It became the greatest centre of medical learning in the ancient world.

Dissection of bodies was illegal in Greece so doctors had not developed detailed knowledge of anatomy and physiology. However, human dissection was allowed for a time in Alexandria. This led to important discoveries. Herophilus, who lived around 350BC, discovered that the brain, not the heart, controls the workings of the body. He also identified parts of the stomach. Erasistratus dissected the brain and began to understand that the brain sends messages to the rest of the body through the nerves. He also dissected hearts and wondered whether the heart was a pump, pumping air and blood around the body. It wasn't until the 1600s that William Harvey, an English scientist, proved that the heart pumps blood around the body.

Did Hippocrates end the belief that gods caused illnesses?

Hippocrates thought that doctors should always look for natural causes for sickness and use natural treatments, but not everybody agreed with him. The best evidence comes from the Asclepeia. An Asclepion was a temple dedicated to Asclepius, the Greek god of healing.

The Greeks continued to believe that the gods affected every part of their lives. If there was a good harvest they said the gods were pleased. If there was an earthquake they said the gods were angry. Asclepius, the son of the great god Apollo, was the Greeks' chief god of healing. By 200BC Asclepeia had been built in every Greek town. Each Asclepion had its own priests who were experienced and skilled healers.

Some Asclepeia were very large, like modern health resorts. The priests encouraged patients, depending on their illness, to take exercise and cleanse themselves in the baths. Patients built up their strength by eating regular meals and had plenty of rest, including time for prayer. The priests also carried out simple surgery, probably while the patient was in a drugged sleep. One recorded example is the removal of fragments of a spearhead from the sufferer's cheek.

Source 1

▲ A carving of the god, Asclepius, treating a patient while another patient lies down. The god was helped by his daughters, Panacea and Hygeia, and by his snake, which could cure blindness by licking the patient's eyelids. Asclepius is usually shown with his snake twined around his staff. Snakes were symbols of health because they could shed their skins and so appear younger and healthier. Harmless snakes were left in the abaton overnight while patients slept.

Source 2

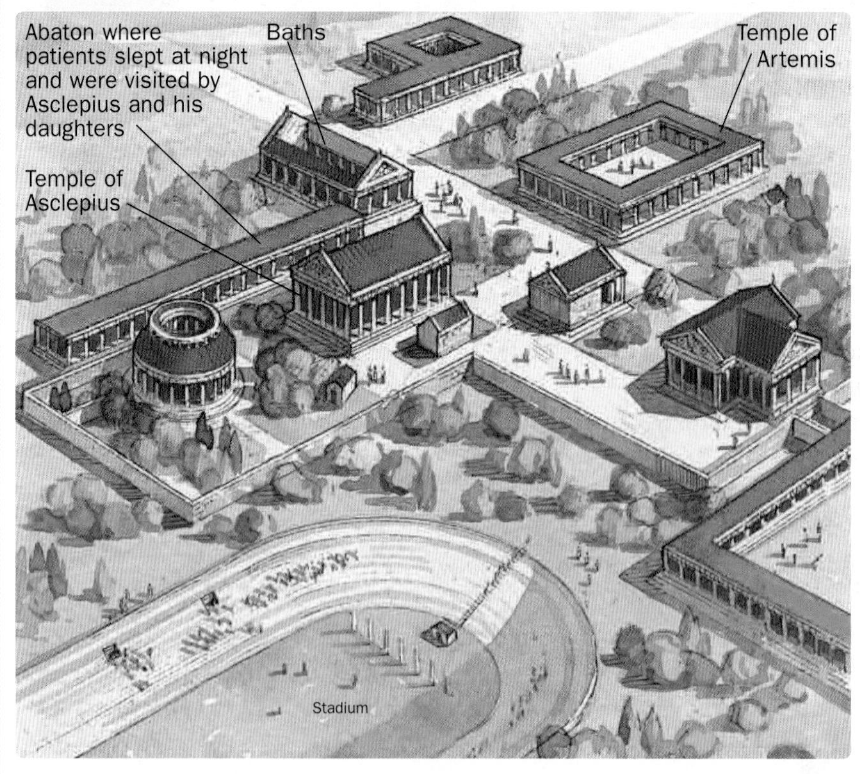

▲ Some Asclepeia were very simple temples but others were much larger. The Asclepion at Epidaurus contained baths, a gymnasium, an athletics stadium, and a theatre seating 14,000 people.

Activities

1. Who was Asclepius and how did people believe he helped the sick?
2. Why did many visitors to Asclepeia feel better?
3. Which treatments at the Asclepeia would Hippocrates have approved of?
4. 'Role of the individual' chart /memory map: update your chart on Hippocrates and your memory map.

Source 3

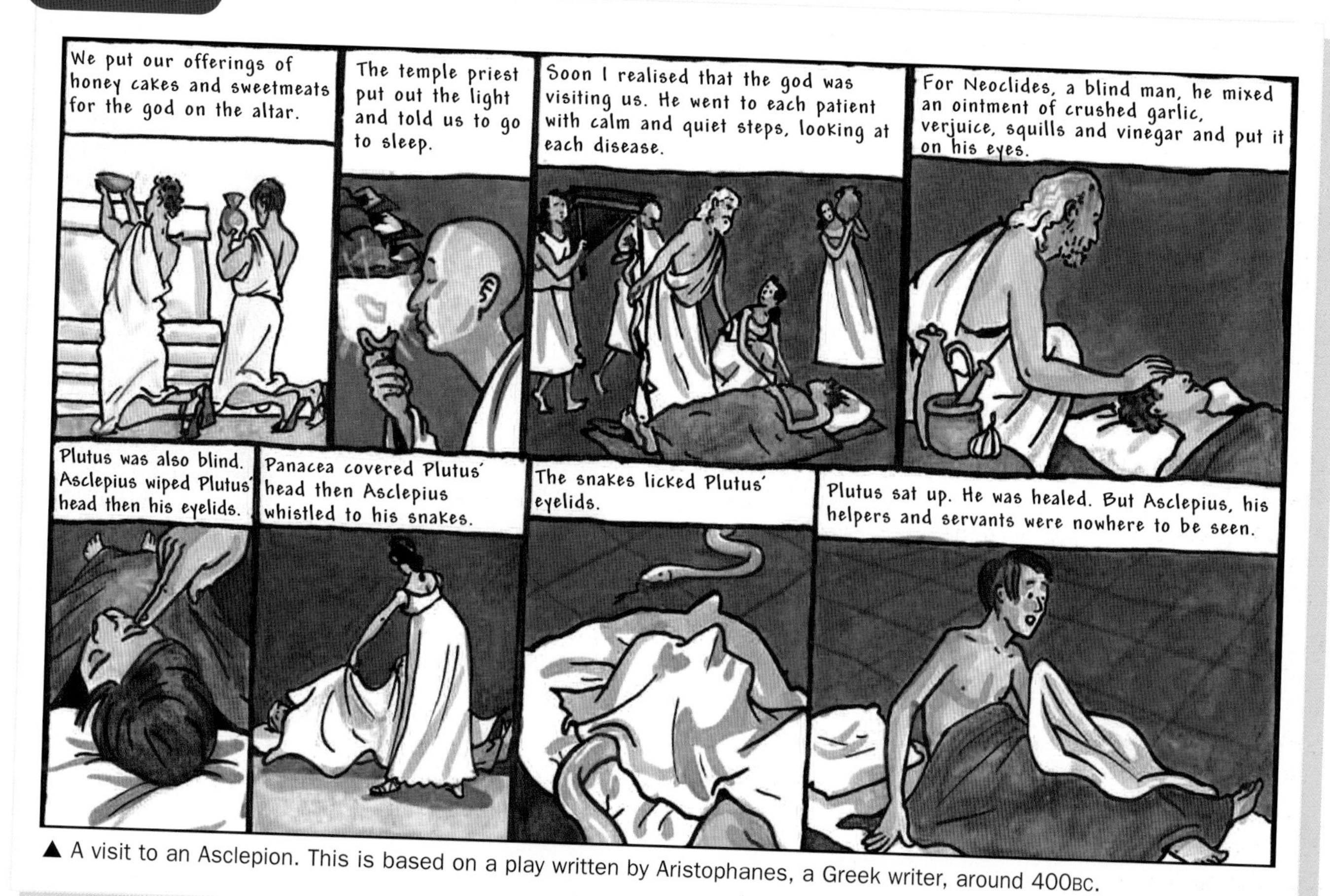

We put our offerings of honey cakes and sweetmeats for the god on the altar.
The temple priest put out the light and told us to go to sleep.
Soon I realised that the god was visiting us. He went to each patient with calm and quiet steps, looking at each disease.
For Neoclides, a blind man, he mixed an ointment of crushed garlic, verjuice, squills and vinegar and put it on his eyes.
Plutus was also blind. Asclepius wiped Plutus' head then his eyelids.
Panacea covered Plutus' head then Asclepius whistled to his snakes.
The snakes licked Plutus' eyelids.
Plutus sat up. He was healed. But Asclepius, his helpers and servants were nowhere to be seen.

▲ A visit to an Asclepion. This is based on a play written by Aristophanes, a Greek writer, around 400BC.

Did Greek cures work?

Many Greeks believed that the god Asclepius could heal them but the evidence also shows that the god and his priests were very practical healers. The ointment mixed by Asclepius in picture 4 of Source 3 might well have helped if the 'blindness' was caused by an infection which made the eyes close up. We now know that garlic acts like an antibiotic to kill infections, while vinegar cleans wounds like an antiseptic. Verjuice is the juice of unripe fruit such as green apples and squill is a plant used in a wide range of cures.

Source 4

◀ Archaeologists have discovered votive stones like this. They were thanksgiving offerings to the god Asclepius, paid for by people grateful for their recoveries. Some were carved in the shape of the affected part of the body. Others have inscriptions, describing the ailment and the cure and giving thanks to Asclepius. The inscription here reads 'Tyche to Asklepios and Hygieia as a thank offering'. Some votive stones record recoveries from serious problems such as a stomach abscess and even complete paralysis.

2.4 Did the Romans just steal the Greeks' ideas… or did they have any good medical ideas of their own?

Greek ideas were important because they were still being used over a thousand years later. The Romans copied Greek ideas but did they have any good medical ideas of their own? Your task is to create a 'washing line' to record your answer.

Activities

1. Sources 1–4 provide evidence to support four of the pieces of information on pages 12–13. Which four pieces are they?
2. The 'washing line' activity is your main activity for pages 34–39. Your task is to decide where the four cards go on the line.

Cause of disease	Treatments
Knowledge of anatomy	Public Health

a. Draw a 'washing line' as in the picture at the bottom of the page.
b. Pencil on your first thoughts on what the Romans borrowed and what their own medical ideas were.
c. As you read pages 36–39 draw the cards onto your line and add evidence that supports their positions.

Source 1

◀ Roman altars found in Britain include inscriptions like this: 'To the holy god Asclepius and to Hygieia, Julius Saturninus set this [altar] up.'

Source 2

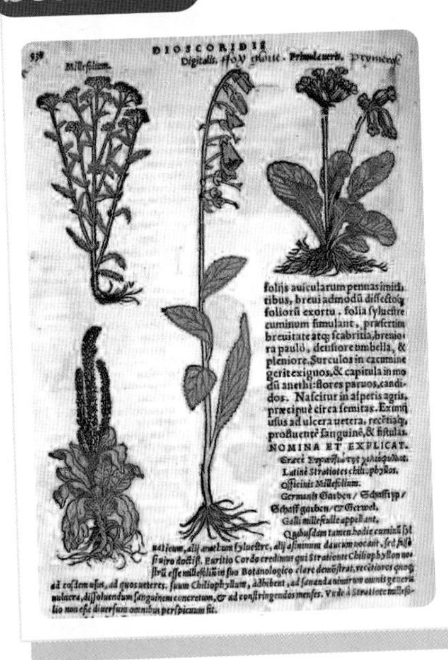

◀ Dioscorides, a Greek surgeon in the Roman army, wrote a book c.AD64 describing many herbal remedies. Modern tests show that at least 20 per cent of the remedies contained ingredients, such as honey or garlic, that would have helped patients by killing infections.

Continuities borrowed from Greece	Minor changes but closely linked to Greek methods	Changes the Romans made

Source 3

From *On Medicine*, a book by Celsus, a wealthy Roman who wrote books on many aspects of medicine:

A surgeon should be youthful or at any rate nearer youth than age; with a strong and steady hand which never trembles, and ready to use the left hand as well as the right; with vision sharp and clear, and spirit undaunted; filled with pity; so that he wishes to cure the patient, yet is not moved by his cries, to go too fast, or cut less than is necessary; but he does everything just as if the cries of pain cause him no emotion.

Source 4

◀ This wall sculpture shows a Roman doctor inspecting the eye of a patient. What are the two objects shown hanging on the wall upside down?

Activities

3 Which clues on the map suggest that the Romans borrowed a lot of Greek ideas?

4 a Which clues suggest that the Romans might have come up with new ideas and methods of their own?

b Which clues can you link to any new ideas you found on pages 12–13?

Londinium
Rome
GREECE
Alexandria
Clue 1 - Many Greek doctors travelled to Rome to make a good living.
Clue 2 - The Roman Empire contained many large cities where people lived cramped together.
Clue 3 - The Romans were skilled engineers and builders.
Clue 4 - The Romans took over Alexandria and its medical library.
Clue 5 - Many of the medical books in Rome were written by Hippocrates and his followers.
Clue 6 - The Romans controlled their empire with a huge army that needed to be kept healthy.
Clue 7 - The Romans were great organisers with good communications throughout their empire.
Clue 8 - The Roman Empire covered all the areas shown in red on this map.

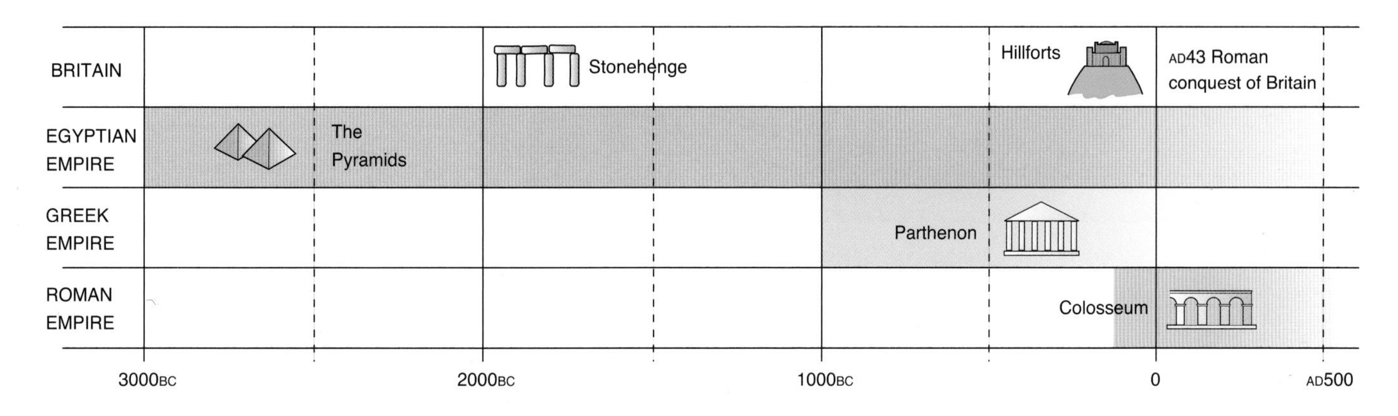

What difference did Galen make?

Now for somebody really important! Claudius Galen is one of the top five most important people in the history of medicine, possibly more important even than Hippocrates. Your task is to find out why – and use a photograph to sum up what you have found. You could even create your own photograph as an example of Even Smarter Revision.

Activities

What can you find out from this page about Galen and why his work was so important in the history of medicine?

I have done as much for medicine as the Emperor Trajan did for the Roman Empire when he built bridges and roads through Italy. It must be admitted that Hippocrates prepared the way but he made mistakes. It is I, and I alone, who have revealed the true methods of treating diseases.

Source 1

From Galen's book *On Anatomy*, written C.AD190:

'Human bones are the subjects that you should first get to know. You cannot just read about bones in books but you must also acquaint yourself with the appearance of each of the bones, by the use of your own eye, handling each bone by itself. At Alexandria this is very easy because the doctors there let their students inspect human bodies. If you cannot get to Alexandria it is not impossible to see human bones. I have often done this where tombs have been broken. On one occasion a river carried a corpse downstream before depositing it on the riverbank. Here it lay, as though prepared by a doctor for his pupils' lesson. Once I examined the skeleton of a robber lying on a mountain-side. If you do not have the luck to do this you can still dissect an ape. Choose apes which most resemble men, which walk and run on two legs, where you will find other parts as in man.'

Source 2

▲ A wall painting in an Italian church showing Galen (left) and Hippocrates. The painting dates from the 1200s, 900 years after Galen died.

Smarter Revision: Digital camera

Revision can be fun. You probably don't believe this but here's how to enjoy revision by thinking hard and being creative. This class wanted to sum up why Galen was so important so they created this picture.

1 They investigated Galen's work and completed a 'role of the individual' chart for him.

2 Then they started thinking creatively – how could they turn this information into a picture they could revise from? In this picture each feature they have included in the photo tells you something important about Galen's work.

3 The class took the picture and annotated it – writing in a short explanation of what each object tells us about Galen.

4 They added two think bubbles to sum up Galen's thoughts – but we've taken off those notes and thought bubbles!

Activities

Either
Annotate your own copy of this picture. All the information is on pages 36–39. The activity on page 38 will help you.

Or
You could even produce your own summary picture of Galen's work. Have fun!

Why was Galen so important?

Activities

1. On your own copy of this page:
   a mark SIMILARITIES between the work of Galen and Hippocrates in BLUE.
   b mark DIFFERENCES between the work of Galen and Hippocrates in RED.
2. 'Role of the individual' chart: build up a chart (see page 27) for Galen.
3. Why is Galen so important in the history of medicine? Write down three reasons AND say which of them you think is the most important.
4. Use this information to place your cards on your washing line on page 34.

Claudius Galen was born in Pergamum in Greece in AD129, the son of an architect. Galen's father had a dream in which Asclepius said that his son would become a physician. Galen began studying medicine when he was 16, even travelling to study at the great medical school in Alexandria. He also became a surgeon at a gladiators' school, gaining experience treating wounds and increasing his knowledge of anatomy.

Age 20, Galen moved to Rome. He was a great showman and put on public performances, dissecting animals and giving talks. He also had a terrible temper, inherited from his mother, whom he said 'bit her maids and was always shouting at my father'. When plague broke out, the Emperor Marcus Aurelius summoned Galen to take care of the royal family and he remained doctor to the emperors for the rest of his life.

The work of Claudius Galen

What really made Galen famous were the 60 books he wrote. They combined Greek ideas with what he learned from his own work in Alexandria and Rome, and presented it all so convincingly that they became the basis for medical teaching and learning for the next 1500 years. For most of that time nobody dared to say that Galen was wrong!

Careful observation
The four humours
• Hippocrates' ideas
• His own ideas about 'opposites'
Dissection and surgery
• Knowledge of anatomy
GALEN
Galen wrote about 60 books on medicine. They were the main books used by medical students for over 1500 years

Diagnosis and the four humours

Galen's work was built on the key ideas in the Hippocratic Collection:

Four humours – Like Hippocrates, Galen believed that illness was caused by imbalances in the four humours.

Observation – Like Hippocrates, Galen told doctors to observe and examine patients carefully, taking the pulse and detailed notes of symptoms. In AD167 Galen made detailed notes on the plague sweeping across the empire, recording how his patients had fever, thirst, diarrhoea, skin rash and spat blood. His notes were so thorough this plague became known as 'Galen's plague'.

Treatments

Galen followed Hippocrates in giving advice on diet and exercise to prevent illness. His most common treatment was bleeding patients to restore the balance of the humours. He used bleeding far more than Hippocrates, who had preferred to interfere with the body as little as possible. Galen also developed the idea of using 'Opposites' to balance the humours. For example, if a patient's symptom was too much phlegm then the illness was caused by cold. Galen's treatment was the opposite of cold – heat! He treated the patient by using hot ingredients such as peppers in his cures. If a disease was caused by heat, then the patient would need a cooling cure, perhaps treating this with cucumber in the medicine or diet.

You have too much phlegm, which is cold and wet. You must take something that is hot and fiery – try a pepper.

Anatomy and dissection

Hippocrates had not done much work on anatomy and had not said that dissection was important. Galen disagreed. He believed that physicians should find out as much as possible about the structure and workings of the body, if possible dissecting human bodies themselves. If this was not possible, he advised doctors to dissect apes because they were most like humans.

Galen demonstrated his discoveries about the workings of the nervous system by dissecting a pig. As the pig squealed on the table, Galen cut into its neck, finding the nerves. He could have cut through the right nerve immediately to stop the pig squealing but that did not appeal to Galen's showmanship. Instead he announced 'I will cut this nerve but the pig will keep squealing.' He cut, and the pig kept squealing. He cut again, building up the tension, and again the pig kept squealing. Then he announced, 'When I cut this nerve, the pig will stop squealing.' He cut and the pig was silent!

Although he often had to dissect animals, not humans, some of Galen's discoveries were important. He proved that the brain, not the heart, controlled speech, and that the arteries, and not just the veins, carried blood around the body. Inevitably he made mistakes because the bodies of apes and pigs are not the same as those of humans, but it was to be well over a thousand years before anyone dared to challenge Galen's findings.

Galen's influence

Galen wrote hundreds of books, covering every aspect of medicine in an extremely detailed and well-organised way. He included the work of earlier doctors such as Hippocrates but also added his own work on treatments and on the structure and workings of the body. It seemed as if Galen had covered everything, so people believed that his books had all the answers. That was one reason why Galen's books became the basis for medical training for over a thousand years.

A second reason why so many people believed Galen was always right was that his ideas fitted in with the ideas of the Christian Church, which controlled education in Europe in the Middle Ages. Although Galen was not a Christian, he believed that the body had been created by one god, who had made all the parts of the body fit together perfectly. This matched the Christian belief that God had created human beings, so for centuries Christians did not dare to question Galen's ideas.

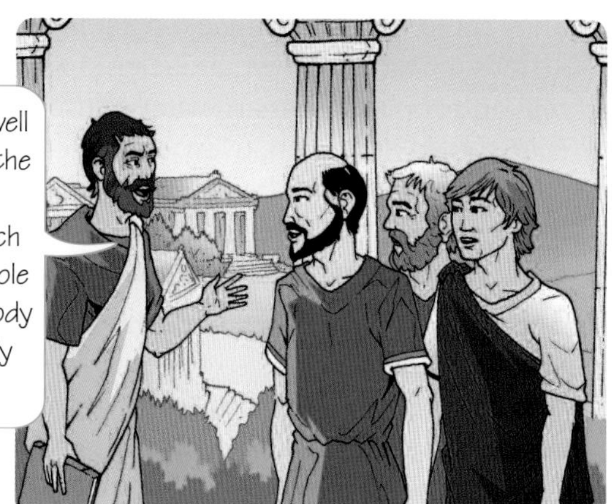

You see how well each part of the body fits together. Each organ has a role to play. The body is wonderfully designed.

Public health – the Romans' big idea

Information

What is public health?
Governments organise public health systems to protect their people from disease. This includes providing, for example, fresh water, sewers and hospitals and making laws to force people to try to prevent diseases spreading.

I am Frontinus, the Water Commissioner of Rome. We Romans have built reservoirs, fountains, water basins. Compare such an array of useful buildings with the idle pyramids or the useless though famous works of the Greeks.

Activities

1 Why was the army so important to the Roman public health system?
2 Make two lists: **a)** the strengths and **b)** the weaknesses of the Roman public health system.
3 Do you think the Roman public health system was an important step forward in the history of medicine?
4 Complete your washingline activity on page 34.

Why did the Romans want to protect the public's health?

Roman rulers needed healthy soldiers to control the Empire. Healthy workers and merchants were needed to keep the Empire fed and prosperous. Therefore they built their towns, villas or army forts in healthy places, away from marshland and polluted water. They tried to keep army forts and cities clean and made sure people had fresh water.

Their public health schemes (see opposite page) used their great skills as builders and engineers. Engineers, often from the army, kept everything running and dealt with repairs.

How successful was Roman public health?

Roman public health schemes were the best there had been – and better than anything in Europe for the next 1500 years. But they were not perfect. What were the problems?

1 They could not stop plagues spreading. In the AD160s a plague (known as Galen's plague) killed 5 million people. A Roman writer said 'plague polluted everything with death. Everywhere fields and towns have no farmers or inhabitants.' Part of the trouble was the army because soldiers carried disease wherever they were sent to fight or defend the Empire.
2 Sewers sometimes spread disease. In York the sewers were too large so water did not flow through quickly enough to clear sewage in the bottom of the sewers. The rough surface of stone sewers also trapped the bacteria that cause disease.

Source 1

▲ A mass grave in Gloucester containing victims of 'Galen's plague'. Their baths and water system could not save them (Source: Oxford Archaeology, www.thehumanjourney.net)

3 Towns could still be dirty places. People had to carry water upstairs. If they did not want to carry it down again they just heaved it out of a window. The poet Juvenal warned: 'Each open window may be a death trap. So hope and pray, poor man, that the local housewives drop nothing worse on your head than a bedpan full of slops!'

The key features of Roman public health schemes in towns

In the countryside little changed. The homes of the rich had bath-houses but across Europe most people's homes did not change.

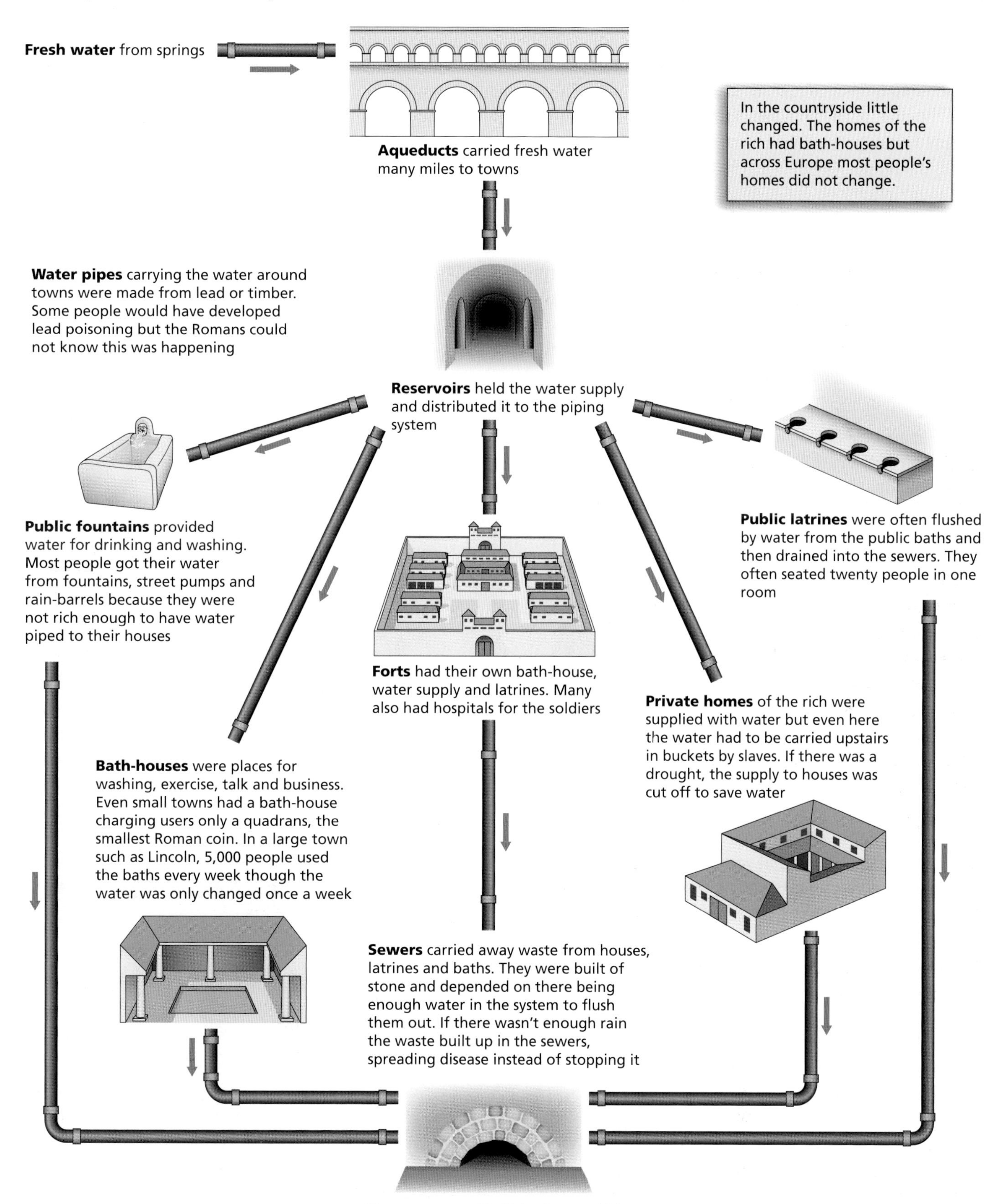

Fresh water from springs
Aqueducts carried fresh water many miles to towns
Water pipes carrying the water around towns were made from lead or timber. Some people would have developed lead poisoning but the Romans could not know this was happening
Reservoirs held the water supply and distributed it to the piping system
Public fountains provided water for drinking and washing. Most people got their water from fountains, street pumps and rain-barrels because they were not rich enough to have water piped to their houses
Public latrines were often flushed by water from the public baths and then drained into the sewers. They often seated twenty people in one room
Forts had their own bath-house, water supply and latrines. Many also had hospitals for the soldiers
Private homes of the rich were supplied with water but even here the water had to be carried upstairs in buckets by slaves. If there was a drought, the supply to houses was cut off to save water
Bath-houses were places for washing, exercise, talk and business. Even small towns had a bath-house charging users only a quadrans, the smallest Roman coin. In a large town such as Lincoln, 5,000 people used the baths every week though the water was only changed once a week
Sewers carried away waste from houses, latrines and baths. They were built of stone and depended on there being enough water in the system to flush them out. If there wasn't enough rain the waste built up in the sewers, spreading disease instead of stopping it
The sewers emptied into rivers, which were used to wash clothes and also for washing and drinking water

2.5 Review: Why was ancient medicine so significant when people didn't even know what made them sick?

You have completed your investigation of each different society. Now it's time to put all those pieces together to see the overall pattern of ancient medicine. Your task is to write the captions to this outline story to answer our main question above.

Activities

By now you should have completed the memory map on pages 14 and 15 recording all the features of ancient medicine. Use that to help you with this task.

1. On your own copy of this story strip write a set of captions to tell the story of ancient medicine. Make sure you include answers to the questions with each picture as they will make sure you also answer our main question about why ancient medicine is significant.
2. On page 7 we set you a task of keep a record of changes and continuities in medicine using living graphs. Now that you have a strong understanding of ancient medicine, go back and update those graphs.
3. People in the Ancient World lived much shorter lives on average than people today. Which two reasons do you think explain why their lives were shorter?

1 What did Prehistoric people believe caused illnesses?

2 What kinds of treatments were used by Prehistoric peoples and which of them continued to be used for many centuries?

3 What was new about Egyptian medicine? Can you suggest at least three developments?

4 What remedies and treatments did the Egyptians use that were similar to those used in prehistoric times?

We need to purge his body to clear the channels.

5 What was Hippocrates' theory about the causes of illness and why was it so important?

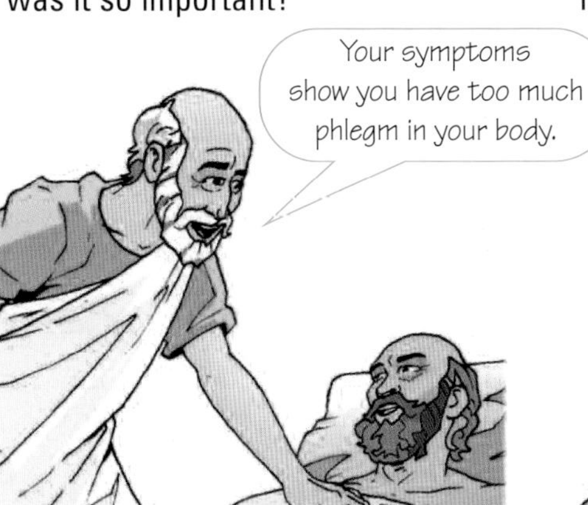

Your symptoms show you have too much phlegm in your body.

6 What methods did Hippocratic doctors use to prevent illness and heal the sick?

7 Which aspects of Greek medicine were not changed by Hippocrates?

8 What was the Romans' big medical idea, and did it make people a lot healthier?

9 Did Galen make any new discoveries or did he just copy the work of Hippocrates?

10 Why did people live much shorter lives than people today?

11 Which parts of ancient medicine had long-lasting importance – and why?

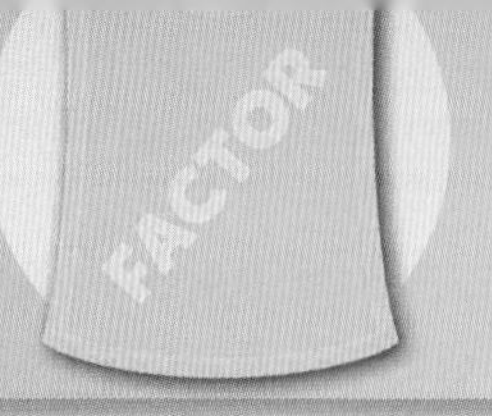

The factor hunt

We have been concentrating on the continuities and changes in medicine but you don't just need to describe **how** medicine and health developed. You need to explain **why** it changed at certain times and stayed the same at others. We began looking at explanations on pages 22–25 and now it's time to take part in a detailed factor hunt. Tracking the factors across the history of medicine will help you do this much more effectively – and get better marks in your exam.

Here's what you need to do, not just here but as you go through the whole history of medicine.

- Identify examples of how each factor affected medicine and health.
- For each example, record whether the factor helped or hindered the development of medicine and health.
- Assess the overall impact of each factor.

Activities

1 In the cartoon on the right how would you finish off Government's sentences 1 and 2?

Factors chart

1 Factor	2 Evidence of factor helping development	3 Evidence of factor hindering development	4 Assessment – did this factor do more to help or hinder development?
War	*Battlefield surgery*		
Government		*It's not the Pharaoh's job to keep people healthy.*	
Religion			

Activities

Prepare a 'factors chart' like the one above. Use the examples below to complete your chart.

First fill in all the factors in the first column.

2 Take each ball in turn and decide which factor it's an example of. Put it in your chart in either column 2 or column 3 of the correct row. Some rows will have several examples in them.

3 Are there any links between two factors? (Think about any balls that might go in more than one row.)

4 Once you have filled up columns 2 and 3 complete column 4, assessing each factor, balancing out the ways it helped and the ways it hindered progress.

5 In one minute, explain to the rest of your class which factor you think had the greatest impact on ancient medicine.

Introducing Development Study questions

By now you should feel like an expert on ancient medicine! However, simply knowing a lot is not enough to achieve a good grade in your GCSE.

This page begins our advice on how to really do well!

Section A: Development Study

Medicine Through Time

You are advised to spend about 1 hour on this section.

Answer Question 1 and ONE other question.

1 Study the sources carefully and then answer the questions which follow.

(a) Study Source A. What dangers faced patients during operations at the beginning of the nineteenth century? [5]

(b) Study Sources B and C. How far do these sources support the impression given of surgery given in Source A? [5]

(c) Do these Sources prove that by the beginning of the nineteenth century surgery had improved little since the time of Paré? Use the sources and your knowledge to explain your answer. [5]

TIMING

It is important to stick to one hour for this section.

If you spend too much time on Section A it will leave you short of time for Section B (the Study in Depth). Both sections are worth the same amount of marks – so time yourself carefully.

Note: We have not included the actual sources. There will usually be a combination of pictures and documents.

ANSWERING QUESTION 1

You must answer this question. It is based on a group of sources. It has three parts, worth a total of fifteen marks. Aim to spend about 25 minutes of your hour on this question.

C THINK CAREFULLY ABOUT WHICH QUESTION YOU CHOOSE

After answering Question 1 you need to make an important choice. You must choose ONE question from questions 2, 3 and 4. Each question is worth 20 marks and is broken down into three parts.

Do not rush your decision. Read all three parts of each question before you make your choice. It is important that you can answer all three parts of the question, not just the first part which only carries 5 marks.

Aim to spend 35–40 minutes on this question.

D LOOK AT THE THEME OF THE QUESTION

Each question has a theme that links the three parts of the question together. For example, Question 2 is exploring the impact of two factors on the development of medicine.

E 'DESCRIBE' QUESTIONS (part (a))

The first part of the question is worth 5 marks. It asks you to describe briefly something from a period. This might be the work of an individual, the impact of a factor like religion or how people tried to prevent disease.

Choose ONE of the following three questions.
You must answer ALL parts of the question you choose.

2 Both religion and chance have had an important impact on the development of medicine.

(a) Briefly describe the impact of religion on ancient Greek medicine. [5]

(b) Explain ways in which chance has had an impact on the development of medicine. [7]

(c) 'Since Roman times religion has hindered, rather than helped, medical progress.' Explain how far you agree with this statement. [8]

F 'EXPLAIN' QUESTIONS (part (b))

The second part of the question is worth 7 marks so spend longer answering 'Explain' questions than 'Describe' questions. You will be asked to explain how or why something has happened. For example, Question 2(b) asks you to explain how a factor (chance) has had an impact on medicine over a long period of time.

G 'EVALUATION' QUESTIONS (part (c))

The third part of the question is worth 8 marks. You will usually be asked to evaluate a statement and explain how far you agree or disagree with it. This question will require you to bring in knowledge from a long period of time. For example, Question 2(c) is asking you to evaluate the role of religion since Roman times.

3 Since the time of the Ancient Greeks there have been many ideas about the cause and the prevention of disease.

(a) Briefly describe how the Romans tried to prevent disease. [5]

(b) Explain why there was so much opposition to smallpox vaccination throughout the nineteenth century. [7]

(c) 'Between the time of the Ancient Greeks and the end of the nineteenth century there has been more continuity than change in ideas about the causes of disease.' Explain how far you agree with this statement. [8]

4

Note: We have not included Question 4.

Answering 'describe' questions

The examiners are not trying to catch you out: they are giving you a chance to show what you know – **and what you can do with what you know.** If you can work out what the question is getting at, you will probably be able to answer it from what you have learned.

To make sure that you stay relevant to the question on the exam paper you will need to practice how to 'de-code' questions.

De-coding exam questions

Step 1: Read the question a couple of times.

Step 2: Highlight each of the following. You could use a different colour for each.

Date boundaries – What time period should you cover in your answer? Stick to this carefully, otherwise you will waste time writing about events that are not relevant to the question.

Content focus – The topic the examiner wants you to focus on.

Question type – Different question types require different approaches. Look for key words, such as 'Describe' or 'Explain', that will help you work out what type of approach is needed.

Marks available – Look at how many marks the question is worth. This gives you a guide as to how much you are expected to write. Do not spend too long on questions that are only worth a few marks.

Look at the exam question below.

You must stick to the date boundaries of the question. In this case it is the Roman period. Details of how people in other time periods try to prevent disease will not gain you any extra marks.

The content focus for this question is on how the Romans tried to prevent disease. This must be the focus of your answer. There is no need to explore other areas of Roman medicine such as surgery or what they thought caused disease.

Briefly describe how the Romans tried to prevent disease.

[5 marks]

Question type: you need to 'describe how' the Romans tried to prevent disease. You are not being asked to 'explain why' they introduced measures to try to prevent disease or whether you think they were successful.

5 marks are available. This indicates that only a short answer is required.
One paragraph would be enough.

Tackling 'describe' questions

Tip 1: Avoid general statements. Make sure you show off your knowledge and give specific examples.

'Describe' questions only carry five marks. It is important that you get to the point quickly and avoid general statements that do not pick up many marks. Look at the example below:

The Romans believed that it was very important to try and prevent disease. They introduced lots of different things to try and stop disease spreading.

This answer contains **general statements**. The answer provides no specific details of *how* the Romans tried to prevent disease. It would only score one mark.

This answer below is a lot better. It gives **specific examples** of what the Romans did to try and prevent disease.

*The Romans used **aqueducts** to bring clean water to towns and built bath houses for people to wash in. They also built **latrines** and **sewers** which were used to take waste away.*

Tip 2: Stay relevant to the question

One of the main problems with 'Describe' questions is that pupils write too much! They include details that are not relevant to the question.

Make sure you stick to the question – **describe** what the Romans did.

You do NOT need to:

- **explain** why they did it, or
- **evaluate** how successful their methods were.

Questions that ask you to explain or evaluate carry more marks and need longer answers. We will provide advice on tackling these types of question later. Describe questions carry less marks and it is important that you stay relevant to the question. If you write too much you could run out of time later in the exam paper.

Activities

Read the answer below. The student has written too much because they have not stayed relevant to the question.

- At times they explain why the Romans introduced public health measures.
- At other times they evaluate how successful these measures were.

On your own copy, cross out the sentences that are irrelevant to the question. You should be left with a good answer!

The Romans tried to prevent disease by improving public health in their towns. This is because they needed fit and healthy people to serve in the army and keep the Empire strong. The Romans thought that dirt was somehow linked to disease although they did not know exactly how because they did not know about bacteria. The Romans built their towns in healthy places, away from marshes and polluted water. They built aqueducts to bring fresh water into the towns and sewers to take waste away. They also built public fountains for people to drink from and public baths for them to bathe in. The Roman public health schemes were the best the world had seen. They were more advanced in preventing disease than the Ancient Greeks or Egyptians. But they were not perfect. There were still outbreaks of epidemic disease. For example, in AD165, an epidemic killed five million people.

Tip 3: Practise makes perfect!

Sample 'describe' questions

1. Briefly describe the impact of religion on medicine in Egyptian times.
2. What medical treatments were provided at a Greek Asclepion?
3. Briefly describe the work of Hippocrates.

Section 3: Why didn't medicine improve during the Middle Ages?

About AD500 the Roman Empire in Europe was destroyed by attacks from Goths, Vandals and other tribes from Germany and the east. Over the next one thousand years medicine did not improve and in some ways got worse. Your task in this section is to find out why medicine did not improve in the Middle Ages.

Medical moments in time: London, 1347

Activities

Work in pairs.

1 You have **five minutes**. What evidence can you find in this picture of:
   - a different kinds of healers
   - b ideas about what caused illnesses
   - c treatments for medical problems
   - d methods of preventing illnesses?
2 You have **three minutes**. How many similarities can you find between medicine in the Middle Ages and medicine in the ancient world?
3 You have **two minutes**. What differences can you find between medicine in the Middle Ages and medicine in the ancient world?
4 What chance do Londoners have of surviving the terrible disease they have heard of? List three pieces of evidence to support your answer.

I treated arrow wounds with the King's army. A blacksmith made me a tool to take the arrow out. Then honey on the wound to help it heal. That'll teach you to walk behind the target at archery practice.
Get this filth cleaned up or I'll fine you two shillings.
Your humours are out of balance. Go to a surgeon who'll bleed you and go again in six months.
A terrible pestilence is killing everyone in France. I've heard it's caused by the planets. What can we do?
You ought to employ more rakers to clean the streets.
Pray to God for forgiveness. God sends plague as punishment for our sins.
Her eye's sore.
My sister has a good remedy – onion, garlic, bull's gall, wine. I'll run and get some.
Physicians trained by reading books by Hippocrates, Galen and Arab doctors such as Ibn Sina and al-Rhazes.
A certain cure for the pestilence! A holy remedy made from finest herbs and dust from the true Holy Cross on which Christ was crucified. Only one silver penny!

3.1 Why couldn't people stop the Black Death?

The pestilence that arrived in 1348 is better known as the Black Death. We can learn a lot about medicine in the Middle Ages from the Black Death. It acts as a linking thread throughout this section, so you need some basic information to begin with. That's what pages 52–55 are for.

The horror of the Black Death!

The Black Death was one of the most frightening outbreaks of disease in history. The epidemic began in China, spread to India and across Europe. In Britain people heard stories of the disease spreading through France. At the time they simply called it 'the pestilence'. What happened next was described by a monk writing at a monastery in Wiltshire:

> In 1348 the cruel pestilence arrived at a port called Melcombe in Dorset. It killed numberless people in Dorset, Devon and Somerset and then it came to Bristol where very few were left alive.
>
> It then travelled northwards, leaving not a town, a village or even, except rarely, a house, without killing most or all of the people there. There was such a shortage of people that there were hardly enough living to bury the dead.

Historians now estimate that at least 40 per cent of the population died, with towns and ports being even harder hit. The plague killed everyone, rich and poor, and they died quickly and painfully. Only remote villages and farms high up on the hills were likely to be safe.

Activities

1. Information speed test! How quickly can you find the answers to these questions?
   - **a** When did the Black Death arrive in England?
   - **b** Which two diseases do historians think were involved?
   - **c** Which two animals probably spread the disease?
   - **d** What percentage of people in Britain died?
   - **e** What were buboes?
2. Use Sources 2–6.
   - **a** Choose three words to describe people's reactions to the Black Death.
   - **b** Why do you think they reacted in these ways?
3. Think back to your work on ancient medicine. Do you think the Black Death would have hit the Romans so hard?

What was the Black Death?

Even now historians are not completely certain what the pestilence was but it was probably bubonic plague. Bubonic plague is carried by rats and spread by fleas. A flea becomes infected when it bites an infected rat, then it passes the disease on to other rats and to humans when it bites them. People bitten by infected rats suddenly felt cold and tired and then discovered painful swellings called buboes in their armpits and groins. Blisters appeared all over their bodies, followed by high fever, severe headaches, unconsciousness for several days and then death.

The impact of the plague was probably made worse by a second disease called pneumonic plague. This was spread by people coughing over others. The victims coughed up blood because the disease attacked their lungs, causing breathing problems. They died more quickly, in a day or two at most.

Source 1

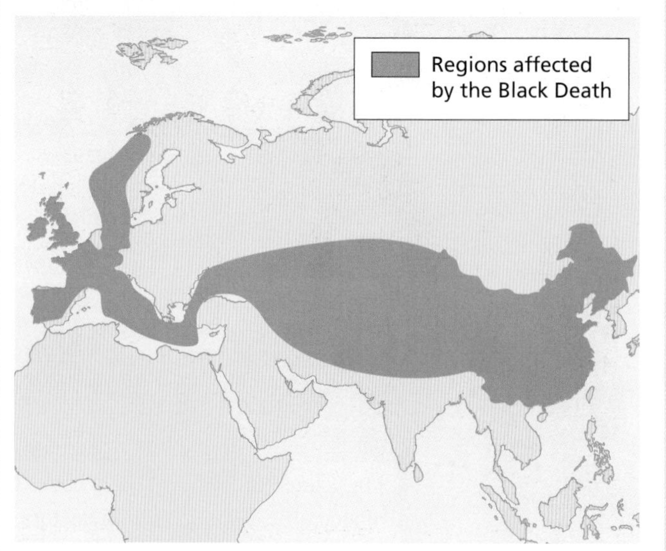

▲ The Black Death spread throughout Asia and Europe, probably carried by rats and fleas on trading ships and in packs of goods carried by merchants.

Source 2

An Irish monk, Brother John Clynn, wrote an account of the plague and concluded:
'I, waiting among the dead for death to come, leave parchment for continuing the work, in case anyone should still be alive in the future and any son of Adam can escape this pestilence and continue my work.'

Source 3

The Italian writer, Petrarch, wrote this letter to a friend in 1350:
'Where are our dear friends now? Where are the beloved faces? Where are the affectionate words, the relaxed and enjoyable conversations? What lightning bolt devoured them? What earthquake topped them? There was crowd of us, now we are almost alonc. We should make new friends, but how, when the human race is almost wiped out; and why, when it looks to me as if the end of the world is at hand?

Source 4

▲ King Death, an illustration in a French book of prayers from the early fifteenth century. The scroll he is holding reads 'Remember man that you are ash [and] into ash you shall return'.

Source 5

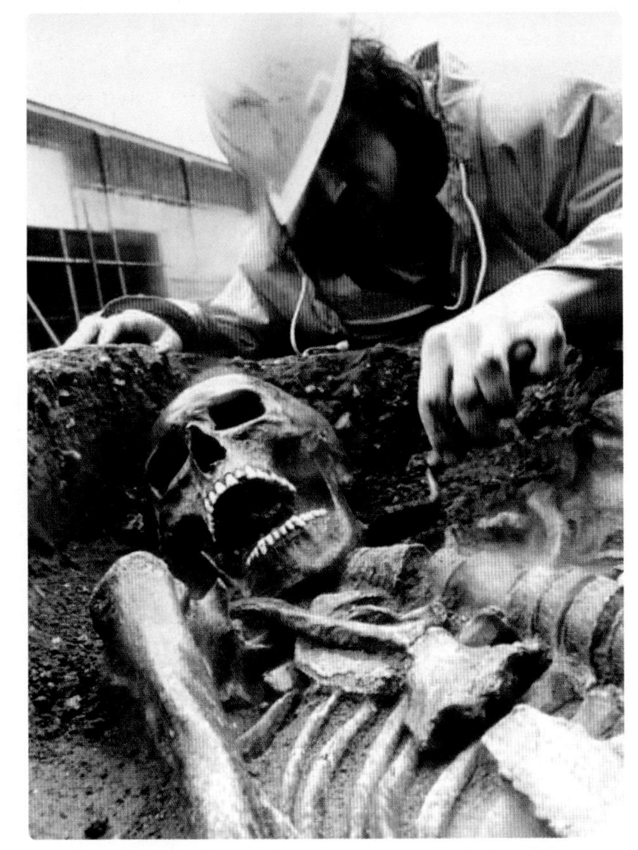

▲ Black Death graves at Hereford cathedral. A chronicler wrote that in London 'they dug broad, deep pits and buried the bodies together, treating everyone alike, except the most eminent'.

Source 6

▲ Words scratched on the church wall in Ashwell, Hertfordshire: '1349 the pestilence 1350 pitiless, wild, violent, the dregs of the people live to tell the tale'.

What did people think caused the Black Death?

What did people think caused the pestilence and how did they try to deal with it? These two quick activities will help you answer these questions. Later in this section you can increase your understanding of these topics.

Activities

1 Which of Sources 1–5 would you use to support each of these statements?
   a The ideas of Galen were still accepted and followed.
   b Some people, at least, connected the Black Death to dirt and bad air.
   c In some places people took the chance to blame and attack outsiders.
   d Science in the Middle Ages was very different from science today.
2 Which of the explanations in Sources 1–5 do you think was the most widely believed? Use Sources 6–10 to help you.

Source 1

A Swedish bishop who had read work by John Jacobus, a French physician, suggested:
'Sometimes the pestilence comes from a privy toilet next to a chamber or some other thing that corrupts the air. Sometimes it comes from dead flesh or from standing water in ditches.'

Source 2

In September 1348 the Prior of Christchurch Abbey, Canterbury wrote to the Bishop of London:
'Terrible is God towards the sons of men ... He uses plagues, miserable famines, wars and other suffering to arise and to terrify and torment men and so drive out their sins. Thus England is struck by the pestilence because of the increasing pride and numberless sins of the people.'

Source 3

By the 1400s the science of astrology was an important part of medicine. Physicians believed the stars and planets affected people's bodies because both were made of the same four elements – air, earth, fire and water. Guy de Chauliac, a French surgeon, blamed the Black Death on two things. One was 'the state of each victim's body – bad digestion, weakness and blockage'. The other was 'the close position of Saturn, Jupiter and Mars in 1345... always a sign of wonderful, terrible or violent things to come'. This fifteenth-century illustration shows the planet Saturn eating his children.

Source 4

▲ A German woodcut showing the burning of Jews in Germany. Minority groups were blamed for the Black Death in many countries. Jews were said to have poisoned water supplies and in some places were burned as people looked for someone to blame.

Source 5

In 1365 a physician called John of Burgundy wrote:
'Many people have been killed by the plague, especially those stuffed with evil humours. As Galen says, the body does not become sick unless it contains evil humours.'

How did people try to treat or stop the Black Death?

Activities

3 Which of Sources 6–10 provides evidence of:
  a the belief that God sent the pestilence to punish sins
  b the ideas of Galen being still followed by physicians
  c public health in British towns being much worse than in Roman towns
  d doctors being helpless to stop the Black Death
  e activity that might have done a little good?

Source 6

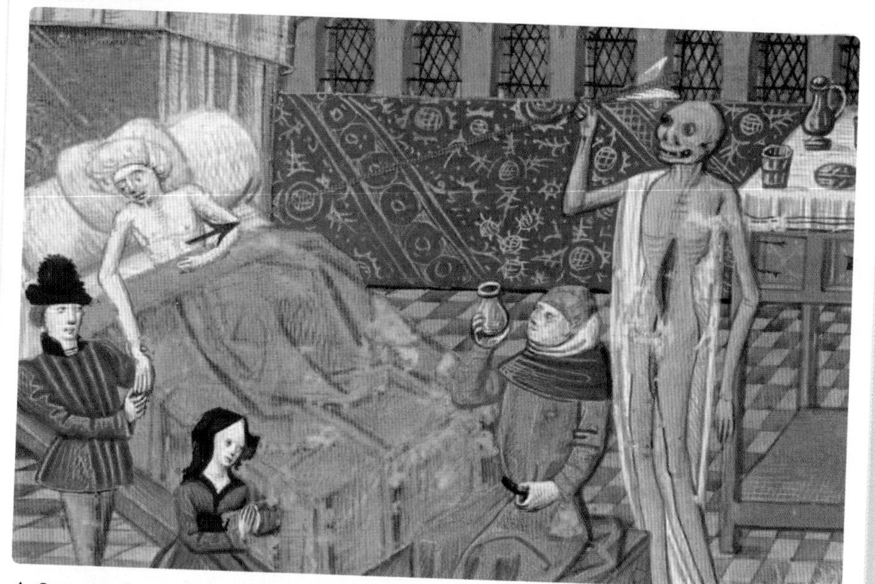

▲ One physician takes the victim's pulse while the other examines his urine, but even they cannot stop 'Death' taking the victim. This warning was in a fifteenth-century French manuscript.

Source 7

◀ The King and bishops ordered that services and procession be held in every church at least once a day, in which people prayed for forgiveness and asked God to put an end to the disease. Some people went further and made candles their own height and lit them in church as offerings to God. In Barcelona, the citizens made a candle 7 kilometres long that they hoped would encircle and protect the city.

Source 8

▲ Flagellants walked through towns as the plague spread, whipping themselves to show God that they had repented their sins and asking God to be merciful.

Source 9

This advice comes from John of Burgundy, author of one of the first books about the plague, written in 1365: 'Avoid too much eating and drinking and avoid baths which open the pores, for the pores are doorways through which poisonous air can enter the body. In cold or rainy weather, light fires in your room. In foggy or windy weather, inhale perfumes every morning before leaving home. If the plague arrives during hot weather, eat cold things rather than hot and drink more than you eat. Be sparing with hot substances such as pepper, garlic, onions and everything else that generates excessive heat and instead use cucumbers, fennel and spinach.'

Source 10

In April 1349, at the height of the Black Death, King Edward III wrote to the Mayor of London:
'Have the filth lying in the streets removed with all speed to places far distant, the city cleansed from all odours so that no great mortality may arise from such smells ... the filth from the houses is infecting the air, endangering people through the contagious sickness which is increasing daily.'

3.2 The Big Story of medicine in the Middle Ages

Pages 50–55 have introduced you to medicine in the Middle Ages. Now use your Smarter Revision techniques to get clear in your mind the key features of medieval medicine. That will set you up for this section's main question about why medicine didn't improve.

	Medicine at the end of the Ancient Period	
Healers	(a) Mothers and family members treated most illnesses. Women with skills and experience were often called to help, e.g. with childbirth. (b) Priests at temples to Asclepius.	(c) Surgeons, e.g. army surgeons, trained by observing others and improved their skills through practice. (d) Specialist doctors trained by reading the books of Hippocrates and Galen.
Ideas about causes of illness	(a) Many believed that illnesses were caused by gods and spirits.	(b) Doctors said that many illnesses had natural causes. They followed Hippocrates' theory that illness was caused when the body's humours were out of balance.
Knowledge of the human body	(a) Doctors knew about many of the main organs and bones from observation of wounds.	(b) At Alexandria discoveries had been made through dissection but dissection was rarely allowed for religious reasons.
Everyday treatments	(a) Remedies were made up from herbs, minerals and animal parts. (b) Prayers, charms and chants used.	(c) Bleeding, purging and other methods used to restore the proper balance of the humours. Galen introduced treatment by 'Opposites'. (d) Rest, exercise and diet.
Surgery	(a) Simple surgery on visible wounds and tumours. (b) Splints for fractured bones.	(c) Trephining (cutting hole in skull). (d) Plants such as opium dulled pain a little but there were no effective anaesthetics. (e) Surgeons used wine, vinegar or honey to clean wounds but could not prevent infections spreading or stop heavy bleeding.
Public health and prevention	(a) The Egyptians and Greeks left people to look after their own hygiene. (b) The Romans built aqueducts, sewers and baths in towns and forts.	(c) Most people in the countryside in the Roman Empire did not have baths or sewers. (d) Even the Romans' public health system could not stop epidemic diseases spreading and killing millions.

Activities

1 On pages 14–15 you built up a memory map for ancient medicine. Use that model to create a memory map for medieval medicine. Do this in pencil at this stage and then finalise your graphs at the end of this section.

2 On pages 6–7 you began to create living graphs which record developments across time. Use the information on this page to fill out your graphs for the Middle Ages. Do this in pencil at this stage and then finalise your graphs at the end of this section.

Medicine c.1400, at the end of the Middle Ages

Little had changed although from the 1200s physicians (specialist doctors) were trained at universities.

- **a** Mothers and family members treated most illnesses. Women with skills and experience were often called to help, e.g. with childbirth.
- **b** Priests said prayers to help the sick and protect from illness.

- **c** Surgeons, e.g. army surgeons, trained by observing others and improved their skills through practice.
- **d** Physicians trained at universities by reading the books by Hippocrates and Galen and some Arab medical writers. In the 1300s there were fewer than 100 physicians in England.

Nothing had changed.

- **a** Many believed that illnesses were sent by God.
- **b** Doctors said that many illnesses had natural causes. They followed Hippocrates' theory that illness was caused when the body's humours were out of balance.

Nothing had changed.

- **a** Doctors knew about Greek and Roman discoveries but did not learn any more.
- **b** Dissection was carried out to illustrate what Galen had said, not make new discoveries.

Treatments were very similar

- **a** Remedies were made up from herbs, minerals and animal parts.
- **b** Prayers, charms and rhymes used.

- **c** Bleeding, purging and other methods to restore the proper balance of the humours, following the methods of Galen.
- **d** Rest, exercise and diet.

Surgeons improved their techniques and instruments a little through practise

- **a** Simple surgery on visible tumours and wounds.
- **b** Splints for fractured bones.

- **c** Trephining (cutting hole in skull).
- **d** Plants such as opium dulled pain but there were no effective anaesthetics.
- **e** Surgeons used wine, vinegar or honey to clean wounds but could not prevent infections spreading or stop heavy bleeding.

The Roman public health systems had disappeared so in towns and wealthy homes public health was worse.

- **a** Town governments employed people and made laws to try to keep streets clean but often had little success.
- **b** It was very difficult to keep towns clean as they were full of animals. Houses were packed together and there were few paved streets.
- **c** Kings were not expected to improve hygiene or protect public health. Their job was to defend the country and keep law and order.
- **d** Epidemic diseases still could not be stopped.

3.3 Why didn't medicine improve in the Middle Ages? Part 1

Now you know that medicine did not change much in the Middle Ages and in some ways got worse. That's strange because people were just as intelligent then as we are today and they wanted to be healthy. So what stopped them improving their medicine and health? We'll tackle this in two stages – you'll find out at half-time that the word 'tackle' has been chosen deliberately!

Using your factors chart to explain why medicine did not improve

Activities

A 'factors chart' will help you build up your explanation throughout this section.

1 Prepare your own version of this chart, on paper or as a spreadsheet.

2 Fill in your factors chart with examples from page 59. You will find plenty of examples of war but there are examples of other factors too.

Factors chart

1 Factor	2 Evidence of factor helping medicine improve	3 Evidence of factor keeping medicine at the same level	4 Evidence of factor hindering development of medicine	5 Assessment – did it do more to help or hinder or just keep medicine static?
War				
Government				
Religion				

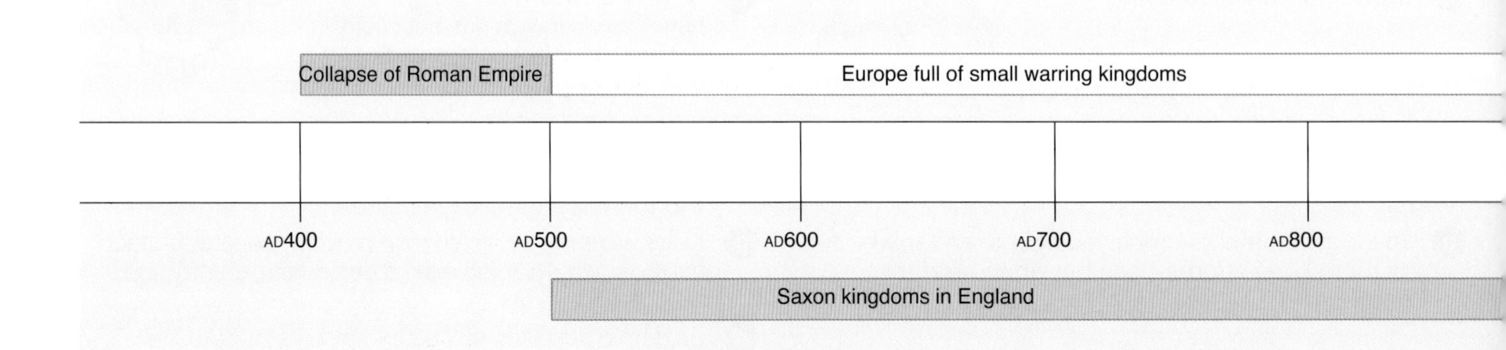

The end of the Roman Empire

After the Roman Empire collapsed, Europe was split into many small kingdoms, frequently invading and fighting each other. Britain, for example, was taken over by tribes of Angles and Saxons who couldn't read and were not interested in Galen, baths or sewer systems. You can see the impact of all this war and destruction below.

Activities

3 Which aspect of medicine do you think the collapse of the Roman Empire and all the wars:
  a hit hardest
  b may have helped?

1 - Without the Roman army there were **no engineers** with the technological knowledge to keep public baths, sewers and aqueducts working effectively.

2 - Invading tribes **destroyed or neglected** public health systems.

3 - Invasions and wars **destroyed libraries** and books in monasteries.

4 - The attitudes of rulers were different. **Kings spent their money on wars,** not on sewers and baths. They were illiterate so had no interest in education.

5 - Wars made **travel more dangerous** so doctors travelled much less to gain experience and education.

6 - All these wars meant there was plenty of **practice for surgeons.**

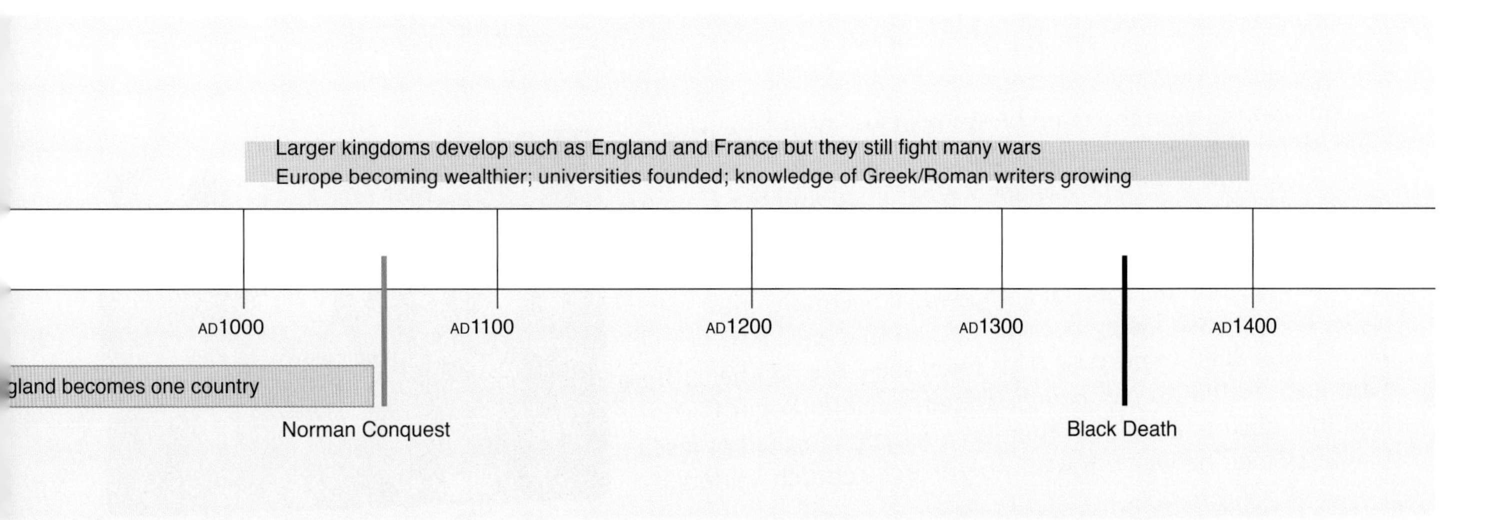

How did Christianity and Islam affect medical developments?

The warfare after the collapse of the Roman Empire nearly destroyed all the medical knowledge built up by the Greeks and the Romans. However, the two great religions, Christianity and Islam, made sure this knowledge was not lost. Firstly, they saved many Greek and Roman medical books from destruction. Secondly, they made sure that physicians continued to read and trust the work of Galen.

Activities

1 Take each development, A–F in turn.
   a Is it an example of the impact of:
      - beliefs and attitudes or
      - communications?
   b Did it improve or hinder the development of medicine, or help to keep it at the same level?
   c Use your answers to a and b to add this evidence to your factors chart.

2 a How similar were Christianity and Islam in their attitudes to medicine?
   b What differences can you find in their attitudes to medicine?

Christian developments

A

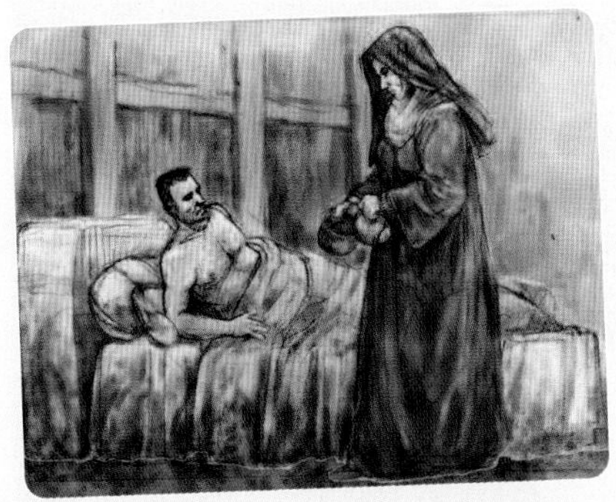

Christians believed that sickness was sent by God to punish people for their sins. Therefore the sick could be healed if they prayed for forgiveness to Jesus Christ and the saints linked to particular illnesses. St Apollonia was the patron saint of toothache because all her teeth had been knocked out when she was murdered because of her religion. In some hospitals, nuns fed the sick and gave them herbal remedies but prayer was the most important treatment. At the end of the hall (or ward) was an altar where priests said mass seven times each day. The patients joined in, hoping that prayer would help them recover.

B

The Christian Church preserved a great deal of knowledge handed down from the Greeks and Romans. Monks in monasteries copied out the Bible, histories and other ancient books, including books by Galen and other medical writers from Greece and Rome.

C

Galen's books were the main books read by physicians in Europe for two reasons. Firstly, the Christian Church controlled the universities where physicians were trained and the Church believed that ancient writings should not be questioned. If people started questioning Galen they might question the Bible so questioning was not a good idea! Secondly, the Church supported Galen because he said that each part of the body had a definite purpose. This fitted the Christian belief that God had created human beings. Therefore when Roger Bacon said that doctors should do their own research instead of just reading Galen he was thrown into prison by church leaders.

Islamic developments

D

The Islamic religion taught people to look after the sick and Arab hospitals were famous for the care they gave patients. The first was founded in Baghdad around 805 and by the 1100s every large town had a hospital. They provided medical care and prayers for the sick.

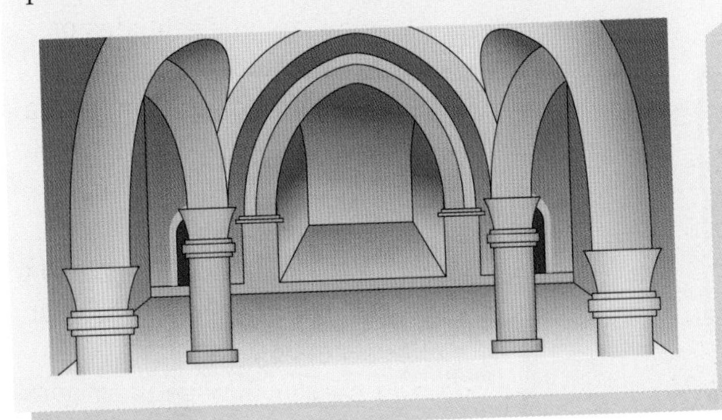

E

Galen

The eighth century was a period of great wealth in the Islamic Empire, when Arab rulers believed it was important to develop education. Many Greek medical books were translated into Arabic by Islamic scholars.

The city of Baghdad was the main centre for collecting and translating medical texts. Without these translations the books by Galen and others could well have been lost amidst European wars.

F

Islamic doctors wrote multi-volume medical encyclopaedias which organised medical knowledge with great thoroughness. They included the work of Galen and other Greek medical writers. These books were later translated from Arabic into Latin and were used in Europe so that European physicians learned more about the work of Galen and Arab doctors. Two of the greatest Arab doctors were:

1 al-Razi (c.860–925) known in Europe as Rhazes. He wrote over 200 books, including his own ideas but also believed 'he who studies the works of the Ancients, gains the experience of their labour as if he had himself lived thousands of years'.

2 Ibn Sina (980–1037) known in Europe as Avicenna. His medical encyclopaedia, *The Canon*, was used to teach European physicians until the 1600s. He included the work of the Greeks and his own methods and was known as the 'Galen of Islam'.

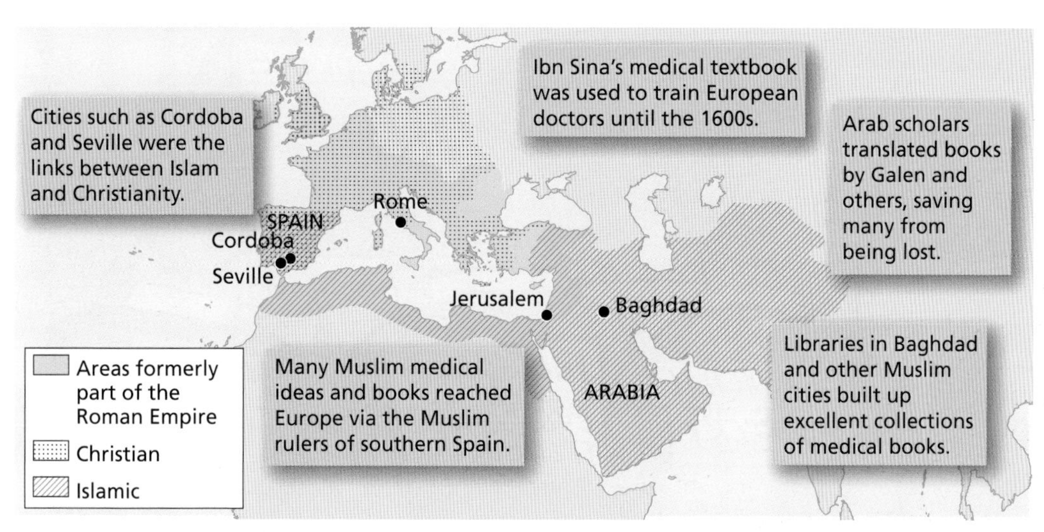
Cities such as Cordoba and Seville were the links between Islam and Christianity.
Ibn Sina's medical textbook was used to train European doctors until the 1600s.
Arab scholars translated books by Galen and others, saving many from being lost.
SPAIN
Cordoba
Seville
Rome
Jerusalem
Baghdad
ARABIA
Areas formerly part of the Roman Empire
Christian
Islamic
Many Muslim medical ideas and books reached Europe via the Muslim rulers of southern Spain.
Libraries in Baghdad and other Muslim cities built up excellent collections of medical books.

◀ After the Roman Empire collapsed, its lands became dominated by two great religions: Christianity and Islam. Europe was full of small countries that spent a lot of time fighting each other, but it was united by Christianity. By AD1000 most people in Europe had become Christians. Islam spread through Arabia, North Africa and into Spain.

3.4 Why didn't medicine improve? A half-time team talk

Now you can see why we said you'd be tackling this enquiry in two stages. This half-time team talk is here to make sure you are on the right lines in building up your factors chart before you start Stage 2 and then decide which factors were most important in preventing medical improvement.

COACH
War, you've been our best player. Great tackles, really pushed them back hard to begin with. But you faded a bit later on. Your only mistake was letting that surgery chap get some practice. But you've had a great game so far.

COACH
You've done well. Stopped them having any creative ideas. Just don't waste time helping people who get injured. Keep it up.

A promising start. Good factor-to-man-marking. You've really pushed Public Health back – he's a danger so stay on top of him in the second-half. I like the way you're teaming up with war – really good team work.
GOVERNMENT

Great start. Really great interceptions stopped them building up any understanding. But their Arab players are making some good passes so be careful.

COACH
What are we paying you lot for? Get stuck in and make some tackles!

Activities

In this match the factors are trying to stop medicine making progress.

1. The coach thinks that War has been the star factor so far, doing most to stop medicine developing. Do you agree? What evidence would you use to support your judgement?
2. Work in pairs. Take one of the topics listed below. Read the topic pages and work out which factors are:
   - **a** putting in the strongest tackles and pushing medicine backwards
   - **b** stopping medicine's development but not pushing it back
   - **c** doing more to help medicine than hinder it.

   Topics:

   Hospitals and healers (pages 64–65)

   Knowledge of the body and causes of disease (pages 66–67)

   Treatments (pages 68–69)

   Surgery (pages 70–71)

   Public health (pages 72–73)
3. Then complete your factors chart as a class using the information you have collected.

3.5 Why didn't medicine improve in the Middle Ages? Part 2

Topic Hospitals and healers – who could you go to for help?

Care for the sick is of great importance. You must help them as you would help Christ, whom you help in helping the sick.

This extract from the rules of the Benedictine monks might make you optimistic about going to a hospital if you were ill. Looking after the sick was an important part of the work of the Christian Church and this led to many hospitals being founded in the Middle Ages. By 1400 there were over 500 hospitals in England, although many had only five or six beds. St Leonard's in York was unusually large with over 200 beds. However, hospitals were very careful about who they took in, as Source 1 shows. So you could not get into hospital if you had a disease that other people might catch!

Occasionally, hospitals were set up to care for particular cases. In London, Richard Whittington, the Lord Mayor, paid for an eight-bed hospital for unmarried pregnant women. In Chester there was a hospital for the care of 'poor and silly persons'. Leper houses were built outside towns to separate the victims of the disease leprosy from healthy people. Leprosy was particularly feared because it rotted people's flesh, a punishment from God for sin.

Source 1

From the rules of the hospital of St John, Bridgwater in the south of England, 1219: 'No lepers, lunatics or persons having the falling sickness or other contagious disease, and no pregnant women, or sucking infants and no intolerable persons, even though they be poor and infirm, are to be admitted. If any such be admitted by mistake they are to be expelled as soon as possible. And when the other poor and infirm persons have recovered they are to be let out without delay.'

▲ The Hotel Dieu in Paris. The King's doctors worked there so this was not typical but it is one of the few illustrations of the inside of a medieval hospital. What evidence can you see of **a)** religion and **b)** medical help?

Information

Islamic hospitals

Islam also taught people to look after the sick, and Arab hospitals were famous for the care they gave patients. Like Christian hospitals they looked after the elderly and infirm but they also provided medical care. The hospital at Cairo, built in 1283, had specialist wards for mental and physical problems, a surgery, pharmacy, library, lecture rooms for teaching and a Christian chapel as well as a mosque.

What kinds of care could the sick get?

Most hospitals were like care-homes today, looking after the poor and elderly. They provided food, rest and, most importantly, prayer. At the end of the hall (or ward) was an altar where priests said mass seven times each day. People believed that God sent sickness to punish them for their sins so they joined in the prayers, hoping that God would realise they were sorry for their sins. Nursing care was provided by nuns who had a good knowledge of herbal and other remedies, often drawn from the books in their library.

Outside hospitals women treated the vast majority of illnesses. Mothers and wives had a wide range of remedies at their fingertips although sometimes the local wise-woman was called in to use her skills and knowledge. Women also acted as midwives. In some towns midwives had to be apprenticed and gain licences and were then paid for their expertise.

If you had a little money or were very worried about your illness you could see a local surgeon. Some surgeons were very skilful, learning through practice as apprentices to experienced surgeons. Guilds of Master-Surgeons required new members to gain licences by passing tests. Some surgeons read books by great European surgeons such as Guy de Chauliac. Women could qualify as surgeons by working as apprentices. Family links played an important part in giving women this opportunity. Records list Katherine, a surgeon in London around 1250, whose father and brothers were surgeons.

Only the rich could afford to go to a physician. Physicians were the highest-ranking doctors because they trained at universities. They treated kings, nobles and wealthy merchants and were well-paid, but there were few of them. In the 1300s there were fewer than 100 physicians in England.

Source 2

In The Canterbury Tales, Geoffrey Chaucer described a physician as:

'Well read was he in Asculapius, Hippocrates, and Hali, and Galen, Serapion, Rhazes, and Avicen…'

Activities

1 **Factor hunt** – what evidence can you find of the effects of
   a religion and
   b lifestyle?
2 a According to the information and sources who did hospitals look after?
   b What kinds of help did hospitals provide?
3 How important a role did women play in medicine?
4 a How does Chaucer (Source 2) show that the physician was well-qualified?
   b How can you tell the man in Source 3 is a physician? (Look at page 68 to see if you are right.)

Source 3

▲ A picture of a physician from about 1400.

Knowledge of the body and causes of disease – what did medieval physicians know?

Activities

1. **Factor hunt** – what evidence can you find on these two pages of the effects of:
   - **a** religion
   - **b** attitudes – conservatism (respect for tradition)
   - **c** attitudes – enquiry?
2. Look back to page 54. Which sources are examples of the ideas about the causes of disease below?
3. Why was new knowledge of the body or of the causes of disease not developed?
4. Why were regular dissections a small step forward?
5. Which new idea about the body was suggested by an Arab doctor?

1 God or the Devil

The most common belief was that God sent illnesses such as the Black Death to punish people for their sins. The Anglo-Saxons also believed that elves and spirits, the Devil's helpers, shot invisible arrows, known as elf-shot, to cause everyday illnesses such as headaches.

2 The four humours

Physicians followed the theories of Hippocrates and Galen and said that illness was caused when the body's humours were out of balance. Greek books were at the centre of university medical training. Many people accepted this theory because physicians were respected for their university training. Islamic doctors also believed in the importance of the four humours because of their studies of Galen.

3 Common-sense – bad air and dirt

A common explanation was that bad air caused illness. At the time of the Black Death many people said that earthquakes had infected the air. Some people did link the bad air to dirt and filth in the streets but could not explain exactly what the link was. Another common-sense belief was that worms caused illness. This sounds strange but archaeological discoveries show that many people suffered from worms in their stomachs and they would have seen these worms in their faeces.

4 Desperate explanations

As the Black Death killed millions, a wide range of other desperate and bizarre explanations were put forward:

- An English monk blamed the outrageous fashions that people had been wearing in recent years.
- When another outbreak of plague in 1361 killed many children, another churchman said God was punishing children who did not respect or look after their parents.
- Minority groups were blamed. Jews were said to have poisoned water supplies and in some places they were burned as people looked for someone to blame.

Knowledge of the body

Source 1

Bodies were dissected as Galen had recommended. In the 1300s human dissections were an important, if small, part of medical education in Italy and Spain. Universities in England copied this in the 1500s.

The physician (in the red robe on the right) was in charge but did not do the dissection. He told the surgeon which parts of the body to dissect. He also told his assistant (middle right) which passages from Galen to read out to illustrate the dissection.
The students had to listen to Galen's words and watch the dissection. They weren't allowed to do anything!

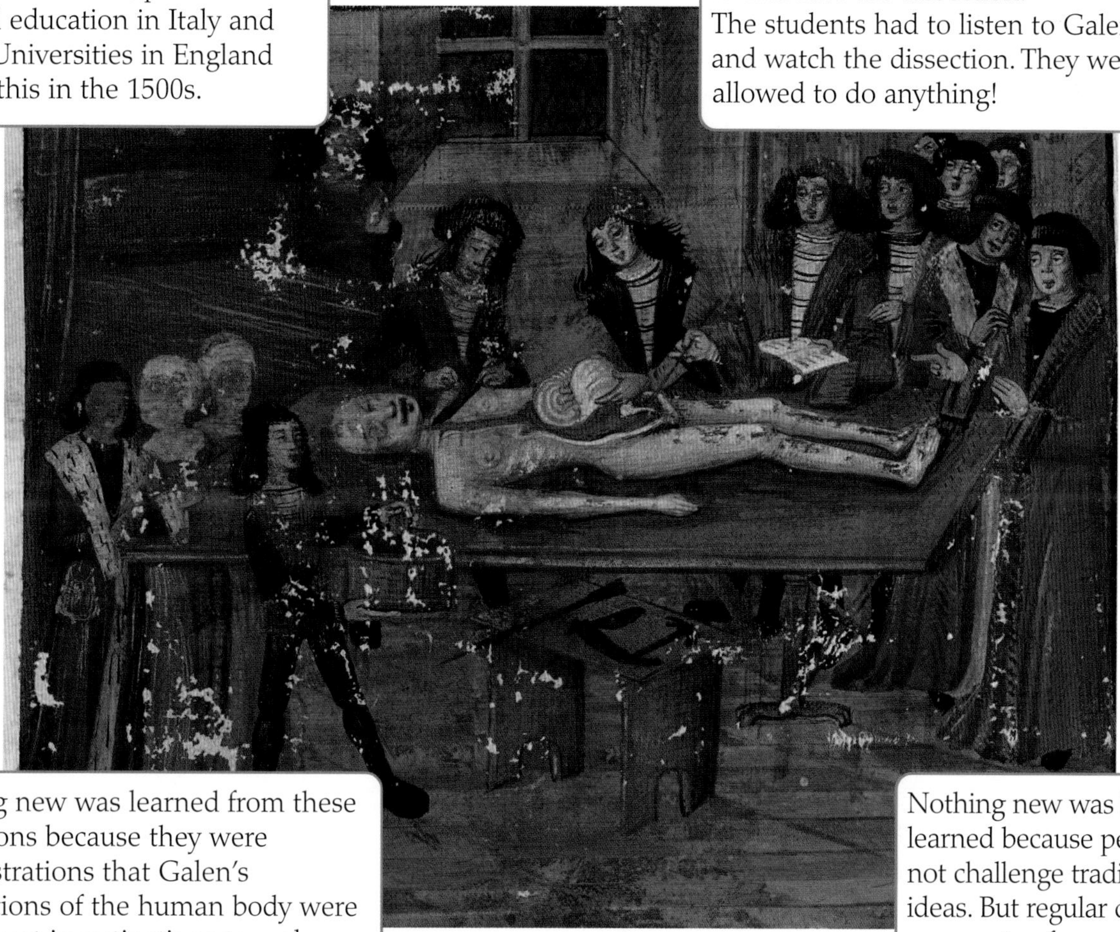

Nothing new was learned from these dissections because they were demonstrations that Galen's descriptions of the human body were correct, not investigations to make new discoveries. Physicians believed that Galen's books contained everything that needed to be learned about the human body.

Nothing new was being learned because people did not challenge traditional ideas. But regular dissections were a step forward because one day someone would use dissection to challenge Galen's descriptions of the body.

BUT

There were new ideas among Arab doctors. Ibn al-Nafis (1200–1288) investigated the anatomy of the heart and was brave enough to challenge Galen. Galen had said that the blood moves from one side of the heart to the other through invisible channels; al-Nafis used his own observations to say that these channels did not exist. He suggested that blood moves from the heart to the lungs and then back to the heart, thus circulating round the body. This idea was correct but nobody built on his work and it wasn't until the 1600s that this discovery was made in Europe.

Treatments – how were the sick treated?

Activities

1. **Factor hunt** – what evidence can you find of the effects of:
   - **a** attitudes – conservatism (respect for tradition)
   - **b** attitudes – enquiry
   - **c** communications
   - **d** religion?
2. What were the most important parts of a physician's equipment and what did he use them for?
3. Which new discovery was made by an Arab doctor?
4. How effective were herbal remedies?

The work of the physician

Diagnosing the illness

Source 1

The physician's most important piece of equipment was his urine chart. The physician matched the patient's urine against the colours, smell and density shown on the chart. He might also taste the urine to check that it was normal.

Wealthy patients sent their urine to their physician to make sure that they were not falling ill. This method of diagnosis (called uroscopy) fitted the Theory of the Four Humours. For example, very white urine was a sign of too much phlegm in the body.

▲ A urine chart

Physicians also followed Hippocrates and Galen by making careful observations of symptoms. This led the Arab doctor al-Razi to describe for the first time the difference between smallpox and measles.

Until then, all infections with rashes had been put together as one illness. Al-Razi carefully noted the differences, writing 'the physical signs of measles are nearly the same as those of smallpox but nausea and inflammation are more severe, though the pains in the back are less. The rash of measles usually appears at once, but the rash of smallpox spot after spot.'

Timing the treatment

Source 2

Once the physician had decided on the treatment he then chose the best time to carry it out. This required knowledge of astrology because they believed that parts of the body were linked to signs of the zodiac and the planets. The Zodiac man showed the doctor when to avoid treating each part of the body. When the moon was in Pisces, for example, the feet should not be treated.

▲ A Zodiac man

The work of the surgeon

Source 3

This kind of chart showed the surgeon where to take blood from. Bleeding, urine and zodiac charts were the three most common illustrations in medical books.

Treatments such as bleeding were carried out by a surgeon. Bleeding was done by warming a bleeding cup, placing it over a small cut and letting the warmth draw blood out of the cut. Alternatively, leeches were used to sink their jaws into the patient and draw off blood, a method still used in the nineteenth century.

People were bled regularly as a way of avoiding illness. One medical book said that bleeding 'clears the mind, strengthens the memory, cleanses the guts, sharpens the hearing, curbs tears, promotes digestion, produces a musical voice, dispels sleepiness, drives away anxiety, feeds the blood and rids it of poisonous matter and gives long life, cures pains, fevers and various sicknesses and makes urine clear and clean'.

Not surprisingly, after that list, bleeding was frequent. In some monasteries monks were bled between seven and twelve times a year to prevent illness. On occasion this was carried out until the monk was on the point of unconsciousness, which means he lost three or four pints of blood!

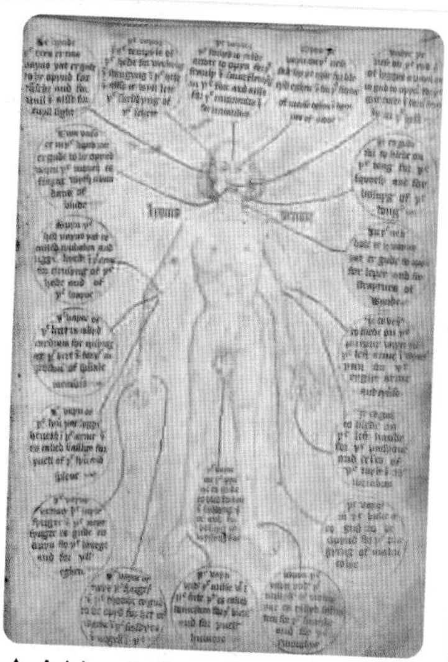

▲ A bleeding chart

Home remedies

Source 4

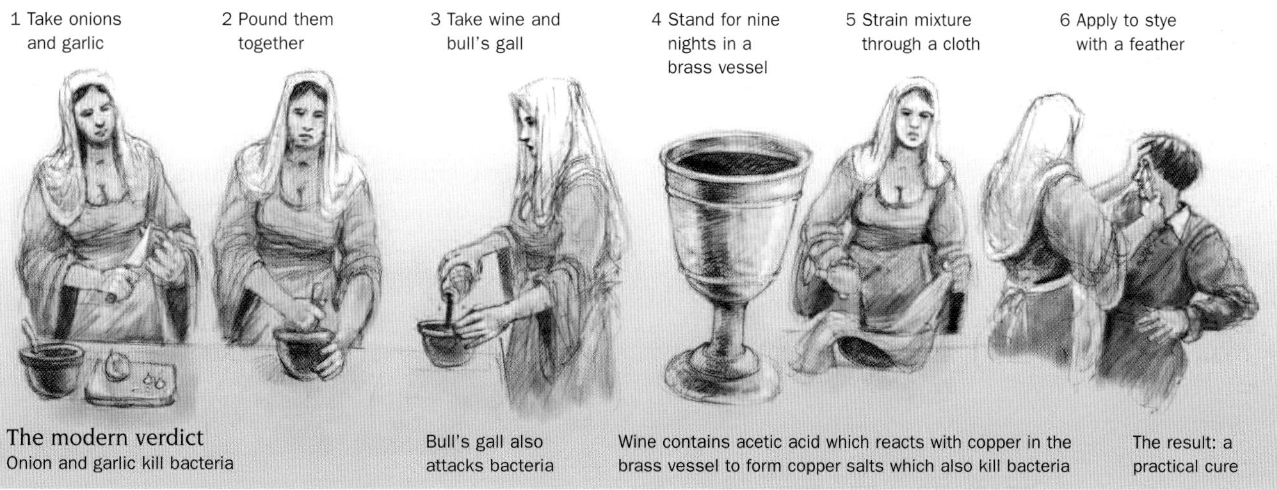

The medieval remedy
1 Take onions and garlic
2 Pound them together
3 Take wine and bull's gall
4 Stand for nine nights in a brass vessel
5 Strain mixture through a cloth
6 Apply to stye with a feather
The modern verdict
Onion and garlic kill bacteria
Bull's gall also attacks bacteria
Wine contains acetic acid which reacts with copper in the brass vessel to form copper salts which also kill bacteria
The result: a practical cure

This cure for a stye comes from Bald's Leechbook, a tenth-century collection of treatments. Many ingredients in such remedies were helpful. Honey and plantain, both very common ingredients for problems such as cuts, wounds and dog-bites, acted like modern antibiotics in fighting infection.

Common remedies were based on plants or herbs, minerals and animal parts. Most women knew these by heart but increasingly they were written down in commonplace books or 'herbals', books illustrating each plant and other ingredient, the exact quantities required and how to mix up the potion. They also included prayers to say while collecting the herbs to increase the effectiveness of the remedy.

Some cures combined all kinds of ideas, a mixture of prayer, magic and folklore, such as this Anglo-Saxon cure written down c.AD900: '[scratch] the neck after the setting of the sun and silently pour the blood into running water. After that, spit three times, then say: Have thou this unheal and depart with it.'

An example of a cure that was less likely to work was for treating quinsy (an abscess in the throat):

'Take a fat cat, flay it well and draw out the guts. Take the grease of a hedgehog, the fat of a bear, resins, fenugreek, sage, honeysuckle gum and virgin wax and crumble this and stuff the cat with it. Then roast the cat and gather the dripping and anoint the sufferer with it.'

Surgery – what kinds of surgery were there?

Activities

1. **Factor hunt** – what evidence can you find on these two pages of the effects of:
   a war
   b attitudes – enquiry?
2. The French surgeon Guy de Chauliac (c.1300–1368) wrote 'The surgeon must be ingenious and able to adapt himself.'
   How do Cases A and B support de Chauliac's statement?
3. Read Case C. Explain which idea was being challenged and how it came to be challenged.
4. Why were surgeons more likely than physicians to have ideas of their own and disagree with Galen?

Case A: The battle of Shrewsbury, 1403

The royal army had beaten the rebels but the 16-year-old Henry, Prince of Wales, lay wounded. An arrow, glancing off a helmet, had thudded through his left cheek and penetrated to the back of the base of his skull. The royal surgeon, John Bradmore, could not see exactly where the arrowhead was but knew it had to be removed. If he left pieces in the wound they would poison and kill the Prince.

First Bradmore designed a metal forcep to pass through the cheek wound, take hold of the arrowhead and pull it out. While a blacksmith made this new instrument, Blackmore kept the wound open by pushing wooden probes through it, each time using a wider probe to enlarge the hole. Each probe was wrapped in clean linen smeared with honey, good for keeping wounds free of infection. When the forcep was made Bradmore pushed it through the wound and removed the arrowhead. For three weeks he dressed the wound with barley and honey. It healed free from any infection.

Case B

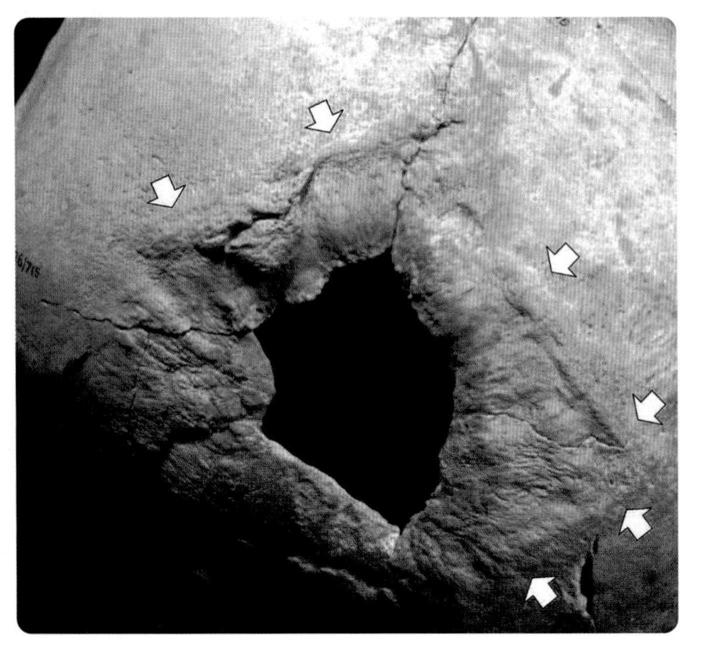

This skull was found in Yorkshire. It belonged to a man who died aged about 40. He had been hit on the head, leaving bone splinters in the brain but a surgeon cut a hole, removed the splinters and the man lived for some time after the operation. Some surgeons could also remove stones that had grown and lodged, extremely painfully, in the bladder.

Case C: What to do with pus

Everyday practice even led a handful of surgeons to dare to disagree with Galen on the lovely topic of pus! Since the Greeks, doctors had said that wounds were more likely to heal if pus (known as praiseworthy pus) developed. They believed the pus carried away poisoned blood that caused infection. Doctors therefore covered wounds in ointments and bandages designed to make pus develop.

Then Hugh and Theodoric, a father and son from Lucca in Italy, dared to say this idea was wrong! Hugh was a surgeon who went on Crusade in 1214 and later taught medicine. Theodoric (1205–1296) was also a surgeon. He wrote 'It is not necessary for pus to form in wounds. There can be no greater mistake! Such a procedure is quite against nature, prolongs illness, prevents healing and hinders the closing up of wounds. My father used to heal almost every kind of wound with wine alone, and he produced the most beautiful healing without any ointments.' Hugh's methods would have been effective. Wine, like honey, attacks infections.

Galen didn't know everything!

Henri de Mondeville (c.1260–c.1320) was another military surgeon and teacher. He taught his students to bathe and cleanse wounds, then close them up quickly without trying to form pus. Henri also wrote a surgical textbook in which he made the two important statements shown on the right, suggesting that surgeons could make new discoveries and challenge Galen's conclusions.

We now know things which were unknown in Galen's time and it is our duty to clarify them in our writings.
God surely didn't use up all his genius on Galen.

Surgeons could read too!

Most surgery was similar to the operations carried out by Greeks and Romans. Surgeons removed small tumours on the skin's surface, sewed up or cauterised large cuts, dealt with dislocations or broken limbs. The most skilful surgeons used extremely fine needles to remove cataracts from eyes, thus restoring or improving sight.

Surgeons did not just rely on practice. They read books too. Roger of Salerno wrote the first European textbook on surgery c.1180. Guy de Chauliac (c.1300–1368) dedicated himself to proving that a surgeon required just as much education and intelligence as a physician. He wrote a seven-volume book, *Chirurgia Magna* (Great Surgery), and filled it with references to the works of great doctors. There are 890 quotations from Galen, 661 from the Arab Ibn Sina and 120 from Hippocrates.

Source 1

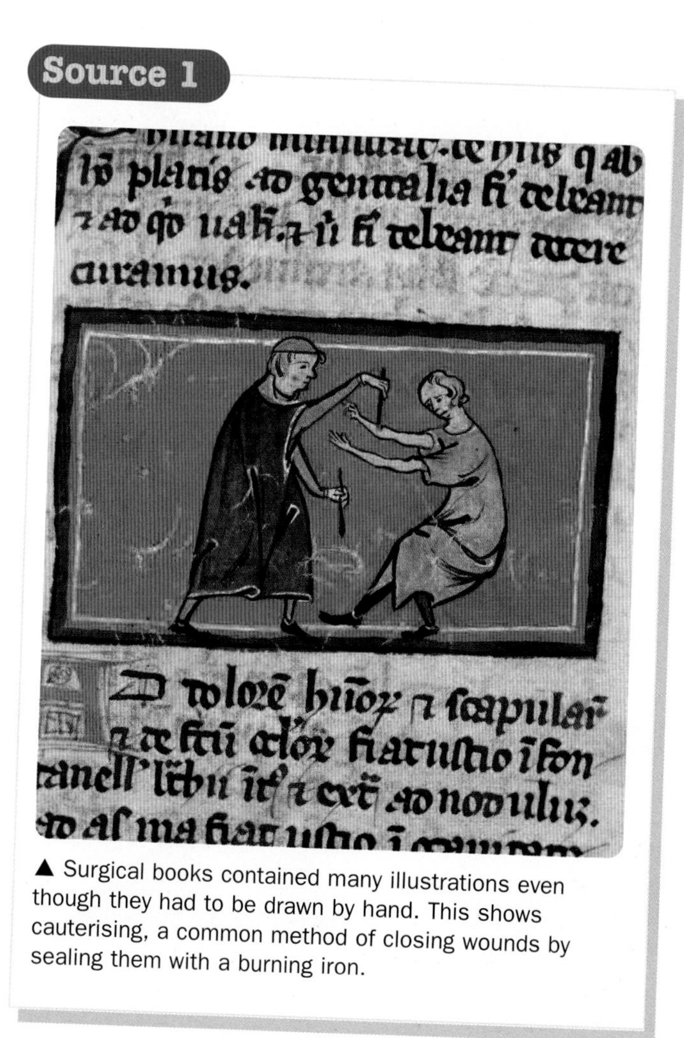

▲ Surgical books contained many illustrations even though they had to be drawn by hand. This shows cauterising, a common method of closing wounds by sealing them with a burning iron.

Source 2

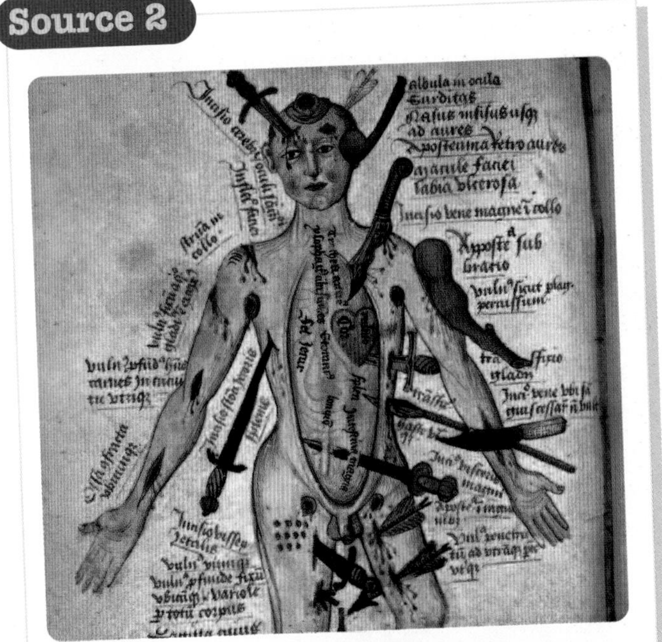

▲ A 'wound man' was a common medical illustration. It showed surgeons how to deal with different kinds of wounds. However, surgeons could not undertake complex surgery inside the body. They did not have enough detailed knowledge of anatomy nor effective anaesthetics. They did use herbs such as mandrake, opium or hemlock, which made patients drowsy, but there was always the danger of using too much of a drug and putting the patient to sleep permanently.

Topic Public Health – why did public health deteriorate?

Medieval towns were much dirtier than Roman towns. Viking Jorvik (York) was a filthy place around AD1000. Water for drinking and cooking was collected from the river or storage pits, which were often next to the cesspits people used as toilets. Pigs and chickens roamed the streets. Rats, mice and hawks scavenged in streets full of rotting fish bones, animal dung, food waste and even human faeces.

Animals were always a problem. People used horses for transport. Cattle, sheep and geese constantly arrived to be butchered for food. But, conditions did improve a little. By 1200 many houses in cities like London and York had stone foundations. A few were built entirely of stone. Cesspits were lined with brick or stone and so were less likely to leak into drinking water supplies.

However, the problems were always greater than the solutions. Medieval towns were dirtier than Roman towns but the Romans had army engineers with good technological knowledge, slaves to do at least some of the building, and the wealth to afford aqueducts and public baths. Even so, the Romans had been no better at stopping plague than people were in the Middle Ages.

Solutions
A Small number of rakers employed to clean streets.
Building public latrines and regulations about where to build private latrines.
Laws to punish throwing waste.
A small number of officials tried to enforce laws.
Problems
People dropping waste and litter - and worse!
Open sewers.
Butchers throwing out waste.
Animals in streets.
Streets were often muddy with open drains along the middle.
Contents of cesspits emptied into streams and rivers used for washing and drinking water.

Why didn't people's efforts work?

▲ King Edward III

We do not have enough officials to punish all the people who break the laws. Londoners will not pay the taxes we need to employ more officials.

▲ Lord Mayor of London

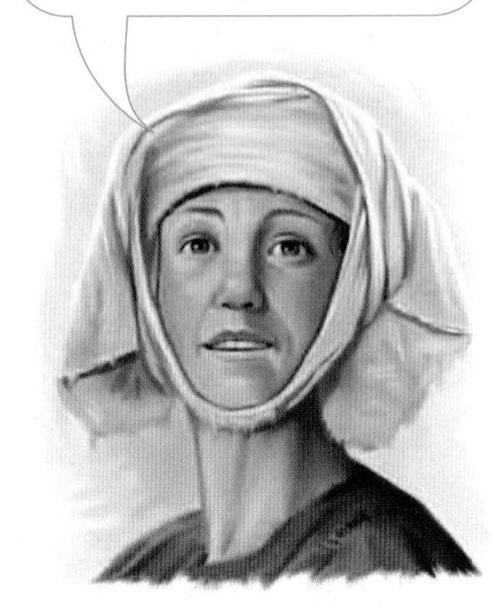

Why should I worry about dirt? God sends the diseases we suffer from. What's illness got to do with dirty streets?

▲ Londoner in 1300s

Activities

1. **Factor hunt** – what evidence can you find on these two pages of the effects of:
   - **a** government
   - **b** lifestyle
   - **c** religion?
2. Study Source 1.
   Was public health always really bad in medieval towns?
3. **a** What was good about the monastery's public health system?
   b Why was the monastery's public health system better than London's?
   c Compare Canterbury Abbey with a Roman fort (see page 41). Which had the better public health system? Explain the reason for your choice.
4. The Romans were not any better at stopping plague than people in the Middle Ages. Why?

The best public health facilities were in monasteries because they could afford them. Monks were better fed than most people, did less physical work and had the advantages you can see in this plan.

Source 1

▼ A plan of the water system at Canterbury Abbey, drawn by the engineer who designed it in the 1100s.

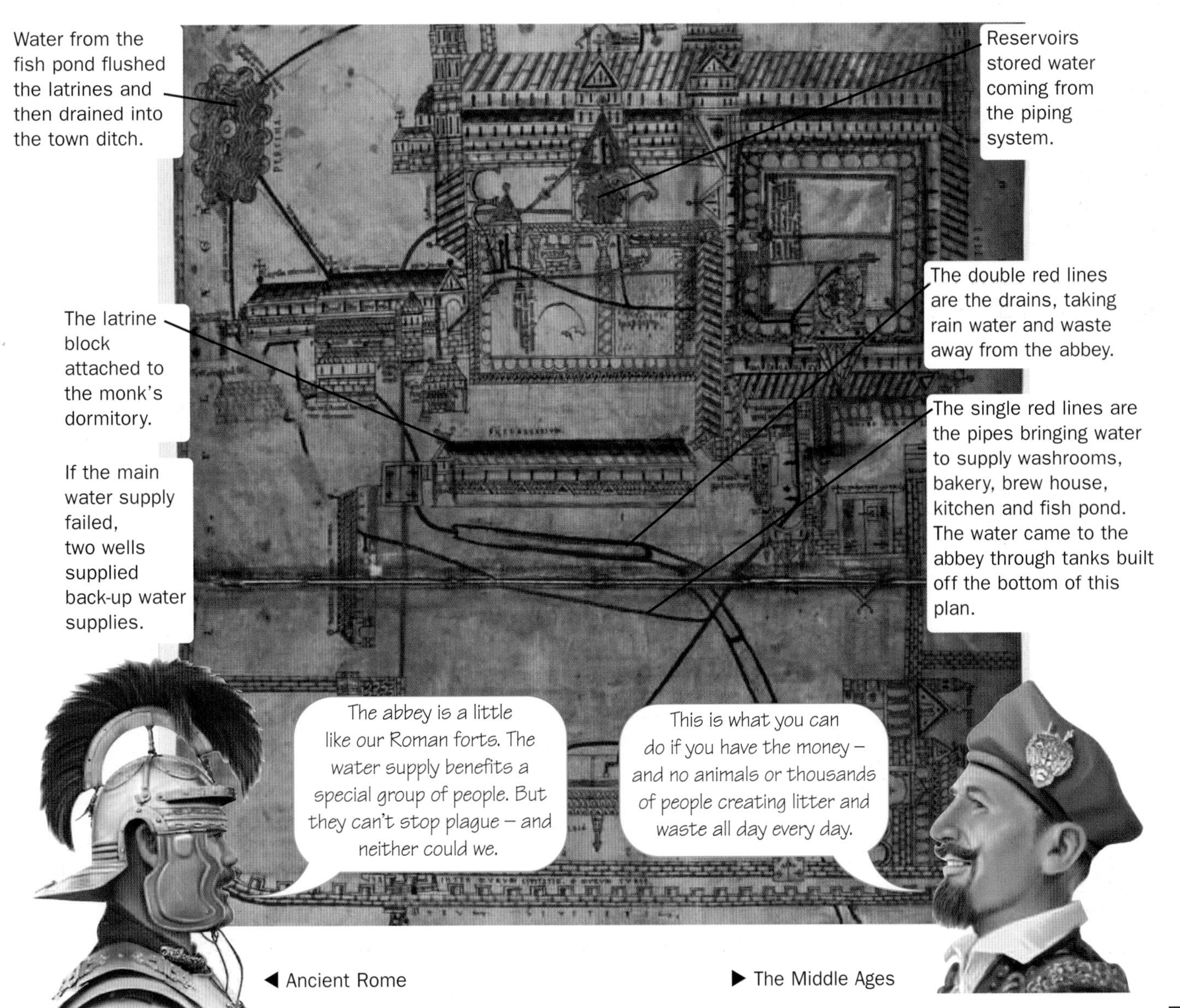

Water from the fish pond flushed the latrines and then drained into the town ditch.
Reservoirs stored water coming from the piping system.
The latrine block attached to the monk's dormitory.
The double red lines are the drains, taking rain water and waste away from the abbey.
If the main water supply failed, two wells supplied back-up water supplies.
The single red lines are the pipes bringing water to supply washrooms, bakery, brew house, kitchen and fish pond. The water came to the abbey through tanks built off the bottom of this plan.
The abbey is a little like our Roman forts. The water supply benefits a special group of people. But they can't stop plague – and neither could we.
This is what you can do if you have the money – and no animals or thousands of people creating litter and waste all day every day.
◀ Ancient Rome
▶ The Middle Ages

Answering 'factor' questions

In the Middle Ages the factors mostly stopped improvements in medicine but there are examples of factors helping to make small improvements.

War, destruction, damage. That's the way to stop people spending time and money on medicine.
WAR

I can help medicine a little. There's so much war that surgeons get plenty of practice and improve their methods a little.

WAR

Some exam questions test your understanding of the impact of factors such as war and religion on the development of medicine. You need to:

1. Identify and **explain** what kinds of effects a factor had – both helping and hindering the development of medicine.
2. Weigh up and **evaluate** that overall impact – did a factor mostly help or hinder?

Look at the question below. Remember what you learnt about de-coding questions on page 48.

You must stick to the date boundaries of the question. In this case it is the **Middle Ages**. Details of the impact that religion had in other time periods are not relevant.

The content focus for this question is on the **impact of religion**. Do not explore the impact of other factors for this question.

Explain ways in which religion had an impact on the development of medicine during the Middle Ages. (7 marks)

Question type: you need to **'explain' ways** in which religion had **an impact on medicine** at the time. A list of ways in which religion had an impact is not enough. Use the advice on page 75 to help you write effective explanations.

7 marks are available. You need to write more than you would for a 'Describe' question worth 5 marks. You will need to explain more than one way in which religion had an impact. Try to aim for three paragraphs. Each paragraph should explain an impact that religion had on medicine during the Middle Ages. Remember that religion may have helped as well as hindered medicine.

Writing effective explanations

Step 1: Identify at least three specific examples of religion either helping or hindering medicine during the Middle Ages. Cover more than one aspect of medicine, e.g. surgery, Public Health, etc.

Use your **factors chart** to help you.

Step 2: Select two or three examples to write about.

Do not try to cover everything! Choose two or three examples where you are confident that you can **explain the specific impact** that religion had.

Step 3: Use connectives to tie in what you know to the question.

Do not 'say' that religion had an impact, **prove it!**

Link religious beliefs and attitudes to specific results/developments.

You can do this by using connectives such as 'this meant that …', 'this led to' and 'this resulted in …' to explain the impact of religion.

Activities

Improve that answer

Look at the answer below. The student has used connectives to link religious beliefs and attitudes to specific developments in one area of medicine.

During the Middle Ages religion had a major impact on the development of medicine. The most common belief was that God sent illnesses such as the Black Death to punish people for their sins. People believed that the sick could be healed if they prayed for forgiveness. This meant that people did not look for scientific ways to explain the causes of disease and that medical treatments did not improve. Also, the Christian church supported Galen's ideas, they controlled universities and said that his work should not be questioned. This resulted in doctors being discouraged from researching and developing new ideas.

That's one paragraph done. Now have a go yourself at producing another paragraph which explains the impact of religion in another area of medicine. You can use the sentence starters and connectives provided or develop your own.

The Islamic religion taught people to look after the sick. This led to…

Looking after the sick was also an important part of the work of the Christian Church and this resulted in …

Sample 'Explain' questions

1. Explain ways in which chance has had an impact on medicine.
2. Explain why Vesalius was able to make so many discoveries about the human body at that time.
3. Explain why there was so much improvement in public health in the nineteenth century.

Historical Source Investigations:
Topic – The Black Death

In your **Historical Source Investigation** exam you will have one and a half hours to answer six questions, using the background information and sources.

You need to use your knowledge and understanding of the period to interpret and evaluate the sources and reach conclusions.

A

Background Information

The Black Death is believed to have started in Asia and spread to England in 1348. It was one of the deadliest outbreaks of disease in history, killing over 40 per cent of the population of England. Heavily populated towns and ports were most badly affected because there was more chance of coming into contact with the disease. The reaction of people in England and elsewhere was a mixture of fear, panic and anger. Does this mean that people had very little understanding of the causes of the disease?

▲ **Source A** *Flagellants whipping themselves. They believed the plague was a punishment from God for their sins. They are punishing themselves in the hope that God will be more merciful.*

Source B

'They went barefoot in procession twice a day in the sight of the people … their bodies naked except for a linen cloth from loins to ankle. Each wore a hood painted with a red cross at front and back and carried in his right hand a whip with three thongs. Each thong had a knot in it, with something sharp, like a needle stuck through the middle of the knot … and as they walked one after the other they struck themselves with these whips.'

A Londoner called Robert Avesbury described the Flagellants' actions.

Source C

'Terrible is God towards the son of men… he often allows plagues, miserable famines, conflicts, wars and other forms of suffering to arise, and uses them to terrify and torment men and so drive out their sins. And thus, indeed, the realm of England, became of the growing pride and corruption of its subjects, and their numberless sins … is to be oppressed by the pestilences …'

Part of a letter from the Prior of the abbey of Christchurch, Canterbury, to the Bishop of London, 28 September 1348.

Source D

'In cold or rainy weather you should light fires in your room, and in foggy or windy weather you should inhale perfumes every morning before leaving home. If however the epidemic occurs during hot weather you must eat cold things rather than hot and also drink more than you eat. Be sparing with hot substances such as pepper, garlic, onions and everything else that generates excessive heat and use cucumbers, fennel and spinach.

Many people have been killed, especially those stuffed full of evil humours. As Galen says in his book on fevers, the body does not become sick unless it already contains evil humours. The pestilential air does no harm to cleansed bodies from which evil humours have been purged.'

Advice written by John of Burgundy in 1365 on how to avoid the plague. This was one of the first books to be written about the plague.

Source E

'Whatever the people said, the truth is that there were two causes, one general, one particular. The general cause was the close position of the three great planets, Saturn, Jupiter and Mars. This had taken place in 1345 on 24th March in the 14th degree of Aquarius. Such a coming together of planets is always a sign of wonderful, terrible or violent things to come. The particular cause of the disease in each person was the state of the body – bad digestion, weakness and blockage, and for this reason people died.'

By Guy de Chauliac, a French doctor in the 1300s.

BACKGROUND INFORMATION

The background information is important. Study it carefully even if you know the topic really well because you can use it to support your answers. Highlight important points. Identify the theme of the paper.

THE SOURCES

Get to grips with the sources quickly but carefully. Read the sources after looking at the Background Information. Spend up to ten minutes reading the sources and working out how the sources and questions relate to each other.

Developments in British Medicine, 1200–1945

THE BLACK DEATH

Study the Background Information and the sources carefully. You are advised to spend at least ten minutes doing this. In answering the questions, you will need to use your knowledge of the topic to interpret and evaluate the sources. When you are asked to use specific sources you must do so, but you may also use any of the other sources if they are relevant.

Answer ALL the questions.

1 Study Sources A and B.
What can you learn from these sources about how people reacted to the Black Death? [6]

2 Study Source C.
How would people have reacted to hearing this explanation of the disease? Use the source and your knowledge to explain your answer. [6]

3 Study Source D.
Are you surprised by the methods being used in Source D to avoid the disease? [8]

4 Study Sources D and E.
How far do these two sources agree about the causes of the disease? [9]

5 Study Source F.
How useful is this source for a historian investigating people's ideas regarding the causes of the Black Death? Use the source and your knowledge to explain your answer. [9]

6 Study **all** the sources.
'People's ideas about what caused the Black Death were completely based on their religious beliefs.' How far do the sources on this paper support that view? Use the sources and your knowledge to explain your answer. Remember to identify the sources you use. [12]

C ALL THE SOURCES

This last sentence is important – although the questions direct you to one particular source, the information in other sources may help you answer a question fully. You can use any source on the paper to support your answer.

D ALL THE QUESTIONS

This statement is crucial. Look at how many marks are allocated to each question as a guide for how much to write. The last question usually carries the most marks, so leave a good 15 minutes to answer. Do not spend too long on questions worth only 5 or 6 marks. For example, you should not spend more than ten minutes answering Question 1.

E INFERENCE QUESTIONS (Question 1)

For this style of question you need to go beyond the obvious clues in the source to explain what you can learn from the source.

F USE YOUR KNOWLEDGE (Questions 2 and 3)

Questions like this test your ability to use your knowledge of the period to put sources in their historical context.

G CROSS-REFERENCING SOURCES (Question 4)

This question asks you to compare what is said in two sources and to reach a judgement on how far they are saying the same thing.

H EVALUATING SOURCES (Question 5)

There is usually a question asking you to evaluate how useful a source is for a particular historical enquiry. Explore the strengths and weaknesses of the source before reaching an overall judgement of how useful the source is.

I EVALUATING A STATEMENT (Question 6)

The final question asks you to use the sources and your own knowledge to evaluate an interpretation or point of view. You must decide the extent to which you agree/disagree with this statement. Before you answer this question, go through the sources and place a tick or cross when you find evidence that supports or contradicts the statement.

Using sources: 'inference' and 'cross-reference': Topic – Medieval Public Health

Using sources effectively: Making inferences

Both your exam papers contain questions which test your ability to use visual and written sources effectively. Look at this sample question:

> Study Source A. What can you learn from this source about health care in monasteries in the Middle Ages? Use the source and your own knowledge to explain your answer. [6]

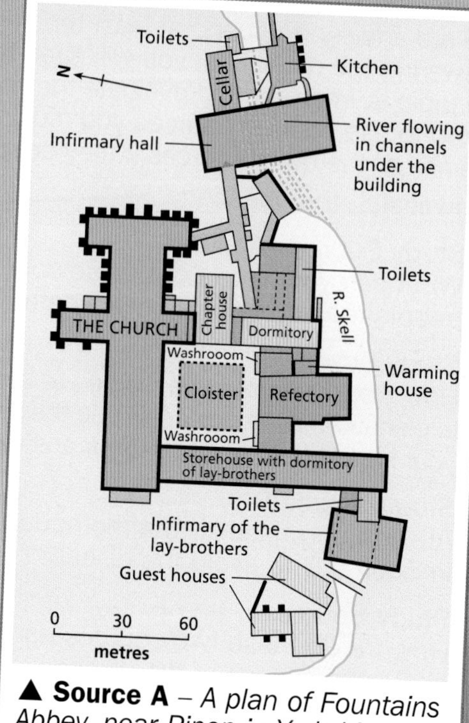

▲ **Source A** – *A plan of Fountains Abbey, near Ripon in Yorkshire, built in the Middle Ages.*

To get high marks you must do more than just describe what you can see in the source – you must also explain it and look beyond it.

Step 1: Identify the clues in the source that can help you answer the question. You could highlight the fact that the monastery is built by the river, the toilets (which are built over the river), the washroom, the drains and the infirmary.

Step 2: Use your knowledge of the topic to go beyond the obvious clues and **explain what the source is saying** about public health. Ask yourself: What do I know that can help me make sense of this evidence? What can I **infer** from this source? This type of question is often known as an **inference question.**

Activities

Read the student answer below. Note how the student **identifies key details and then explains what they say about health care.**
Now complete the answer.

In Source A there are different rooms for the healthy and the sick (the infirmary). The building appears to have been carefully planned and gives the impression that medical care in the monasteries was very well organised. There are also good facilities, such as water pipes and washrooms. This suggests that people in the monastery realised the importance of keeping clean. There are also toilets, which are built over the river. This suggests...

They are usually worth five or six marks so you should not spend too long on these questions. The key thing to remember is ...

Stick to the focus of the question.

- Only bring in your own knowledge if it is relevant to the question and helps to explain the meaning of a source. The focus here is on health care in monasteries so there is no need to impress the examiner with your knowledge that health care in towns was very different! You will not gain any extra marks as it is not what the question asks.
- Focus on what you can learn from the source. There is no need to evaluate how trustworthy the source is. Once again you will waste valuable time and pick up no extra marks.

Using sources effectively: Cross-referencing

Sometimes you are asked to compare the messages given in two different sources. This skill is known as cross-referencing. Look at the question below:

> Study Sources B and C.
> How far do these two sources provide a similar impression of public health in Medieval towns? [8]

Some students answer this type of question poorly because they waste time describing what each source says before they begin to answer the question. Approach A below would score very few marks. Approach B is a lot better. The student picks up marks from the start as the entire answer is focused on the question making direct comparisons between the sources.

Source B

The streets often had open sewers running down the middle of them. These sewers became clogged with rubbish and excrement thrown from the windows. Pigs, dogs and rats roamed through the streets. Towns such as London sometimes tried to clean up the streets, but not very often. People had no idea that dirty conditions could lead to disease.

Extract from L. Hartley, History of Medicine (1984)

Source C

Order – to cause the bank of the River Thames and the streets and lanes of the city to be cleansed of dung, dungheaps and other filth and to keep them clean. In the time of the King's ancestors the streets used to be cleansed of refuse and filth but now, in crossing the River Thames, the King has observed filth and other refuse accumulated on the bank. Noisome smells arise therefrom, whereby great danger may arise to men dwelling in the city.

A Royal Order by Edward III in 1349

Approach A

▼ *Paragraph 1* – Lengthy description of Source B

Source B tells us that they had open sewers running down the middle of the streets and that people threw their excrement from windows onto the street. It also tells us that pigs, dogs and rats . . .

▼ *Paragraph 2* – Lengthy description of Source C

Source C shows us that there were dungheaps and filth all over the streets of London. Rubbish is everywhere and the area around the Thames is full of . . .

▼ *Paragraph 3* – The answer ends with a broad statement, such as:

Source C therefore supports Source B

Approach B

▼ *Paragraph 1* – Similarities between the sources

Source B gives the impression that people did not keep the streets clean. For example, we learn that excrement was thrown into the streets and . . . Source C gives a similar impression. We are told that . . .

▼ *Paragraph 2* – Differences between the sources

Source B gives the impression that very little was done to stop the streets becoming so unhygienic and that . . . However, Source C is an order from the King to clean the streets. It suggests that . . .

▼ *Paragraph 3* – An overall judgement about how far the sources agree

Overall, the two sources do give a very similar impression of public health at the time. As it states in Source B, sometimes people did try and clean up the streets but this was very rare. This is shown by . . .

Remember to plan your approach to cross-referencing questions carefully.

✗ Do not go through everything that Source A tells us, then everything Source B tells us and leave it to the examiner to pull out the similarities and differences!

✓ Instead make direct comparisons as you go through your answer.

Activities

Complete your answer to this question in the style shown in Approach B.

Section 4: Why was the medical Renaissance important when it didn't make anyone healthier?

The Renaissance is the period of European history between around 1400 and 1600. It is famous for discoveries in science, geography and art. There were also breakthroughs in medicine but, by 1700, people were no healthier than in the Middle Ages. So, if they weren't any healthier, why were these medical discoveries important?

Read all about it! Great medical discoveries! Nobody will notice for centuries!

Activities

1. Sources 1–4 were all important developments in the period of the Renaissance. How do you think each development influenced medicine?
2. Which breakthroughs do you think each of the three medical pioneers shown on page 81 made use of in his work?
3. Think about the three medical discoveries made by these pioneers. Why do you think they did not immediately lead to people being healthier and living longer?

Renaissance breakthroughs

Source 1

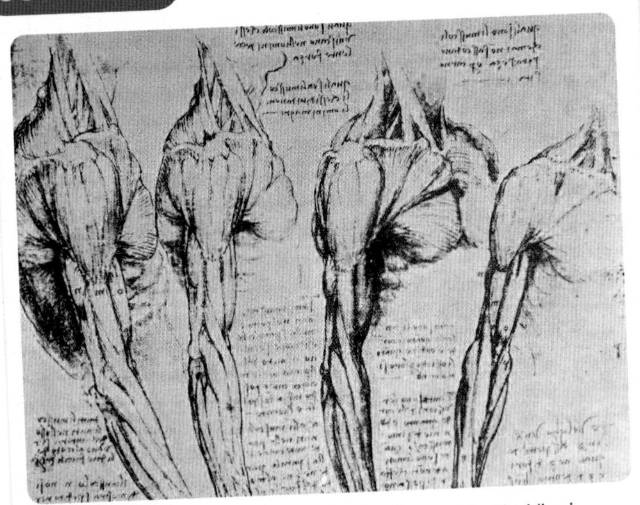

▲ Drawings of parts of the body by Leonardo da Vinci (1452–1519). Da Vinci gave this advice to young artists: 'The painter who has knowledge of sinews, muscles and tendons will know exactly which sinew causes the movement of a limb. He will be able to show the various muscles in the different attitudes of his figures. You will need three dissections to have a complete knowledge of the arteries, three more for the membranes, three for the nerves, muscles and ligaments, three for the bones and cartilages. Three must also be devoted to the female body.'

Source 2

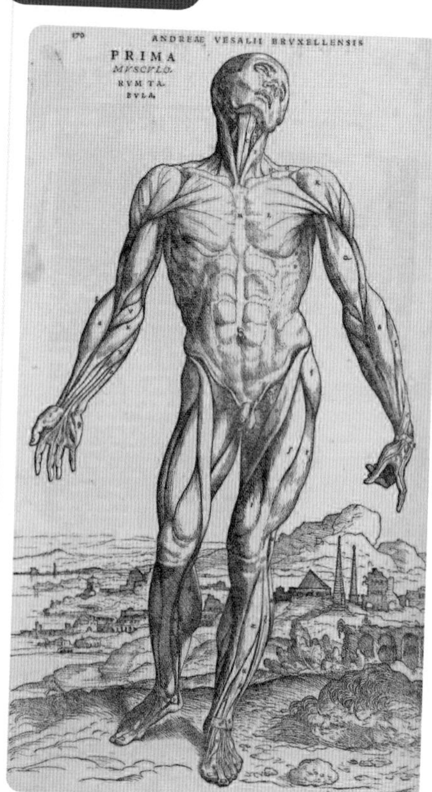

◀ The printing press was invented by Johannes Gutenberg in the 1450s. By 1500 printing presses were being used throughout western Europe. Some books were highly illustrated such as this page from Andreas Vesalius' book on anatomy, *The Fabric of the Human Body* (1543).

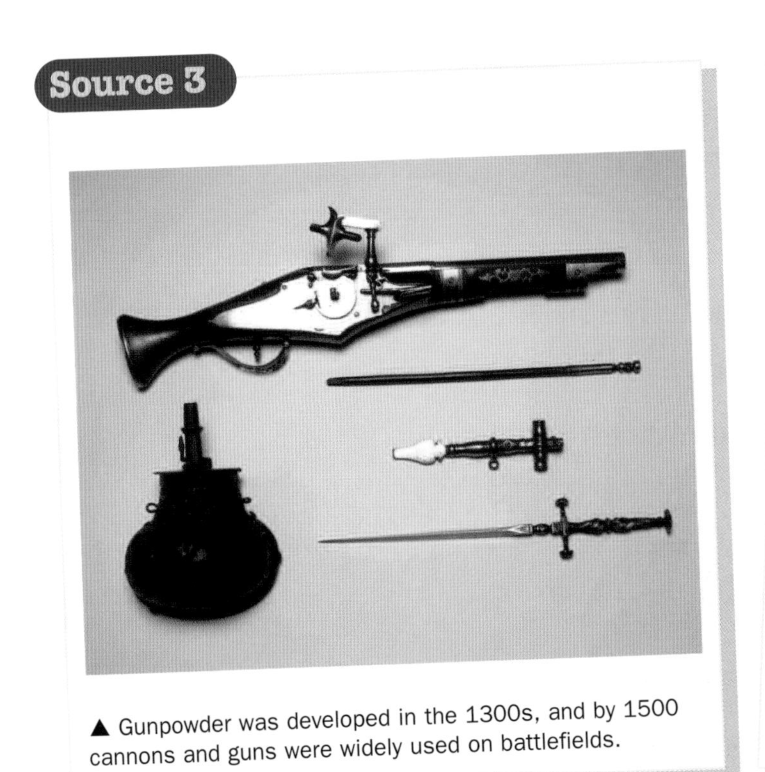

Source 3

▲ Gunpowder was developed in the 1300s, and by 1500 cannons and guns were widely used on battlefields.

Source 4

◀ The first effective microscopes were developed in the 1600s by instrument makers including Robert Hooke in England and Antoni van Leeuwenhoek in Holland. They allowed people to see things they could not see with the naked eye.

Renaissance medical pioneers

▲ Andreas Vesalius made new discoveries about the anatomy of the human body.

▲ William Harvey discovered that the blood circulates around the body.

▲ Ambroise Paré pioneered new surgical methods for treating gunshot wounds and stopping bleeding.

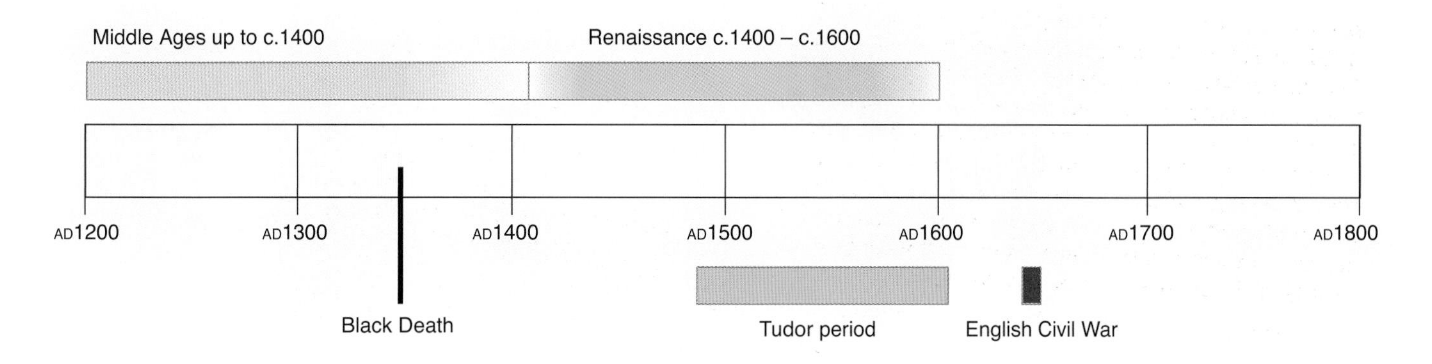

4.1 What was re-born in the medical Renaissance?

Renaissance means 're-birth'. In general the Renaissance period was a time of 're-born' interest in all things Greek and Roman, their books and ideas, buildings and sculptures. But, in medicine, interest in the Greeks and Romans had never gone away because physicians had kept reading and relying on Galen. So what exactly was being re-born in the medical Renaissance?

The Renaissance struggle: conservatism versus enquiry

In the Big Fight of the Middle Ages, conservatism beat enquiry. This wasn't surprising as conservatism had the experienced and powerful Christian Church in his corner. Enquiry only had a couple of surgeons in his corner suggesting new moves but they did not hurt conservatism at all. What happened next?

Then came the Black Death. Afterwards many of the survivors were better-off because employers had to pay higher wages to attract workers. Many people had spare time and spare money and they spent some of this time and money on education.

Wealth and education helped trigger the Renaissance, the re-birth of interest in the Greeks and the Romans. Educated people during the Renaissance thought that the Greeks and Romans were just like them – intelligent and thoughtful. They looked down on the people of the Middle Ages as ignorant.

They made new translations of Galen. Greeks and Romans, like Galen, had never gone away in medicine. Medieval doctors had studied them in detail. In universities in the 1500s scholars were still reading translations of Galen but now they were worried. The translations had been made in the Middle Ages. What if they were wrong? What if vital knowledge had been missed out or misunderstood by ignorant people in the Middle Ages? They decided to make new translations to make sure they were right. They published new editions of Greek and Roman books, including nearly 600 editions of Galen's books.

Better make sure this is right. Can't trust those medieval monks to get things right.

This work changed attitudes. In the Middle Ages, people respected traditional ideas and simply copied Greek knowledge and ideas. They did not challenge them. But in the Renaissance, people realised that the Greeks loved enquiry – asking questions, challenging old ideas (like the gods causing disease) and suggesting new ones (the Theory of the Four Humours). If the Greeks could ask questions and challenge old ideas, then so could they, the people of the Renaissance.

Those Greeks asked questions and challenged old ideas. Maybe enquiry is more important than tradition?

So what was re-born? It was not just interest in Greek and Roman ideas that was re-born but, far more importantly, their love of enquiry and willingness to challenge existing ideas. Once they began to ask questions and look carefully some people began to realise that Galen had not known everything – and had even made mistakes!

What? Why? Who? Is Galen right?

ENQUIRY

But not everyone agreed. Many people still conservatively stuck to tradition, not daring to think for themselves, still saying it was wrong to challenge Galen. So what developed was a battle between attitudes – between people defending the old ideas and people fighting for new ones.

We can't let this upstart Enquiry win. Old ideas have always been right and we're not going to think differently.

Activities

1. What exactly was being re-born in the Renaissance?
2. Conservatism beat enquiry in the Middle Ages.
   a. What kinds of changes in medicine do you think would be needed to change the result and give enquiry a knock-out victory over conservatism?
   b. Look at the possible results on the right. Which do you think was the likely result by 1700?

The Big Fight 1400–1700 – how will it end?

So who did win the Big Fight between the attitude twins – conservatism and enquiry? Your task is to create your own commentary on the great conservatism versus enquiry contest. Your commentary will link all the topics in this section together by assessing how much medicine really changed between 1400 and 1700. And there's a bonus – you will have begun your revision months before you complete your course and take your exam!

Activities

Over the next twelve pages you will be gathering information to fill in the Big Story chart on the opposite page. You could do this on computer. You will then use the chart to write your own audio commentary on the big fight of 1400–1700. Each topic in the table will be one 'round' in the big fight.

Stage 1: get an overview

Use pages 86–87.

- **a** Pencil information about each topic into column 3 of your Big Story chart.
- **b** On a separate sheet of paper draft first ideas for your commentary for each 'round'. Just a sentence to summarise what happened will be enough at this stage. This is your set of starter ideas to build on.

Remember:
Round 1 is Knowledge of the Human body
Round 2 is Surgery
Round 3 is Healers
Round 4 is Ideas about causes of disease
Round 5 is Treatments
Round 6 is Public Health.

Stage 2: fill in the detail

Now work through the tasks on pages 88–99. Some of them will get you working in groups or listening to other groups present, but all the time it is your responsibility to fill in your Big Story chart.

Stage 3: decide on the winners of each round

Complete the final column of your chart giving points to each boxer: conservatism or enquiry. Use the table to help you.

If there are...	Then Conservatism gets...	And Enquiry gets...
No discoveries at all	3	0
Traditional ideas that still dominate medicine even if one or two new ideas begin to be accepted	2	1
Really important discoveries that completely change this aspect of medicine	1	2
Really important discoveries that completely change this aspect of medicine	0	3

Stage 4: write your commentary

- **a** Now you are ready to write your commentary. It should say in sports-commentator style: who is winning this round (is it a close run thing or an easy win?); which punches (evidence) have the biggest impact?
- **b** Record your commentary as a podcast. You can also listen to it for revision.

The Big Story of medicine during the Renaissance

	Medicine c.1400, at the end of the Middle Ages	The impact of the Renaissance – medicine c.1700	Who won this round: conservatism or enquiry? Which were the strongest punches?
Round 1 Knowledge of the human body (pp. 88–91)	Doctors knew about Greek and Roman discoveries but did not learn any more. Dissection was carried out to illustrate what Galen had said, not make new discoveries.		
Round 2 Surgery (pp. 92–93)	**a** Simple surgery on visible tumours and wounds. **b** Splints for fractured bones. **c** Trephining (cutting hole in skull). **d** Plants such as opium dulled pain a little but there were no effective anaesthetics. **e** Surgeons use wine, vinegar or honey to clean wounds but could not prevent infections spreading or stop heavy bleeding.		
Round 3 Healers (pp. 94–95)	**a** Mothers and family members treated most illnesses. Women with skills and experience often called to help, e.g. with childbirth. **b** Priests said prayers to help the sick and protect from illness. **c** Surgeons, e.g. army surgeons, trained by observing others and improved their skills through practice. **d** Physicians trained at universities by reading the books by Hippocrates and Galen and some Arab medical writers.		
Round 4 Ideas about causes of disease (pp. 94–99)	**a** Many believed that illnesses were sent by God. **b** Doctors said that many illnesses had natural causes. They followed Hippocrates' theory that illness was caused when the body's humours were out of balance.		
Round 5 Everyday treatments (pp. 96–97)	**a** Remedies made up from herbs, minerals and animal parts. **b** Prayers, charms and rhymes. **c** Bleeding, purging and other methods to restore the proper balance of the humours, following the methods of Galen. **d** Rest, exercise and diet.		
Round 6 Public health and prevention (pp. 98–99)	**a** Town governments employed people and made laws to try to keep streets clean but had little success. **b** It was very difficult to keep towns clean as they were full of animals, houses were packed together and there were few paved streets. **c** Kings were not expected to improve hygiene or protect public health. Their job was to defend the country and keep law and order. **d** Epidemic diseases still could not be stopped.		

Medical moments in time: London 1665

Activities

This drawing helps you to develop a quick overview of how medicine was changing and whether conservatism was still beating enquiry in 1665. You can add this to your Big Story chart on page 85.

1. Divide the six topics among the class. What evidence can you find to start your chart? Who is winning each round?
2. What evidence helps to explain why people were no healthier nor living longer than in the Middle Ages?

Plague struck in 1665. The Mayor of London ordered watchmen to guard houses to make sure the sick and their families stayed shut up.
It's not plague. Your humours are out of balance, that's all. You just need bleeding.
House owners were ordered to sweep the streets outside their homes.
Taverns and theatres were closed to stop plague spreading.
I saw many gunshot wounds as an army doctor. I'll dig out the bullet but it'll hurt. But we don't use boiling oil on wounds any more thanks to that Frenchman, Paré.

Physicians trained at universities, reading books by Greek, Roman and Arab writers. They studied discoveries by Vesalius and Harvey but new ideas were rarely accepted immediately.

4.2 What did people discover during the medical Renaissance?

Pages 88–93 tell you about the three most important developments of the medical Renaissance. They make it look as if medicine is changing completely, as if enquiry has won. But is it that simple? Were these punches really knocking out conservatism or just the start of a much longer contest?

Activities

Pages 88–93 will help you complete the first two rows of your Big Story chart on page 85: 'Knowledge of the body' and 'Surgery'.

1 Work in groups. Each group tackle one of the developments:
- Vesalius and anatomy (pages 88–89)
- Harvey and blood (pages 90–91)
- Paré and surgery (pages 92–93).

Report your findings to the rest of the class.

2 'Role of the individual' chart: convert your findings into 'role of the individual' charts for revision.

Pioneer 1 Andreas Vesalius – breakthroughs in anatomy

Biography

- Born 1514, died 1564.
- Father a doctor, studied medicine in Paris and Padua, Italy.
- Professor of Surgery in Padua.
- Wrote *The Fabric of the Human Body* (1543), a detailed and fully illustrated description of human anatomy.

Anatomy – the story so far

1. Doctors believed Galen had given a fully correct description of anatomy.
2. Dissection was carried out to show Galen was right, not to check or challenge him, even though Galen had said it was important to learn by dissecting human bodies. He sometimes had to use animals because human bodies were not available.

Vesalius' achievements – Galen could be wrong!

The Fabric of the Human Body was the first highly illustrated book on human anatomy.

Vesalius respected Galen's work but proved that Galen was sometimes wrong by showing that

- the human jaw bone is made from one bone, not two as Galen said
- the breastbone has three parts, not seven as Galen said
- blood does not flow into the heart through invisible holes in the septum – such holes do not exist.

He showed that doctors could learn more about anatomy and had to carry out human (not animal) dissection to learn more.

Source 1

▲ The title page of Vesalius' *The Fabric of the Human Body* tells us about his attitudes to dissection. Vesalius is shown in the centre, dissecting the body himself. In the Middle Ages, professors sat and read Galen aloud while demonstrators did the dissection. Galen and other Greek doctors are shown at the same level as Vesalius, not higher up as if superior. Students crowd round the body so they can see what Vesalius is doing rather than simply listening to Galen being read out.

How did he do it?

Vesalius made great use of the new invention of printing. He chose the best printer and supervised the engraving of the illustrations and the printing himself. Printing meant that everything came out the same with no mistakes – which was not the case in books copied by hand. Without printing his work would not have had such an impact. Thousands of copies were printed quickly and used all over Europe.
TECHNOLOGY

Vesalius was inventive and determined. Once he stole the body of a criminal from the gallows to dissect and he worked at Padua where dissection was encouraged. He insisted on making sure every detail of his book was printed correctly.
INDIVIDUAL GENIUS

In Italy many artists were already interested in dissection to improve their own work. Vesalius used them to illustrate his book.
ART

Vesalius respected Galen but believed that it was vital to ask questions and challenge traditional ideas by carrying out as many human dissections as possible.
ATTITUDES – ENQUIRY

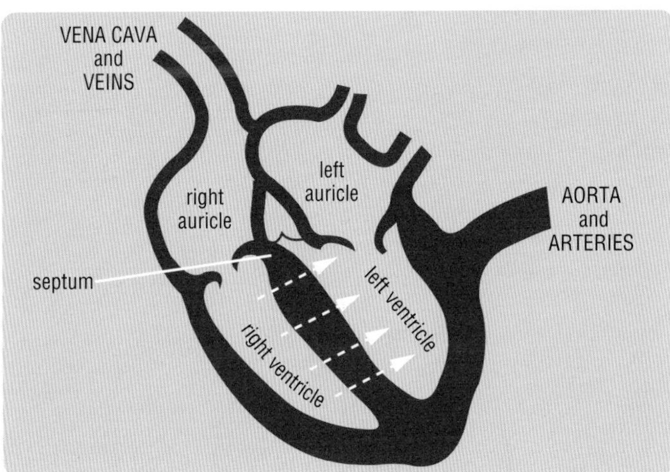
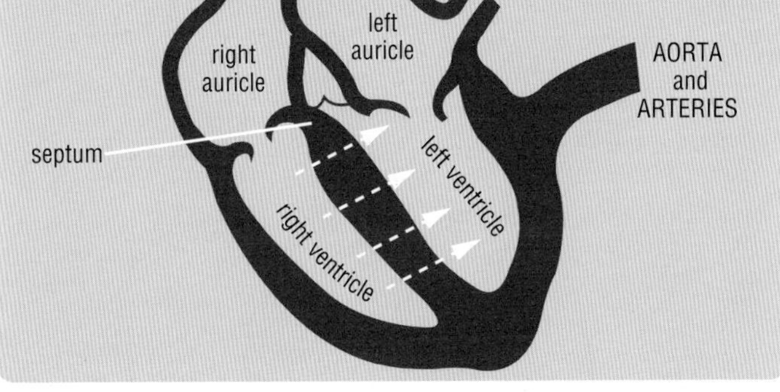
VENA CAVA and VEINS
left auricle
right auricle
AORTA and ARTERIES
septum
left ventricle
right ventricle

▲ Diagram showing Galen's idea about how blood reached the heart. Vesalius's dissection proved this was not true.

But...

WARNING

DON'T EXAGGERATE

- **Many doctors refused to accept that Galen could be wrong.** Some said that Vesalius's work only showed that the body had changed since Galen's time. The heavy criticism led Vesalius to leave Padua and work for the Emperor Charles V.
- **Nobody was healthier as a result of Vesalius's work.** His work was only the start. Many more discoveries were needed before people would live longer, healthier lives.

Stepping stones to the future

1 Vesalius' insistence on enquiry began to change attitudes and encourage others to follow his example.

2 Doctors realised there was more to be learned – Galen had not discovered everything or got everything right.

3 Accurate knowledge of anatomy was vital for the building up of medical knowledge and paving the way for better treatments later.

4 His book spread knowledge AND his attitude, showing others the way forward.

Improved medicine and health

Pioneer 2 William Harvey – discovering the circulation of the blood

Biography

- Born 1578, died 1657.
- Studied medicine in Cambridge and Padua, worked as a doctor in London.
- Published his book *An Anatomical Account of the Motion of the Heart and Blood*, in 1628, which described how the blood circulates round the body.
- Became doctor to King Charles I.

Source 1

▲ A water pump being used to fight a fire in the 1600s. Pumps like this had valves to direct the flow of water.

Blood – the story so far

Galen had said:

1 new blood was constantly manufactured in the liver to replace blood burned up in the body just like wood is burnt by a fire

2 blood passed from one side of the heart to the other through invisible holes in the septum. This had been challenged by Ibn al-Nafis (1210–1288) and Vesalius but neither could provide an alternative explanation.

Two other doctors had made discoveries that paved the way for Harvey:

- Realdo Columbo (1516–1559) said that blood moved along the veins and arteries
- Fabricius (1533–1619), Harvey's tutor at Padua, proved there are valves in the veins.

Despite these pieces of knowledge, nobody could explain how blood moved around the body!

Harvey's achievements

Harvey proved that the heart acts as a pump, pumping blood around the body. He did this by:

- dissecting live cold-blooded animals whose hearts beat slowly so he could see the movement of each muscle in the heart
- dissecting human bodies to build up detailed knowledge of the heart
- proving that the body has a one-way system for the blood – he tried to pump liquid past the valves in the veins but could not do so
- calculating that the amount of blood going into the arteries each hour was three times the weight of a man. This showed that the same blood is being pumped round the body by the heart.

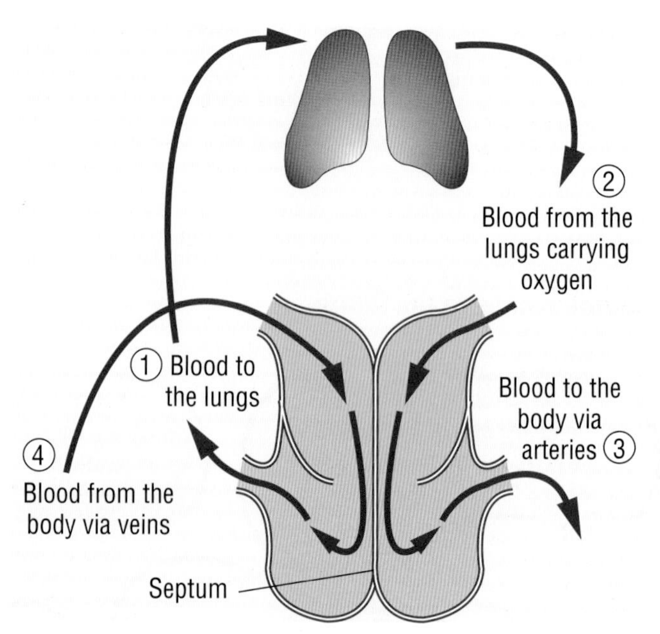

▲ A simplified version of the circulation of the blood. Blood leaves the heart (1), then passes through the lungs (2) and back to the heart and then around the body along arteries (3). Then blood comes back to the heart along veins (4) before starting its circulation around the body again.

How did he do it?

Mechanical water pumps in London may have given Harvey the idea that the heart is pumping blood.
TECHNOLOGY

Harvey's discovery was the result of careful dissection, observation of detail and experiment.
ATTITUDES
ENQUIRY

Harvey was exceptionally thorough in his work, spending many hours repeating experiments and going over every detail.
INDIVIDUAL GENIUS

Harvey had read the work of earlier doctors and was able to use it to build up his theory.
COMMUNICATIONS

Source 2

◀ Harvey could not explain everything about the circulation of the blood. He did not know how blood moves from the arteries to the veins but later in the 1600s Professor Marcello Malphigi used one of the first effective microscopes to discover the capillaries, which carry blood from arteries to veins. The development of microscopes was a vital technological development helping to transform medical knowledge.

But…

- **There was still much more to discover about the blood.** Doctors could not make blood transfusions until they discovered blood groups in 1901.
- **Harvey's discovery was only gradually accepted.** Some doctors ignored his theory. Others said that he was wrong because he was contradicting Galen. It was nearly fifty years before the teachers at the University of Paris taught Harvey's ideas rather than Galen's.
- **Harvey's discovery did not make anyone better.** The writer John Aubrey noted 'All his profession agree Dr Harvey to be an excellent anatomist, but I never heard any that admired his treatment of the sick.' Harvey himself said that after he published his discovery fewer patients came to see him. Many thought his idea mad.

Stepping stones to the future

1 Harvey's discovery laid the groundwork for future investigation of the blood and physiology (the workings of the body) – see Source 2.

2 Many aspects of medicine depend on understanding the blood system. Surgery, for example, could not develop until after Harvey's discovery.

3 Harvey proved that Vesalius was right about the importance of dissection. He wrote 'I prefer to learn and teach anatomy not from books but from dissections.'

Improved medicine and health

Pioneer 3 Ambroise Paré – breakthroughs in surgery

Biography

- Born 1510, died 1590
- Learned surgery as apprentice to his brother, then worked at Royal Hospital, the Hotel Dieu, Paris.
- From 1536 spent 20 years as an army surgeon, then was surgeon to kings of France.
- Most famous surgeon in Europe because of his books *Ten Books on Surgery* and *Apology and Treatise.*

Surgery – the story so far

1. Practice in wartime had helped surgeons make minor improvements to techniques but there had been no major breakthroughs.
2. Gunpowder in gunshot wounds was thought to be poisonous so wounds were treated by pouring boiling oil onto them to kill the poison or by ramming an oil-soaked cloth into the wound and binding it up. Both were extremely painful.
3. Open wounds and amputations were closed by putting a red-hot iron called a cautery onto the wound to seal the blood vessels. Cauterising a wound was also incredibly painful.

Source 1

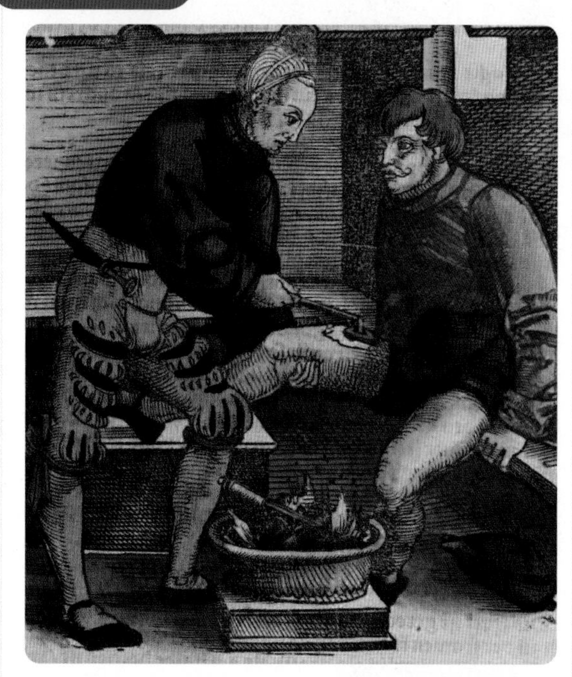

▲ A wound being cauterised. In reality the patient would have been struggling and screaming with pain. This wood engraving dates from around the 15th–16th century.

Paré's achievements

- Paré changed the treatment of gunshot wounds. He replaced the use of boiling oil on wounds with his own mixture of egg yolks, oil of roses and turpentine.
- He used ligatures to stop bleeding – silk threads tied around individual blood vessels. He did this instead of using a cauterising iron, which he called the 'old and too cruel way of healing'.
- He designed and arranged the making of false limbs for wounded soldiers, and included drawings of them in his books to spread the idea.

Source 2

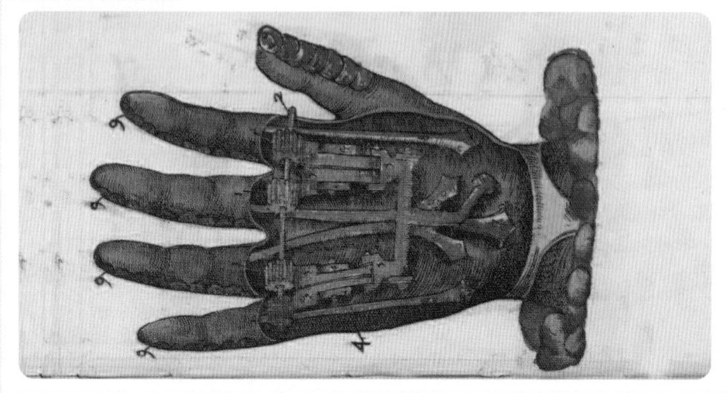

◀ Skilled armourers sometimes made the false limbs designed by Paré. The best even allowed the user to hold a sword and fight. This wood engraving appeared in 1564.

How did he do it?

Paré was determined, intelligent, willing to try new ideas. He didn't give in to critics who said new ideas were mistaken.

Paré only tried his new remedy for gunshot wounds when he ran out of boiling oil. Read his own description in Source 1 to see how important chance was in his work!

As an army surgeon, Paré had plenty of practice and opportunities to try new methods.

Printing spread Paré's ideas much more quickly and widely than the new ideas of medieval surgeons such as Theodoric of Lucca.

Paré was willing to learn from his work and did not rely on reading books. He wrote angrily in reply to physicians and critics: 'How dare you teach me surgery, you who have done nothing but look at books. Surgery is learned with the eye and the hand.'

Source 3

Paré's description of his breakthrough in treating gunshot wounds in the middle of a battle:

'Other surgeons applied the oil, as hot as possible, into the wounds. I took courage to do as they did. Eventually I ran out of oil. I was forced instead to use an ointment made from egg yolks, oil of roses and turpentine. That night I could not sleep, fearing what would happen because the wounds had not been cauterised and that I should find those on whom I had not used the burning oil dead or poisoned. This made me rise up very early to visit them. To my surprise I found those to whom I gave my ointment feeling little pain, and their wounds without inflammation or swelling, having rested reasonably well during the night. The others, on whom I used the boiling oil, were feverish, with great pain and swelling around the edges of their wounds.'

- **Stopping bleeding with ligatures was slow.** Fifty-three ligatures had to be tied when a thigh was amputated. In the chaos of war, using a cautery was faster and could be effective.
- **Ligatures were dangerous** because the thread could carry infection deep into a wound, causing death. A better antiseptic than turpentine or wine was needed but this wasn't discovered for another 300 years, in the late 1800s.
- **Paré's discoveries were still small-scale** compared with the major problems facing surgeons – they had no effective anaesthetics, they had no effective antiseptics to stop infection and they did not understand about blood groups or have fast ways of stopping major bleeding.

Stepping stones to the future

1 Parés work became widely known through his books, which were written in French and translated into other everyday languages so that they could be read by more surgeons then if they had only been in Latin.

2 Paré encouraged surgeons to think for themselves and try new methods. He showed that improvements were possible.

3 Ligatures did stop bleeding, although other improvements were needed (see warning) before they were widely used.

Improved medicine and health

4.3 Did new discoveries help the sick?

It looks as if enquiry was winning thanks to the work of individuals but conservatism was fighting hard. Use pages 94–99 to complete your chart (from page 85) and decide who really won the Big Fight.

Healers and their training

1 Physicians

University-trained physicians still accepted Hippocrates' theory that illness was caused by an imbalance in the body's humours. Their training still concentrated on the writings of Greek doctors, especially Galen, and Arab doctors such as Ibn Sina. They also read the work of Vesalius, Paré and Harvey but were often reluctant to accept that Galen could have been wrong. Therefore Harvey's discovery was not accepted immediately. Like their ancient and medieval predecessors, physicians also advised their clients on how to stay healthy through a good diet and exercise.

Physicians also watched dissections taking place. However, even in the 1660s, a century after Vesalius had shown how important human dissection was, they still sometimes had to make do with dissecting animals. When Samuel Pepys (who wrote a famous diary in the 1660s) feared he was going blind he took advice from London's leading expert on eye problems, Dr Daubeny Turberville. Pepys tried green lenses in spectacles, eye-drops, pills and even bleeding and purges. On 3 July 1668 Pepys wrote that he had been with Turberville and several other doctors to 'dissect several eyes of sheep and oxen, to my great information; but strange that Turberville should be so great a man and yet to this day has seen no eyes dissected or but just once …'.

Activities

1. Work in teams. Each team will tackle one topic:
   Healers (pages 94–95)
   Treatments (pages 96–97)
   Public health (pages 98–99)
   Record what you find in the correct row of your Big Story chart then report back to the class.
2. All teams will have discovered something about 'Ideas and disease' because there is evidence about that on every page. Pool your findings and add the details to your Big Story chart.
3. Discuss: Why do you think Thomas Hobbes, one of the greatest philosophers in history, said 'he had rather have the advice or take medicine from an experienced old woman, who had been at many sick people's bedsides, than from the learnedest but unexperienced physician'?

Source 1

◀ Uroscopy, examining the appearance of urine, was still one of the most common means of diagnosing illness in the seventeenth century.

2 Women healers

Women still played a major part in everyday medicine. Wealthy ladies often provided care for local families. As a child, Lady Grace Mildmay (1552–1620) was set to read William Turner's book *A New Herbal* by her governess, and later read books by Galen and Ibn Sina. She also kept records of her patients and the treatments she used. Women continued to work as midwives, although the first handbooks for midwives were written by men who had little practical experience. The first English handbook by a woman was *The Midwives Book* by Mrs Jane Sharp in 1671.

However, wealthy patients were becoming less willing to go to women healers and preferred fashionable physicians instead. This was nothing to do with experience or effectiveness but wanting to be seen to be going to the most expensive doctors! Women were still not allowed to go to university so could not match the theoretical knowledge of men, no matter how good their practical skills.

Another development which downgraded women's role was a secret discovery. About 1620 Peter Chamberlen invented the obstetrical forceps, used to free a baby from the womb during a difficult birth without hurting or killing baby or mother. The Chamberlens, refugees from France, passed the design from father to son until the death of the last of the family in 1728 revealed their secret. After this, male physicians said that only men should use forceps because only they had been to university to gain anatomical knowledge.

Source 2

MARGARET COLFE.
HAVING BEEN ABOVE FORTY YEARS A WILLING NURSE, MIDWIFE, SURGEON AND, IN PART, PHYSICIAN TO ALL BOTH RICH AND POOR, WITHOUT EXPECTING REWARD.
(LEWISHAM, 1643)

PRUDENCE POTTER.
HER LIFE WAS SPENT IN THE INDUSTRIOUS AND SUCCESSFUL PRACTICE OF PHYSIC, SURGERY AND MIDWIFERY.
(DEVON, 1689)

DOROTHY BURTON.
HAS EXCELLENT SKILL IN SURGERY, SORE EYES, ACHES ETC AND HAS DONE MANY FAMOUS GOOD CURES UPON POOR FOLKS THAT WERE OTHERWISE DESTITUTE OF HELP.
(1629)

▲ Some memorials put up to women healers

3 Quacks

There had always been quacks, healers with no training, although the word was new. Many were simply out to make as much money as possible by selling their charms, potions or bottles of medicine. Some did very well indeed. Joanna Stephens (died 1774) claimed to have a remedy that would dissolve bladder stones without needing painful surgery. Parliament paid £5,000 to buy the recipe from her!

Source 3

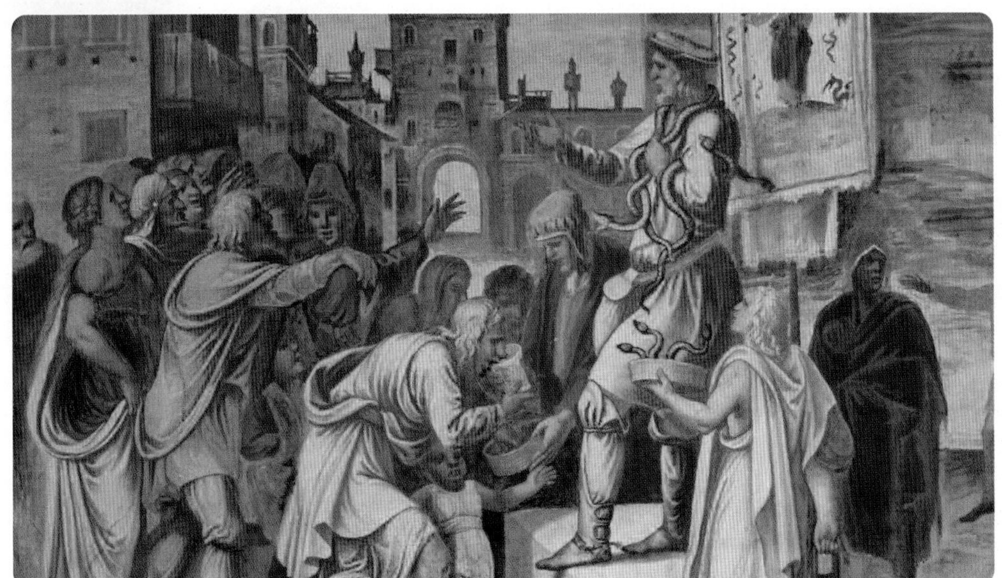

◀ Arriving with a fanfare of drum and trumpet, quacks were often accompanied by a capering clown and chattering monkey to draw the crowds. Some pretended to be from faraway places, such as Turkey, to add a sense of mystery and excitement.

Were everyday treatments changing – and doing more good?

1 Bleeding and purging

Source 1

◀ Bleeding was still one of the most common medical treatments and was recommended as a method of preventing illness, too.

2 Herbal remedies

Many home remedies were handed down through generations from mother to daughter. Girls learned how to mix up remedies, using ingredients such as honey, which we now know kills some bacteria. More people were writing down home remedies because more people could now read and write. Mary Doggett noted a remedy for scurvy which used a mixture of horseradish roots, white wine, water and a quart of orange juice or twelve thinly cut oranges. We know that scurvy, which leads to internal bleeding and death, is the result of not eating enough fruit and vegetables so long practice had produced an excellent remedy, even if Mary did not know why it worked.

Source 2

Of Borage.

Buglossum.

▲ The printing revolution meant that more people had books in their homes containing advice on herbal remedies. One of the most popular was Nicholas Culpepper's *The Complete Herbal* which recommended simple homegrown herbal remedies.

3 New ingredients from abroad

European travels to America and Asia led to the arrival of new ingredients for medicines. Rhubarb from Asia was widely used to purge the bowels. Ipecacuanha from Brazil was prescribed for dysentery and used to make people vomit. The bark of the cinchona tree was imported from South America because of its effectiveness in treating fevers. In Europe it became known as quinine and helped many who suffered from malaria.

Less helpfully, opium was imported from Turkey and used as an anaesthetic. Tobacco was greeted as a cure-all when it arrived from America, being recommended for toothache, poisoned wounds, joint pains and as protection from plague. A schoolboy at Eton College commented that he had never been flogged so much as during the Plague of 1665, when he was beaten for not smoking often enough!

4 The bezoar stone – testing a magical cure

In 1566 a visitor to King Charles of France gave the king a bezoar stone, which came from the stomach of goat-like animals. The visitor insisted that it would cure all poisons but when King Charles asked Ambroise Paré, his surgeon, Paré said that it could not possibly cure all poisons because a hot poison needed a cold antidote and vice-versa. Paré then suggested a test on a live patient! A cook who had been sentenced to death for theft was offered the chance to live if he took poison and then the bezoar stone. If the bezoar stone worked he would be free! The cook accepted the chance, took poison and then the stone. He died in agony several hours later. It was another triumph for experiment and enquiry, though not so good for the cook.

Source 3

From James Woodforde's diary (Woodforde was a parson in Norfolk and Somerset):
27 May 1779 'My maid Nanny taken very ill with dizziness and a desire to vomit but could not. Her straining to vomit brought on the hiccups which continued very violent. I gave her a dose of rhubarb before going to bed.'
1 March 1778 'Ben brought me a letter saying that Juliana is in a decline on account of lately having had measles and catching cold after, which has affected her lungs. She has been bled seven times.'
17 May 1778 'Ben brought letters which gave the disagreeable news of Juliana's death.'
11 March 1791 'The stye on my eye was still swelled and inflamed very much. As it is commonly said that rubbing the eyelid with the tail of a black cat would do it much good, and having a black cat, I made a trial of it. Very soon after dinner I found my eyelid much abated of swelling and almost free of pain. Any other cat's tail may have the above effect in all probability but I did my eyelid with my own black tom cat's tail.'
16 March 1791 'My eyelid rather better. Just before dinner I washed it well with cold water and the evening appeared much better for it.'

Source 4

▲ Between 1660 and 1682 over 92,000 people visited the King's court, believing that if Charles II touched them they would be cured from scrofula, a skin disease known as the King's Evil.

Source 5

Two suggestions from the 1660s on how to help plague sufferers:
'To draw the poison from the plague sore, take the feathers from the tail of a chicken and apply the chicken to the sore. The chick will gasp and labour for life. When the poison is drawn by the chicken, the patient will recover.'
'Wrap in woollen clothes, make the sick person sweat, which if he do, keep warm until the sores begin to rise. Then apply to the sores live pigeons cut in half or else a plaster made of yolk of an egg, honey, herb of grace and wheat flour.'

Source 6

From *The New London Dispensary*, published in 1682:
'To cure malaria, take the hair and nails of the patient, cut them small and either give them to birds in a roasted egg or put them in a hole in an oak tree or a plane tree. Stop up the hole with a peg of the same tree.'

Had public health improved?

1 Plague – the disease that would not go away

After the Black Death of 1348 plague never completely disappeared. Leicester, for example, suffered ten outbreaks of plague between the 1550s and 1640s. In 1604, 30 per cent of the people of York died from plague. Outbreaks like these happened all over the country.

One major reason was that towns were still overcrowded and full of dirt. The Government did issue some orders, such as saying that bundles of straw had to be hung as a warning outside the homes of plague victims and that people who came from infected houses should carry a white stick in public. However, little was done to enforce regulations because of the cost of employing people to do this at a time when there was no police force.

2 How did people explain plague? Old and new ideas

On 7 June 1665 Samuel Pepys noted in his diary 'I did in Drury Lane see two or three houses marked with a red cross upon the doors and "Lord have mercy upon us" writ there.'

Many people still believed that plague was sent by God as a punishment for their sins.

In 1665 the government ordered days of public prayer and fasting so that people could publicly confess their sins and beg God to be merciful.

Others blamed the malevolent movements of planets or poisonous air, just as in the fourteenth century.

However there were also signs of a more scientific approach based on observation of the evidence. From the weekly Bills of Mortality (see below), some observers linked dirt and disease after realising that the highest numbers of deaths were in the poorest, dirtiest parishes where people lived crammed into the worst housing.

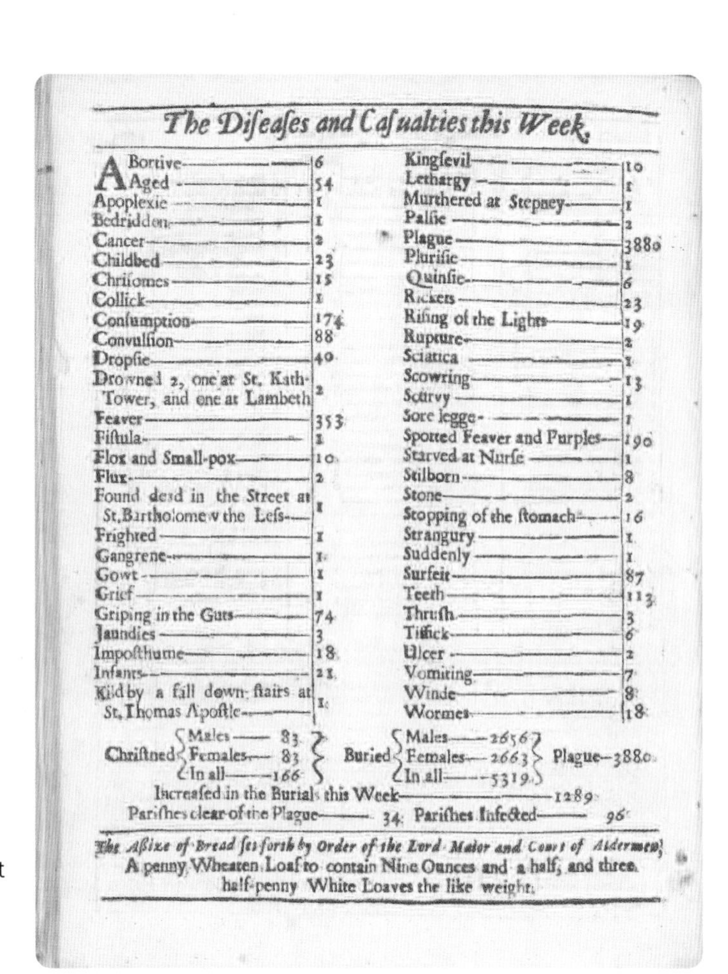

The Diſeaſes and Caſualties this Week.

Abortive	6	Kingſevil	10
Aged	54	Lethargy	1
Apoplexie	1	Murthered at Stepney	1
Bedridden	1	Palſie	2
Cancer	2	Plague	3880
Childbed	23	Pluriſie	1
Chriſomes	15	Quinſie	6
Collick	1	Rickets	23
Conſumption	174	Riſing of the Lights	19
Convulſion	88	Rupture	2
Dropſie	40	Sciatica	1
Drowned 2, one at St. Kath-Tower, and one at Lambeth	2	Scowring	13
Feaver	353	Scurvy	1
Fiſtula	1	Sore legge	1
Flox and Small-pox	10	Spotted Feaver and Purples	190
Flux	2	Starved at Nurſe	1
Found dead in the Street at St. Bartholomew the Leſs	1	Stilborn	8
Frighted	1	Stone	2
Gangrene	1	Stopping of the ſtomach	16
Gowt	1	Strangury	1
Grief	1	Suddenly	1
Griping in the Guts	74	Surfeit	87
Jaundies	3	Teeth	113
Impoſthume	18	Thruſh	3
Infants	21	Tiſſick	6
Kild by a fall down ſtairs at St. Thomas Apoſtle	1	Ulcer	2
		Vomiting	7
		Winde	8
		Wormes	18

Chriſtned: Males 83, Females 83, In all 166. Buried: Males 2656, Females 2663, In all 5319. Plague 3880

Increaſed in the Burials this Week — 1289

Pariſhes clear of the Plague — 34 Pariſhes Infected — 96

The Aſſize of Bread ſet forth by Order of the Lord Maior and Court of Aldermen; A penny Wheaten Loaf to contain Nine Ounces and a half, and three half-penny White Loaves the like weight.

▶ In 1665, another outbreak of plague killed around 100,000 people in London, a quarter of the city's population and many thousands more all over Britain. A general mortality bill for the year 1665, listing the number of deaths in each parish and the overall different causes of death. This kind of evidence demonstrated how the plague hit the crowded, poorest parishes hardest.

3 Preventing plague spreading – old and new ideas

Doctors had no cures for the plague. Many physicians followed their wealthy clients out of London. Some stayed, including Dr George Thomson, who carried out an autopsy on a plague victim, hoping to learn more. Thomson caught plague but survived. Perhaps his own remedy – putting a dried toad on his chest – worked.

Methods of preventing the spread of plague were, however, more carefully thought out and organised. The Mayor of London ordered that victims be shut up in their homes, and watchmen stood guard to stop anyone going in or out. When anyone died, the body was examined by 'women searchers' to check that plague was the cause. Their findings were confirmed by surgeons. Bedding had to be hung in the smoke of fires before it was used again.

Other regulations showed that people were making a connection between dirt and disease, even if they could not explain the link scientifically.

Householders were ordered to sweep the street outside their doors. Pigs, dogs, cats and other animals were not to be kept inside the city. Plays, bear-baitings and games where banned to prevent the assembly of large crowds. These methods helped a little but it took a combination of cold weather, the disease reaching the end of its natural course and then the Great Fire of London to put an end to the Great Plague.

▲ In 1666 London was destroyed by fire and was completely rebuilt to the design of the architect, Christopher Wren. In place of the narrow, dirty streets and wooden buildings were stone and brick buildings with wider, better-paved streets. For a time London was healthier but, as the city became more and more crowded again, the benefits of the rebuilding began to fade.

Evaluating change within a period

'During the Renaissance period there was more continuity than change in medicine.' Explain how far you agree with this statement. [8]

This question is challenging. It tests your knowledge of medicine in the Renaissance **and** your ability to use this knowledge to **evaluate** change and continuity. It is not simply a case of saying whether you agree or disagree with the statement. As 8 marks are available, the examiner expects you to **explore both sides of the argument**. You should spend 12–15 minutes answering this type of question.

Follow steps 1-3 below to achieve a high grade on questions evaluating a statement.

Step 1: The argument for

Look back at the table you produced for the boxing match. **Select** two or three examples that you can **use** as evidence to prove that there was continuity during this period. Selection is important. In the exam you will not have time to write everything down.

Avoid making general points without fully explaining them and backing them up with an example.

Look at the following answer.

There was a great deal of continuity during the Renaissance. The same ideas about what caused illness continued.

The student starts by making a general point. They would score just one mark if they stopped here. They are simply saying something, they are not proving anything!

However, the student goes on to score extra marks by **proving their point**. They compare ideas about the cause of disease at the start and the end of the period.

At the start of the period doctors believed that many illnesses had natural causes. They followed Hippocrates' theory that illness was caused when the body's humours were out of balance. By the end of the Renaissance period little had changed. People continued to believe that many illnesses were caused when the humours in the patient's body were out of balance. Therefore they continued to use bleeding and purging to correct the balance.

Step 2: The argument against

What evidence could you use from your table and commentary to argue against the statement? Select evidence and use it to prove that there was also change during this period. This will help form a good second paragraph. Remember: back up points with good explanations and specific examples.

Step 3: The conclusion

This is a crucial part of your answer. It is usually the part that pupils forget or answer poorly. You have been asked to evaluate the extent to which you agree or disagree with the statement. It would be easy to sit on the fence by writing a neutral answer and avoiding reaching a final conclusion. Sitting on the fence is dangerous. Your answer collapses and you lose marks! Instead, you need to be confident and reach an overall judgement. Imagine that you could put the evidence on scales. Which side would the scales tip – towards change or continuity? Which side has the strongest evidence to support it? How many rounds in the 'Big Fight' did conservatism (which leads to continuity) win? Write down your opinion and explain the key reason you have come to your conclusion.

Change Continuity

What makes an effective conclusion?

Things to avoid:

- A detailed summary of everything that has already been said.
- A one-sentence conclusion which reaches an overall judgement but does not explain it or show that there are two sides to the argument.
- A weak conclusion, that sits on the fence and does not reach an overall judgement.

How to structure a conclusion

Things to do:

- Focus on the question. You could use words or phrases from the question in your final paragraph.
- Compare the strengths of the two slides of the argument. Show that you recognise that there is evidence that agrees *and* disagrees with the statement.
- Come to an overall judgement. To what extent do you agree or disagree with the statement?
- Support your judgement. Explain your main reason for coming to this conclusion.

In some ways the Renaissance was a period of change.

Knowledge of anatomy and how the body worked was revolutionised.

However, overall I agree with the statement. There was far more continuity than change during the Renaissance.

Treatments did not improve for ordinary people and life expectancy did not improve.

The key breakthrough in medicine was still to happen.

Activities

1. Look at the model conclusion on the left. Spot the ways in which the student has applied the four pieces of advice above.
2. Do you agree with the student's conclusion? If you do not, write your own conclusion. Remember to follow the four key pieces of advice on how to structure a conclusion.

Sample 'Evaluation' questions

1. 'Since Roman times religion has hindered, rather than helped, medical progress.' Explain how far you agree with this statement.
2. 'Between the time of the Ancient Greeks and the end of the nineteenth century there has been more continuity than change in ideas about the causes of disease.' Explain how far you agree with this statement.

Smarter revision: Concept map

So far this section has mostly been investigating the changes and continuities in medicine. To finish we'll concentrate on **why** medicine was slow to change with the help of a concept map. On this page we're going to show you how to build up a concept map.

Using concept maps

The students on the opposite page are building a concept map. Concept maps help you develop good explanations. They will:

- help you identify the factors that explain why medicine changed or stayed the same
- show how the factors worked together
- show which factors were the most important (that's what the crowns are for!).

Activities

We have built up this concept map for you. It explains why medicine was slow to develop. It's almost finished. All you have to do is copy it and finish it off.

1. The factors linked to the question with red string were important in hindering medical developments.
   The pink cards on the right provide evidence of this. On your own version of the map write or place the cards in the correct places on the red string.
2. The green string links the factors that worked together to prevent progress.
   The green cards explain these links. On your own version of the map write or place the cards in the correct places on the green string.
3. The crown shows which factor we think was most important in hindering medical progress. Do you agree – and why?

A. Opposition to Vesalius' criticism of Galen.

B. Prayers said in 1665 to prevent plague.

C. Continued belief in Theory of Four Humours.

D. Opposition to Harvey's ideas about blood.

E. Touching for the King's Evil.

F. Governments did not try to improve public health except in emergencies.

G. The Church still supported many traditional ideas.

H. Kings still believed their task was making decisions about war and religion, not improving living standards and health.

Why was medicine so slow to change during the Renaissance?

Evaluating sources:
Topic – Quack Doctors

Look at the source questions below. You should be able to use your inference and cross-referencing skills to answer Questions 1 and 2. Remember to use the advice on pages 78–79 to help you. The advice opposite will help you answer Questions 3 and 4. These questions test your ability to place sources in their historical context and to evaluate how useful sources are for a particular enquiry.

Quack doctors: Background information

A 'quack' is someone who practises medicine without any training, knowledge or skill. In the Renaissance period many quacks were out to make as much money as possible by selling their charms, potions or bottles of medicine.
They travelled around the country often selling their treatments in the street. Many people tried their treatments in the hope what they offered could cure their illnesses. There were many warnings during the eighteenth century, usually from the medical profession, who feared them as rivals.

Source A

'The patient is informed that the doctor has thirteen lords and dukes with him that morning. Presently he enters; there is a general distribution of snuff, which, he assures them, is a cure for all diseases. When the people remind him of his advertisements of free treatment he replies that he charges fees so that he can supply medicines to the poor. To one woman who says she has no money, he answers that it makes no difference at all, but he happens to be very busy that morning.'

An eye witness description of the quack John Taylor in 1740.

Source B

'I was at Tunbridge in 1748, where I met with Taylor the famous Quack. He seems to understand the anatomy of the eye perfectly well; he had a fine hand and good instruments and performs all his operations with great skill.'

A description of John Taylor by a doctor in 1748.

Source C

'My wife walked to Whitesmith to see a quack perform wonders. He has a stage built there and comes once a week to swindle poor deluded creatures out of their money. He sells packets which are to cure people of more illnesses than they ever had in their lives for one shilling each, by which means he makes £9 a day.'

An extract from the diary of Thomas Turner, a Sussex grocer, written in July 1760.

1 Study Source A.
What impression of Quacks is given in this source? [6]

2 Study Sources A, B and C.
How far do Sources B and C support the impression of quacks given in Source A? [8]

3 Study Sources C and D.
Are you surprised that so many people visited Quacks during the seventeenth and eighteenth centuries? [8]

4 Study Source E.
How useful is this source for finding out about Quacks in the eighteenth century? [8]

Source D

'It would be a great mistake to dismiss all these unqualified practitioners merely as grasping charlatans, for they could only get away with selling their unproven cures because the qualified practitioners had nothing better to offer. If the physicians, surgeons and apothecaries had been able to provide effective and safe forms of treatment, the quacks would not have flourished.'

An extract from Vernon Coleman's The Story of Medicine (1985).

Source E

1. Never trust those who pretend that the good of mankind is their only reason for offering their medicine for sale.
2. Conclude the advertiser to be a fool, who pretends that his medicine will cure different illnesses which have no connection to each other
3. Do not believe lists of causes where the medicine is said to have worked, these are usually invented by the quack.

A list of rules for identifying quacks, written by a doctor in 1767.

Using sources effectively: Placing sources in their historical context

To answer Question 3 effectively you need to combine details in the sources with your own knowledge of a period. It is important that you **consider the historical context**. To us today, it might be surprising that so many people visited untrained quacks who sold cures that rarely worked. However, the question asks you to **consider this in light of what you know about the seventeenth and eighteenth centuries**.

Remember that, despite Vesalius and Harvey, treatments had not improved and there was still no understanding of what caused disease. Source D points out that had doctors at the time been able to offer better treatments the quacks would not have made so much money.

Using sources effectively: Evaluating sources

Question 4 asks you to evaluate how useful Source E is for finding out about quacks. There is more to this question than meets the eye. That is why it is worth 8 marks. You need to consider the strengths and limitations of Source E.

Remember: the question is asking you how useful the source is, not how useless. There will not be any sources that are completely useless. Do not get bogged down telling the examiner what is wrong with the source. Begin and end your answer positively.

Use the grid to develop an effective answer.

	Strengths	Limitations
STEP 1: CONSIDER CONTENT **What** do we learn? (Use your inference skills.) • Consider the source's **content** but do not fall into the trap of repeating what the source says in your own words. • Explain how the source can be used. Explain why it contains useful information.	*Source E is useful because…* *…it helps us understand how quacks worked. We learn that they advertised their products and gave lists of people they had helped.* *…it shows that not everybody at the time believed in quacks. The author of the set of rules states that quacks did not tell the truth and tricked people into buying their medicine. He also suggests that the cures offered by quacks did not work.*	What do we not learn? What is missed out? What else would you want to know? *However, Source E is…* *…only a set of rules. It does not provide us with specific examples of quacks who have tricked people by selling them worthless cures.*
STEP 2: CONSIDER THE PROVENANCE OF THE SOURCE • What is the **nature** of the source? What **type of source** is it? • What are the **origins** of the source? **Who** wrote or produced the source? **When** was it produced? • What was the **purpose** of the source? Why was it produced? • **How typical** is the source of the period and other sources. Do other sources back it up?	*Source E is a set of rules for identifying quacks, written by a doctor in the eighteenth century. He would have some medical knowledge and this may have helped him see through the way quacks worked.* *The criticisms he makes are supported by other sources. For example…*	*However, we need to be careful about totally trusting the impression of quacks given in source E. The source was produced by a doctor who may have seen quacks as a threat to his business. Quacks and doctors were rivals at the time. Some doctors may have exaggerated how bad quacks were to get more business for themselves.*

STEP 3: REACH AN OVERALL JUDGEMENT

Always end with a conclusion in which you reach a judgement.

- How useful is the source (very, quite)?
- What is your key reason for reaching this judgement?

Overall, the source is…
extremely / very / quite /not very
useful for a historian studying…

We have reached 1750 and, although changes have begun to take place, people are not living longer and are no healthier. This section rapidly summarises everything you have done so far, investigates one of the greatest discoveries in medical history and then takes you on a quick tour of the medical breakthroughs that finally improved health and life expectancy.

5.1 Why hadn't life expectancy improved by the 1750s?

	Prehistory	Ancient Egypt	Ancient Greece	Ancient Rome
Ideas about causes of disease	Gods and spirits	Blocked channels	Four Humours	Bad air
Public Health	Hunter-gatherers avoided some problems through constant travelling	Individuals took care of themselves		Aqueducts sewers Baths in forts and towns
Everyday Treatments	Herbal remedies Prayers and charms	Purging	Bleeding and purging Rest exercise and diet	
Surgery	Simple surgery – external growths Splints for fractured bones Trephining		Honey, wine and vinegar used Herbal anaesthetics, eg. opiur	
Individuals			Hippocrates Galen	

Activities

1 Life expectancy had not increased since Ancient times.
   a How do each of the four themes in the top four rows of the table below help to explain this?
   b Which theme do you think is most significant in explaining why life expectancy had not increased?
2 What medical changes and discoveries do you think were needed to make significant progress in the future?
3 Living graph: look at the living graphs you began on page 7. Use the details on this page to make sure they are complete to 1750.

1750

	Middle Ages	Renaissance
	Gods and spirits →	
	Four Humours →	
		Bad air →
	Planets and stars	
ion .n	Monastries developed their own facilities Kings did little to improve public health	Towns had laws to prevent dirt and disease but they were poorly enforced
	Herbal remedies →	Herbal remedies →
	Prayers →	
	Bleeding and Purging →	
	Rest exercise and diet →	
→	Burning cauteries to close up wounds	Paré – soothing oils instead of burning oil for gunshot wounds
→	Military surgeons made minor improvements	Paré – ligatures to stop bleeding
tiseptics →		
.drake →		
n Sina	Rhazes	Vesalius Paré Harvey

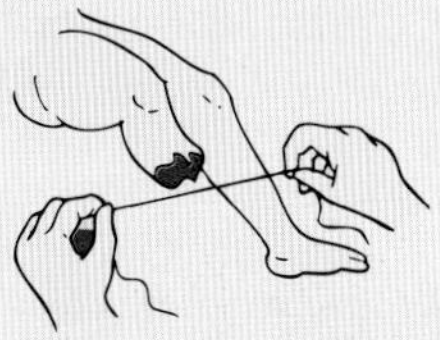

Which factors played the biggest part in hindering progress?

Activities

This activity helps you think about which factors did most to prevent medical progress. Take each factor in turn. The bubbles show examples of this factor in action.

1. Give each example a mark out of 3, using the table on the right.
2. Add up the marks for all the examples of that factor give each factor a total.
3. Decide which factors get the gold, silver and bronze medals for preventing progress.

Marks	Impact on medicine
3	Example of factor pushing medicine back significantly
2	Example of factor pushing medicine back a little
1	Example of factor preventing progress but not pushing medicine back

War examples

a Destruction after the end of the Roman Empire.

b Medieval kings spent money on war, not public health.

Lifestyle examples

a In prehistory the first farming settlers caught and spread diseases.

b Medieval towns were dirty and crowded, spreading disease.

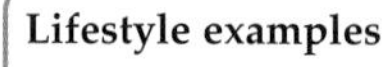

Religion examples

a Egyptian religion prevented detailed dissection.

b The Christian church in the Middle Ages supported Galen and opposed enquiry and change.

c Throughout history people believed that their gods sent diseases so there was no need to look for other explanations.

Attitudes – conservatism examples

a Support for traditional Greek ideas of Hippocrates and Galen during the Middle Ages.

b Continued opposition to new ideas and discoveries during the Renaissance.

Government examples

a Rulers in Egypt and Greece and in the Middle Ages did not believe it was their responsibility to improve people's health.

Evaluating change and continuity across periods

'Between the time of the Ancient Greeks and 1750 there was far more continuity than change in ideas about the causes of disease.' Explain how far you agree with this statement. [8]

Top tips

- Explore both sides of the argument. Look at evidence that supports and challenges the statement.
- Avoid making general points without fully explaining them and backing them up with a specific example.
- Make sure you write an effective conclusion. Reach an overall judgement and explain the key reason for coming to this conclusion.
- Remember the tips on page 100 about questions that ask you to evaluate statements. Structure your answer as you did on page 100 when you evaluated change during the Renaissance.

This exam question presents a new challenge. It requires you to evaluate change and continuity across a number of periods – over 3000 years of history!

The key here is to make sure that you **keep focused on the question**. You must select your examples very carefully. this question is about causes of disease. The statement claims that 'there was far more continuity than change '**in ideas about the causes of disease**'. You will waste time and pick up no marks if you explore surgery, public health or treatments. Focus on ideas about the cause of disease.

Step 1: Look at pages 106–107. **Select** two or three examples as evidence to prove there was **continuity in ideas about the causes of disease**. Use this as the basis for your first paragraph.

Step 2: Now select any examples of ideas about the cause of disease **changing**. These examples help you write a good second paragraph.

Step 3: Keep focused on the question during your conclusion. The statement claims that there was '**far more** continuity than change'. This is a strong claim – be very clear about **the extent to which you agree or disagree** with this statement in your conclusion. Where would you stand on this line? Does everyone in your class agree with you?

5.2 What does the story of Jenner and vaccination tell us about medicine in 1800?

Source 1 is titled 'The Curse of Humankind'. It probably doesn't make a lot of sense to you so you'll have to take our word for it when we say it's really interesting! Your task is to find out exactly what it's telling us – about the story of vaccination and about how far medicine had developed by 1800.

Activities

1. Look carefully at the picture. What can you work out in answer to the questions before reading pages 111–113?
2. Now read pages 111–113 and come back and answer the questions round the picture. (Remember to use your speed-reading skills.)
3. Who or what is the 'curse of humankind?' and what is the artist's attitude to vaccination?
4. Think back to the struggle between enquiry and conservatism. What evidence is there in this picture about the strength of each of the two attitudes around 1800?

Source 1

▲ 'The Curse of Humankind', drawn by Isaac Cruikshank in 1808.

Smallpox – the story so far

Smallpox killed more children than any other disease in the 1700s. Survivors were often severely disfigured by scars from the scabs that formed on the skin.

To stop people catching smallpox the technique of inoculation was used in China and other parts of Asia and Africa. This involved spreading pus from a smallpox pustule into a cut in the skin of a healthy person. If the person was lucky they got a mild dose of smallpox and did not catch it again because their body had developed antibodies against smallpox – although they did not know this. If the person was unlucky they got a bad case of smallpox and died.

Lady Mary Wortley Montagu watched inoculation carried out in Turkey where her husband was British Ambassador. During a smallpox epidemic in England she had her daughter inoculated in front of important doctors and the method rapidly became popular.

Inoculation became big business. Robert and Daniel Sutton became very wealthy by carrying out many thousands of inoculations, charging up to £20 per patient. However, there were dangers with inoculation:

The person inoculated could get a strong dose of smallpox and die.

The person inoculated could pass smallpox onto someone else.

Most people could not afford inoculation so were not protected.

Some people thought that the milder disease of cowpox seemed to give protection against smallpox so deliberately infected themselves with cowpox. However, no doctors had written about or tested this idea scientifically.

Jenner's achievements

Jenner learned a lot from the surgeon John Hunter, who told his students to observe patients carefully and experiment to test their ideas. Jenner's discovery of vaccination followed Hunter's advice exactly. Jenner had long known the story that milkmaids who caught cowpox never seemed to get smallpox and he kept this idea in his mind, thinking about how to test it.

In the 1790s Jenner carried out experiments to test the theory, observing and recording all the details carefully (see Source 2). Then in 1798 he published his book describing vaccination and presenting his evidence, describing 23 different cases. He called this method vaccination because the Latin word for cow is *vacca*.

Activities

5 How did inoculation come to be used in Britain?

6 Why did Jenner believe that vaccination was an improvement on inoculation?

Edward Jenner – Biography

- Born 1749 Died 1823
- Aged 13 apprenticed to a surgeon for 6 years. Aged 21 studied with John Hunter in London, the greatest surgeon of the time.
- 1772 began work aged 23 in Berkeley, Gloucestershire as a country doctor but kept in touch with Hunter about medical developments.
- 1798 published his book *An Enquiry into the Causes and Effects of Variola Vaccinae, known by the Name of Cowpox*. This showed that vaccination could save people from catching smallpox.

Source 2

Extracts from Dr Jenner's casebook, published in 1798:

Case 16

'Sarah Nelmes, a dairy maid, was infected with cowpox from her master's cows in May 1796. A large sore and the usual symptoms were produced.'

Case 17 James Phipps

'I selected a healthy boy about 8 years old. The matter was taken from the cowpox sore on Sarah Nelmes' hand and inserted on 14 May 1796 into the boy by two cuts each half an inch long. On the seventh day he complained of uneasiness, on the ninth he became a little chilly, lost his appetite and had a slight headache and spent the night with some degree of restlessness but on the following day he was perfectly well.

In order to ascertain that the boy was secure from the contagion of smallpox he was inoculated with smallpox matter but no disease followed. Several months later he was again inoculated with smallpox matter but again no disease followed.'

How did Jenner develop and spread vaccination?

Jenner, following Hunter's advice, tested the connection between cowpox and smallpox in experiments, collecting evidence carefully as proof that catching cowpox really did protect people against smallpox.
ATTITUDES
ENQUIRY

In 1798 Jenner published his own account of his discovery, spreading the details of his method worldwide. By 1803 vaccination was being used in the USA and in 1805 Napoleon had the whole of the French army vaccinated.
COMMUNICATIONS

In 1802 and 1807 Parliament gave Jenner £30,000 to develop his work on vaccination. Fifty years later, in 1852, vaccination was made compulsory in Britain, helping to cause a huge drop in smallpox cases.
GOVERNMENT

Jenner had the insight to realise that the link between cowpox and smallpox was important and the determination to carry on and publish his research despite opposition and criticism.
INDIVIDUAL GENIUS

Source 1

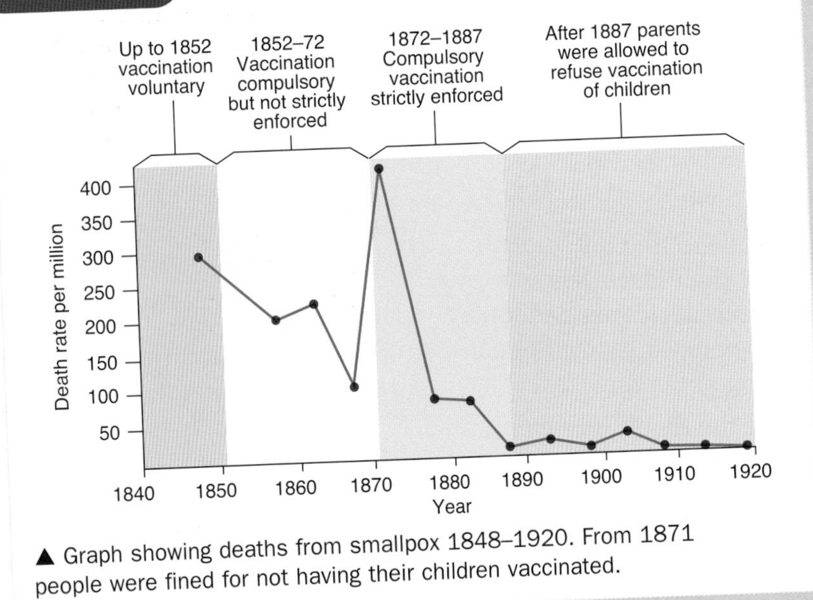

Up to 1852 vaccination voluntary
1852–72 Vaccination compulsory but not strictly enforced
1872–1887 Compulsory vaccination strictly enforced
After 1887 parents were allowed to refuse vaccination of children
Death rate per million
400
350
300
250
200
150
100
50
1840
1850
1860
1870
1880
1890
1900
1910
1920
Year

▲ Graph showing deaths from smallpox 1848–1920. From 1871 people were fined for not having their children vaccinated.

But...

WARNING

DON'T EXAGGERATE

- **Many people opposed vaccination.** An Anti-Vaccine league was formed in 1866.
- **Governments could not decide how much to force people to be healthier.** The graph shows the changes in laws about vaccination being compulsory.
- **Jenner did not know that germs cause disease** so did not know exactly how vaccination worked. Therefore it was not possible to learn from this discovery how to prevent the spread of other diseases.
- **In the later 1800s other factors played a part in keeping people healthier**, such as clean water supplies, cleaner housing and a better diet.

1 An excellent example of experiment and enquiry and showed that a killer disease could be beaten, encouraging other doctors and scientists to solve medical problems.

2 Used worldwide.

3 Vaccination made compulsory in Britain in 1852, leading to a significant reduction in deaths. Other factors like public health reforms played a part in this.

4 In 1980 smallpox was declared eradicated from the world.

Improved medicine and health

Why was there opposition to vaccination?

1 It's against God's laws to give people an animal disease.

2 Smallpox is a punishment for sin. The only cure is prayer and living a godly life.

3 It will cost us inoculators our jobs and profits.

4 The Royal Society says this idea is too revolutionary. They refused to publish Jenner's book.

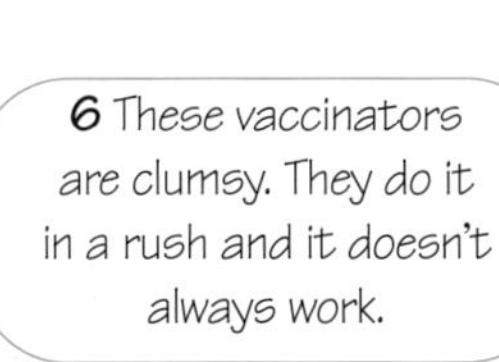

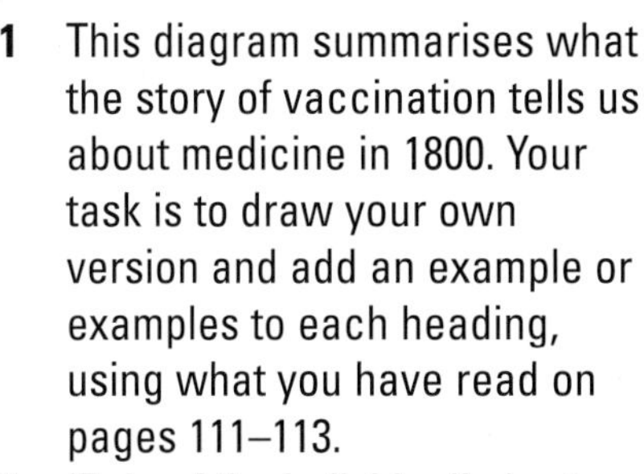

5 I've never heard of Jenner – why should we believe a country doctor?

6 These vaccinators are clumsy. They do it in a rush and it doesn't always work.

7 I've got enough to worry about finding work and food. I don't have time to have my children vaccinated.

8 The government shouldn't interfere in people's lives. It's got no right to fine people who don't get their children vaccinated.

Activities

1. This diagram summarises what the story of vaccination tells us about medicine in 1800. Your task is to draw your own version and add an example or examples to each heading, using what you have read on pages 111–113.
2. 'Role of the individual' chart: create a 'role of the individual' chart for Jenner, to help your revision.
3. Remember to go back and finish Activity 2 on page 110.

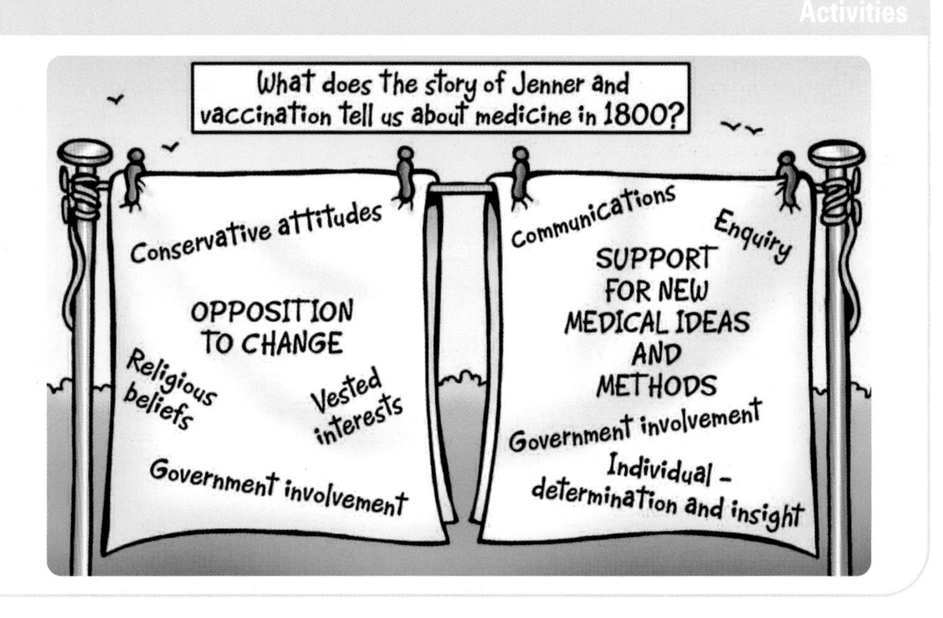

Reaching overall judgements using sources and your own knowledge:

Topic – Jenner and vaccination

Sometimes questions on your exam papers ask you to use all the sources and your own knowledge to reach an overall conclusion. You will usually have to evaluate a statement. You will be asked how far the sources on the exam paper support a point of view. The following question is a good example:

> Study **all** the sources.
> 'The main reason that people opposed Jenner was because they believed that his methods were unsafe.'
> How far do the sources on this paper support that view? Use the sources and your knowledge to explain your answer. Remember to identify the sources you use.
> [10]

Jenner and the development of vaccination

Background information

The number of poor people who accepted free vaccination from organisations set up for that purpose remained very low. Some people were worried that vaccination was unsafe. Things were made worse by the fact Jenner could not explain why vaccination was not successful every time. Some people caught smallpox after they had been vaccinated. Anti-vaccinists claimed that smallpox inoculation could not fail because it was not possible to contract smallpox twice.

Source A

The Suttons in eleven years inoculated 2,514 people, for large fees. They also sold, for anything between fifty and a hundred pounds, to doctors living far away from them, the secrets of their methods. They had their own inoculation house in Ingatestone in Essex where patients were prepared for the operation and rested after it.

An account of the Sutton family business. They inoculated people with smallpox matter in the 1760s and 1770s. This extract is from Doctor Jenner of Berkely by Dorothy Fisk, published in 1959.

Source B

'Jenner's book was published in 1798. He was only a country doctor, and most leading doctors did not accept his ideas, though some did. Neither Jenner nor anyone else could offer any explanation of how vaccination worked. Many of the doctors and others who copied him took far less care than Jenner. There was at this time no knowledge that germs cause infection, and there were no antiseptics, so things often went wrong. One doctor, for instance, vaccinated patients in the same room as he inoculated others with smallpox. It was easy to get the diseases mixed up, and as a result patients often died.'

An extract from Medicine Through Time by J.Scott and C.Culpin (1996).

Source C

'The cowpock – or – the Wonderful Effects of the New Innoculation' by James Gillray. This cartoon was published by the Anti-Vaccine Society in 1802.

Source D

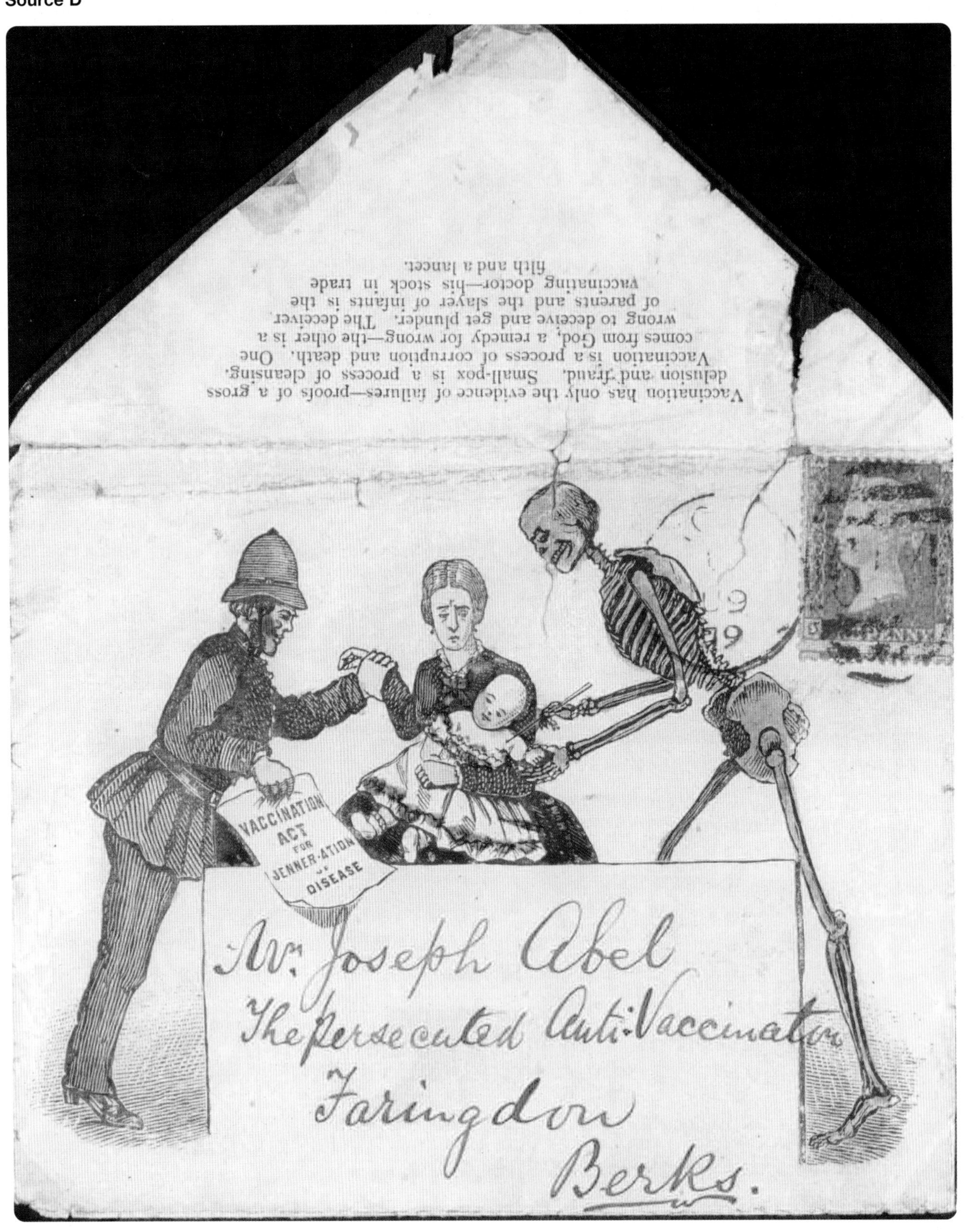

Anti-vaccination propaganda, 1899

Plan your approach to the question

You have already been given advice on how to tackle questions that ask you to evaluate a statement (see pages 100–101). Remember it is not simply a case of saying whether you agree or disagree with the statement. Ten marks are available so the examiner will expect you to explore **both sides of the argument**. Plan to include three paragraphs.

- Paragraph 1: explore the evidence that supports the statement.
- Paragraph 2: explore evidence which disagrees with the statement.
- Paragraph 3: your conclusion. You need to reach an overall judgement. To what extent do you agree or disagree with the statement? Remember to explain your thinking.

Use the sources

You **must** base your answer on the sources on the exam paper. You will not achieve a good grade if you ignore the sources and simply write an answer based on your own knowledge. You do not have to use all the sources but try to use most of them (at least three in this example). Make sure you refer to the source you are using by letter so that the examiner can see which sources you are using to support your answer.

Step 1: Decide which sources support the statement. Use these in paragraph 1. Make sure you explain how they support the statement. Refer to specific details in the source. For example:

Source A does suggest that people opposed Jenner because they thought his methods are unsafe. Jenner is shown vaccinating a terrified looking woman. People who have been vaccinated have parts of cows growing out of their bodies. On the right of the picture...

Step 2: Decide which sources disagree with the statement. Explain why in paragraph 2. If you are using written sources use short, specific quotes to support your answer. For example:

However, there was more than just one reason why people opposed Jenner's new methods. As we can see in Source B, some doctors were making a lot of money from the old method of inoculation. Some people may therefore have exaggerated the dangers of vaccination to protect their own business. In addition Source C indicates that some people opposed Jenner's methods for religious reasons. The writing on the envelope states that smallpox 'comes from God' and is 'a remedy for wrong'. This suggests that some people thought that vaccinations were going against God's wishes.

Step 3: Write an effective conclusion. Use the advice on Pages 100–101.

5.3 When and why did life expectancy improve after 1800?

Jenner's breakthrough begins the story of huge medical improvements. Pages 118–123 give you an overview of these changes so you can begin thinking about why they have happened. But first travel back in time to 1848 and then to 1935 – how quickly was medicine and health changing?

Activities

1. What evidence can you find in the 1848 picture of:
   a. changes in medical methods, ideas and attitudes
   b. continuities in medical methods, ideas and attitudes from the Middle Ages or earlier?
2. What adjectives would you use to describe the degree of change between 1665 (see page 86) and 1848?
3. In 1848 the average life expectancy was still only around 40 for men and a few years lower for women. Which factors do you think explain why:
   a. life expectancy was still low
   b. life expectancy might improve later in the 1800s?

Medical moments in time: London, 1848

In 1848 the government passed a Public Health Act setting up a national Board of Health. It said:
• local taxes could be charged to improve water supply and sewers
• the Board of Health could force towns to improve water supply and sewerage if the local death-rate was very high
• local Boards of Health with Medical Officers could be set up.
Hold your arm out. Bleeding does you good. And I've a good laxative that'll clear out your whole body.
50,000 people dead from cholera. It's worse than 1832.
It's this miasma of bad air that's causing it. People need clean air.
Toilets and cesspits were cleaned out by night-soil men and the waste was carried through streets on carts.
It's consumption. He's been coughing all week.
Back home people with coughs ride a donkey in a circle seven times. Worth trying?
There's talk of taxes to pay for cleaning streets and building sewers and water pipes.
I'll pay for where I live but not for keeping anyone else clean.
WINE ALES
TAILOR
CARRIAGES
EEL PIES

Activities

1 What evidence can you find in the 1935 picture of:
   a changes in medical methods, ideas and attitudes since 1848
   b continuities in medical methods, ideas and attitudes with the Middle Ages or earlier?
2 What adjectives would you use to describe the degree of change between 1848 and 1935?
3 In 1935 the average life expectancy was just over 50 for men and a few years higher for women. Which factors do you think explain why life expectancy had improved since 1848?
4 Create your own version of 'Medical moments in time' for today.
   a Include details that show changes since 1935.
   b Explain why life expectancy in many parts of Britain has risen to nearly 80.
   c Describe any problems that continue to threaten people's health.

Medical moments in time: London, 1935

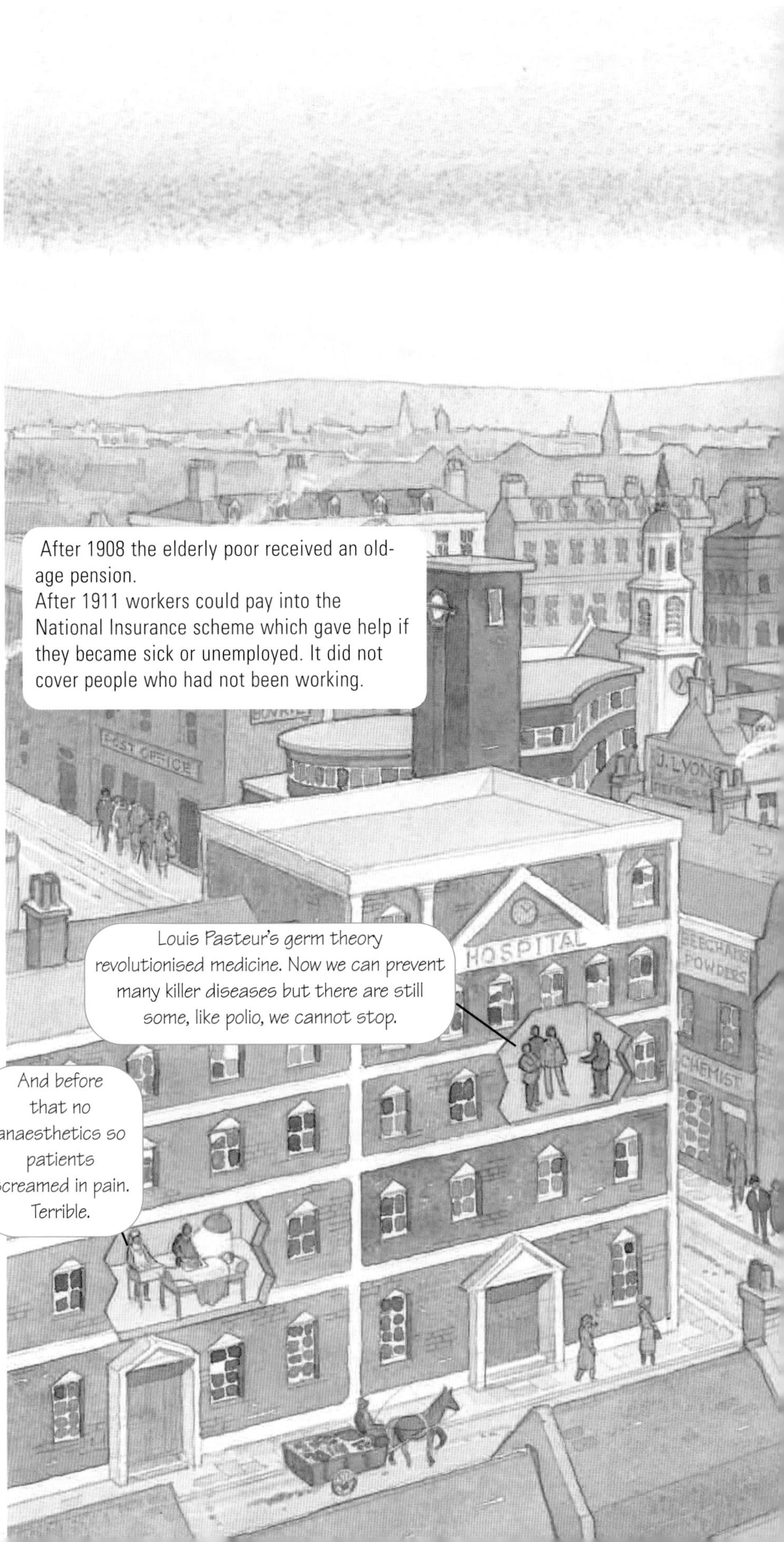

After 1908 the elderly poor received an old-age pension.
After 1911 workers could pay into the National Insurance scheme which gave help if they became sick or unemployed. It did not cover people who had not been working.
POST OFFICE
J. LYONS
HOSPITAL
BEECHAMS POWDERS
CHEMIST
Louis Pasteur's germ theory revolutionised medicine. Now we can prevent many killer diseases but there are still some, like polio, we cannot stop.
Only 70 years ago surgeons wore old clothes and there were no antiseptics. Germs were everywhere in operating theatres!
And before that no anaesthetics so patients screamed in pain. Terrible.

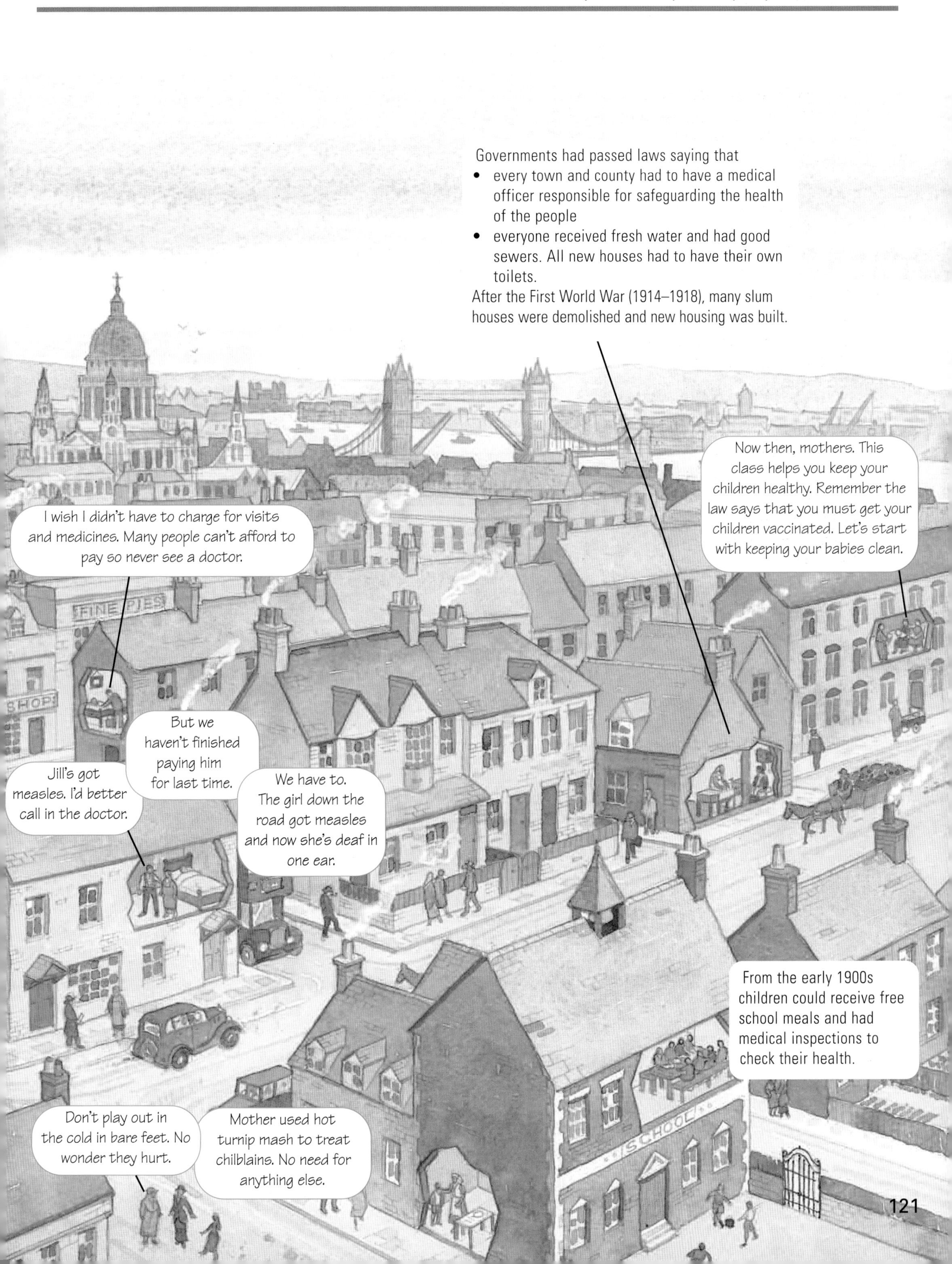
Governments had passed laws saying that
• every town and county had to have a medical officer responsible for safeguarding the health of the people
• everyone received fresh water and had good sewers. All new houses had to have their own toilets.
After the First World War (1914–1918), many slum houses were demolished and new housing was built.
I wish I didn't have to charge for visits and medicines. Many people can't afford to pay so never see a doctor.
Now then, mothers. This class helps you keep your children healthy. Remember the law says that you must get your children vaccinated. Let's start with keeping your babies clean.
FINE PIES
SHOPS
But we haven't finished paying him for last time.
Jill's got measles. I'd better call in the doctor.
We have to. The girl down the road got measles and now she's deaf in one ear.
From the early 1900s children could receive free school meals and had medical inspections to check their health.
Don't play out in the cold in bare feet. No wonder they hurt.
Mother used hot turnip mash to treat chilblains. No need for anything else.
SCHOOL

What were the key breakthroughs in medicine after 1800?

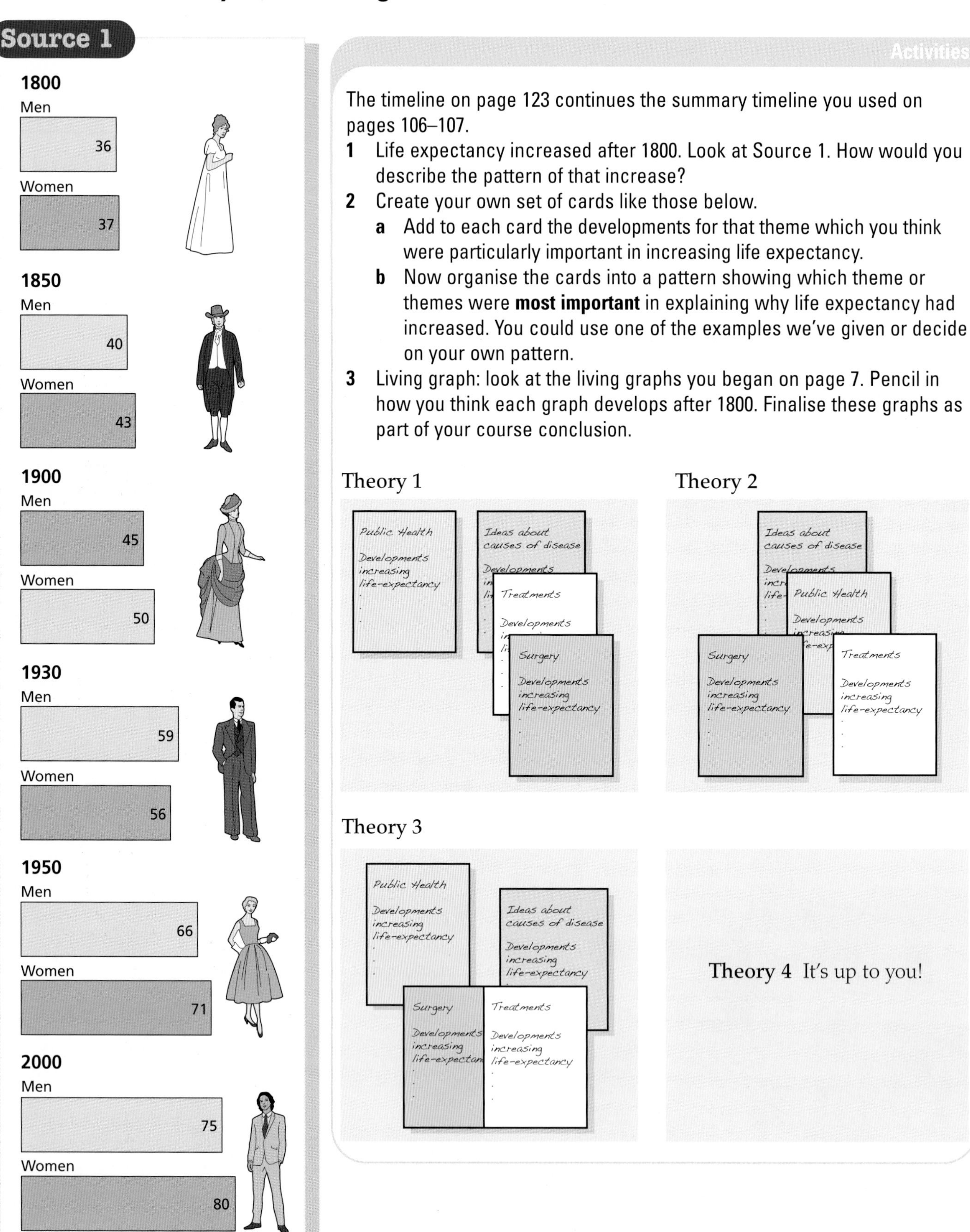

Activities

The timeline on page 123 continues the summary timeline you used on pages 106–107.

1 Life expectancy increased after 1800. Look at Source 1. How would you describe the pattern of that increase?
2 Create your own set of cards like those below.
   a Add to each card the developments for that theme which you think were particularly important in increasing life expectancy.
   b Now organise the cards into a pattern showing which theme or themes were **most important** in explaining why life expectancy had increased. You could use one of the examples we've given or decide on your own pattern.
3 Living graph: look at the living graphs you began on page 7. Pencil in how you think each graph develops after 1800. Finalise these graphs as part of your course conclusion.

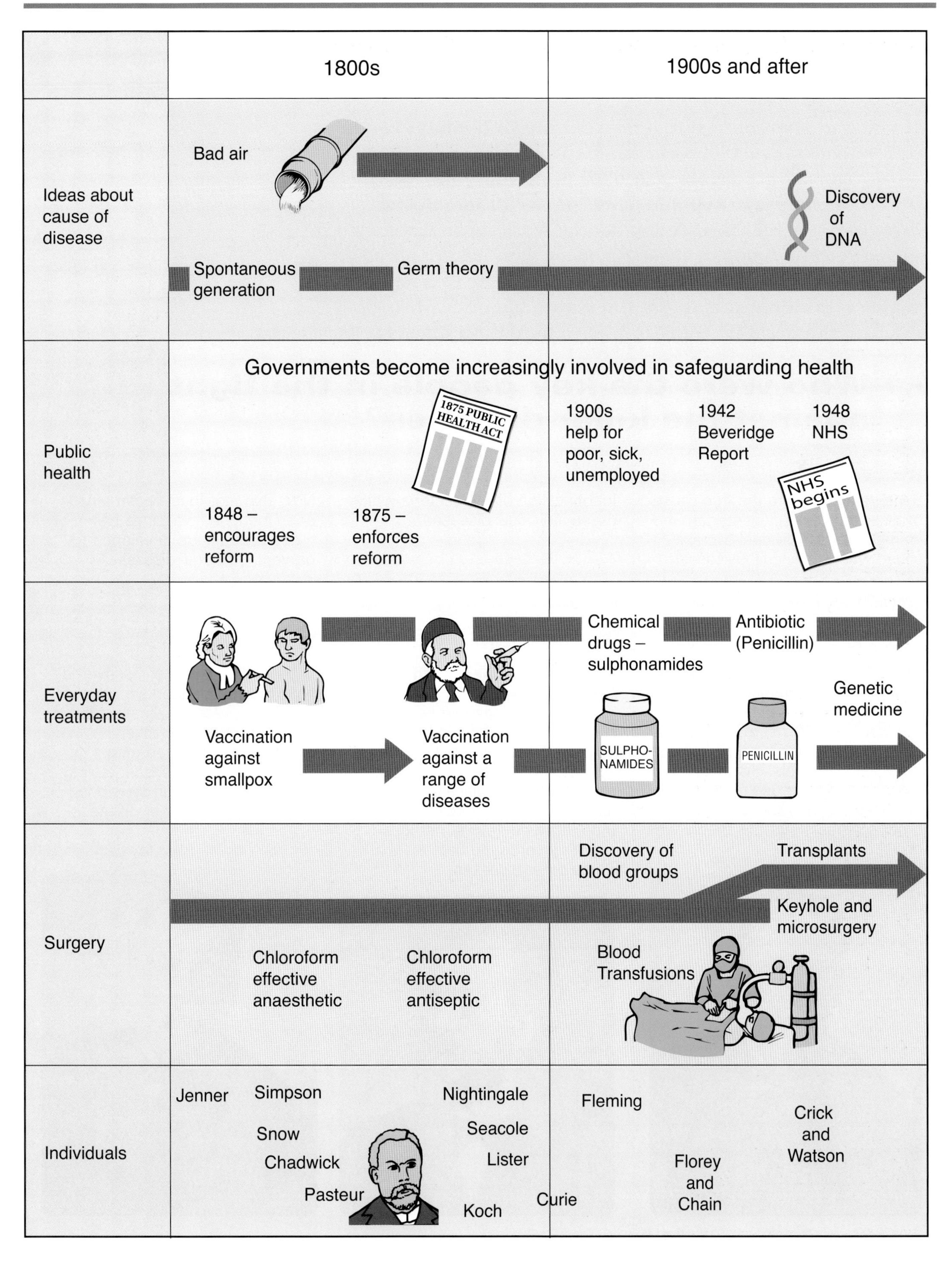
1800s
1900s and after
Ideas about cause of disease
Bad air
Discovery of DNA
Spontaneous generation
Germ theory
Public health
Governments become increasingly involved in safeguarding health
1875 PUBLIC HEALTH ACT
1900s help for poor, sick, unemployed
1942 Beveridge Report
1948 NHS
NHS begins
1848 – encourages reform
1875 – enforces reform
Everyday treatments
Chemical drugs – sulphonamides
Antibiotic (Penicillin)
Genetic medicine
Vaccination against smallpox
Vaccination against a range of diseases
SULPHO-NAMIDES
PENICILLIN
Surgery
Discovery of blood groups
Transplants
Keyhole and microsurgery
Chloroform effective anaesthetic
Chloroform effective antiseptic
Blood Transfusions
Individuals
Jenner
Simpson
Nightingale
Fleming
Crick and Watson
Snow
Seacole
Chadwick
Lister
Florey and Chain
Pasteur
Koch
Curie

Section 6: Fighting disease after 1800: Which medical hero deserves the statue of honour?

If you had been born into a poor family in London, Leeds or Manchester in 1800 your life expectancy was as low as 18. The chances were still very high that you would die from cholera or typhoid, smallpox or tuberculosis, diphtheria or measles. Today deaths from these diseases are very rare. Some of these diseases have disappeared completely. Through this section your task is to decide which individual should get the statue of honour for making the greatest contribution to defeating disease.

6.1 Who were the key people in the fight against the killer diseases?

Discovery 1	Discovery 2	Discovery 3
Bacteria (germs) are the true cause of diseases BUT scientists cannot identify which individual bacteria cause which individual diseases.	Identification of the bacteria which cause individual diseases.	Now that individual bacteria had been identified, vaccines based on those bacteria are developed to prevent individual diseases.
Understanding ▶	**Prevention** ▶	
Who did what?	**Who did what?**	**Who did what?**
Louis Pasteur published his **germ theory** in 1861. He had carried out a series of experiments to prove that bacteria (germs) make milk and beer go bad and that bacteria cause diseases in animals. His theory was that germs also cause human diseases. In 1864 he convinced other scientists that this theory was correct.	In the 1870s **Robert Koch** and his research team developed the scientific methods that helped scientists to identify specific bacteria. Koch then made the first discovery of the bacterium that causes a human disease – tuberculosis. Other scientists then followed Koch's methods and discovered the bacteria that cause other diseases.	In the 1880s **Pasteur** discovered how vaccination works and developed vaccines, firstly against animal diseases – chicken cholera, anthrax – and then against a human disease, rabies. Other scientists then developed vaccines against other diseases.

Activities

1. Work in a pair and examine one of these six discoveries. You have one minute to explain to the rest of the class **why** that discovery was so important. Include, briefly, information on:
   - **a** before the discovery – what was thought or what couldn't be done
   - **b** what the discovery was and who made it
   - **c** what the discovery led to.
2. Can you spot links between any two discoveries?
3. Can you see evidence of the impact of any of the factors on page 9?

Discovery 4

The first cures for people who have already become sick with diseases. These cures attack the bacteria developing in the body. They are made from chemicals and called sulphonamide drugs.

Cures

Who did what?

In 1909 **Paul Ehrlich** (below, who had been part of Koch's research team) developed the first chemical cure for a disease. This was Salvarsan 606, which he called a 'magic bullet' because it homed in on and destroyed the harmful bacteria that cause syphilis. It wasn't until the 1930s that **Gerhard Domagk** developed Prontosil, the second chemical 'magic bullet', to cure blood poisoning. Scientists then discovered that the important chemical in these cures was sulphonamide and drug companies then developed more sulphonamide cures for diseases such as pneumonia.

Discovery 5

A second group of cures which attack bacteria. These cures are based on other bacteria which kill the bacteria causing a disease. They are called antibiotics.

Who did what?

Magic bullets could not kill staphylococcus germs which caused major infections and often killed the victims. These germs were beaten when **Fleming**, **Florey** and **Chain** developed the first antibiotic medicine, penicillin. In 1928 Alexander Fleming made the initial discovery that penicillin killed bacteria and later Howard Florey and Ernst Chain developed Fleming's idea into a medical treatment.

Discovery 6

Treatments for diseases which have genetic causes rather than being caused by bacteria. These are based on the discovery of DNA and knowledge of the genetic make-up of the body.

Prevention and cures

Who did what?

In 1953 **Francis Crick** and **James Watson** discovered the structure of human DNA and how it is passed on from parents to children. In the 1990s the Human Genome Project, a world-wide project, began working out exactly how each part of human DNA affects the human body.

Note – the discovery of DNA is not part of your course so we aren't going to ask you any questions on this or consider Crick and Watson for a place on the statue **but** this development could, in time, have even more impact on medicine than Pasteur's germ theory.

What could your statue look like?

Activities

Here is an outline design for the statue that you can develop in your own way – or you could come up with your own design!

1. What initial ideas do you have for your statue now that you have read pages 124–125?
   a. Think about how many individuals you want to include – one, two or more?
   b. What else could you include on the statue base, besides individual people?
   c. Should Edward Jenner (see below) be part of this statue? What are the reasons for and against including him?
   d. What about the base of your statue? We have shown it as interlocking links because no single element was responsible for conquering disease. How else could you present it?
2. Now use the two case studies on pages 128–131 and 132–133 to fill out your knowledge of the battle against disease. Then return to this task and complete the design of your statue.

Edward Jenner

In 1798 Jenner had proved that vaccination prevents people catching smallpox. This discovery saved many thousands of lives but Jenner did not understand what caused smallpox or exactly how vaccination worked. Therefore this method could not be transferred to preventing other diseases.

Recap: What did they think caused disease in the early 1800s?

Activities

Before we look at the case studies here are some questions as a reminder of what people in the early 1800s thought caused disease.

3 Why was 'bad air' a logical explanation for disease?
4 Why did the microscope make a breakthrough possible?
5 Explain the theory of spontaneous generation in your own words.
6 Why hadn't Jenner's discovery of vaccination changed ideas about what caused diseases?

Fading beliefs

Two ideas, supernatural explanations and the theory of the Four Humours, had dominated explanations of the causes of disease for thousands of years but in 1800 both were fading fast.

The popular explanation – bad air/miasma

The idea that bad air causes diseases had been around for centuries. People could see rotting food and flesh and even faeces in the streets. They knew that this dirt gave off terrible smells and they assumed that these smells caused and spread disease. They called these poisonous fumes miasma. This made even more sense in the early 1800s when towns were more crowded and filthy than ever before.

Towns are filthier today than ever and the air smells really bad. So it's logical there's more disease than ever before.

The microscope – a key development

In the 1600s a Dutchman, Anthony van Leeuwenhoek, made a microscope that magnified things by 300 times. He wrote descriptions of what he saw, including tiny living organisms that he found in food, water and human waste. He called them 'animacules' but nobody connected these organisms with diseases. In the 1800s Joseph Lister developed a much more powerful microscope, magnifying things 1000 times. Now scientists could study these 'animacules' in detail.

The latest theory – spontaneous generation

Scientists used the new microscopes to study the micro-organisms (which we call bacteria or germs) on rotting food and tried to work out where these organisms were coming from. They decided that the organisms were spontaneously (automatically) generated (created) by the process of decay in, for example, meat and then the organisms spread disease. This was the theory of spontaneous generation.

Case study 1: How did Pasteur and Koch make their breakthroughs?

For hundreds of years the names of Hippocrates and Galen had dominated medicine. In the 1800s they were finally replaced by Louis Pasteur and Robert Koch. Pages 128–131 help you work out how they achieved so much. Do they deserve to be on the statue by themselves because they achieved everything through their own genius – or should they share the statue with other people or things?

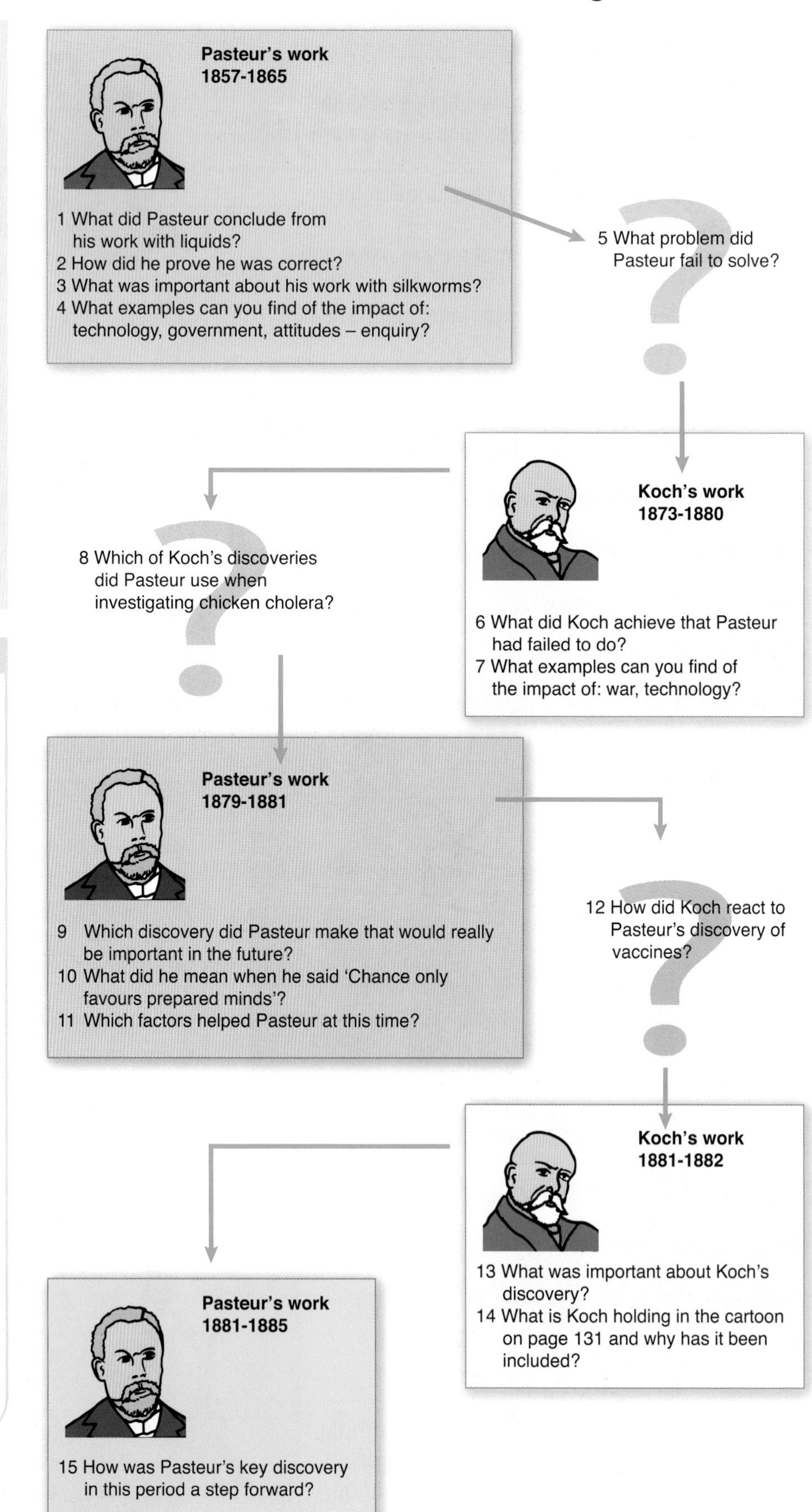

Pasteur's work 1857-1865
1 What did Pasteur conclude from his work with liquids?
2 How did he prove he was correct?
3 What was important about his work with silkworms?
4 What examples can you find of the impact of: technology, government, attitudes – enquiry?
5 What problem did Pasteur fail to solve?
Koch's work 1873-1880
6 What did Koch achieve that Pasteur had failed to do?
7 What examples can you find of the impact of: war, technology?
8 Which of Koch's discoveries did Pasteur use when investigating chicken cholera?
Pasteur's work 1879-1881
9 Which discovery did Pasteur make that would really be important in the future?
10 What did he mean when he said 'Chance only favours prepared minds'?
11 Which factors helped Pasteur at this time?
12 How did Koch react to Pasteur's discovery of vaccines?
Koch's work 1881-1882
13 What was important about Koch's discovery?
14 What is Koch holding in the cartoon on page 131 and why has it been included?
Pasteur's work 1881-1885
15 How was Pasteur's key discovery in this period a step forward?

Activities

1. Draw your own version of this diagram and as you read through pages 129–131 write notes on it to explain the developments. Use the questions 1–15 on the diagram to help you.
2. Choose each man's two major achievements and explain why you chose them.
3. The work of the two men was often linked together. Choose one link and explain how it led to a new discovery.
4. Which two factors played the greatest part in their discoveries? Explain your choices.
5. Who do you think made the greater contribution to the development of medicine – Pasteur or Koch? Jot down two or three reasons for your choice.

Louis Pasteur (1822–1895): biography

Born in France, Pasteur was a university scientist, not a doctor. He loved to demonstrate his experiments in public, especially if he could show that he was right and someone else was wrong. He was also a hugely determined man. He suffered a stroke in 1868 and was paralysed down the left side of his body but kept working and went on to make some of his greatest discoveries.

Source 1

▲ Pasteur in his laboratory. Which vital piece of equipment is shown?

1 Louis Pasteur – his work from 1857 to 1865

- He helped the alcohol industry in Lille. The alcohol was going sour. Pasteur studied the liquid under his microscope and saw two differently-shaped **micro-organisms**: one in the fresh liquid, one in the sour liquid. He concluded that it was the organism that was making the alcohol go sour. Next he was asked by the government to help the wine and milk industries. He suggested that gently heating the liquids (**pasteurisation**) would kill these organisms or bacteria, making them safe to drink.
- As a result of this work Pasteur was convinced that **germs** in the air were causing the liquids to go sour and perhaps causing disease. His ideas were mocked by scientists who believed in the theory of **spontaneous generation** but he had the support of the Emperor of France and the government, who believed that Pasteur's success was making France respected abroad. They paid for his research assistants and a new laboratory to carry out his experiments with specially designed equipment. Improvements in technology made it possible to have much more precisely designed flasks.
- In 1864 he carried out a series of experiments (see Source 2) that convinced scientists that his **germ theory** was correct and that the theory of spontaneous generation was wrong. He showed that **bacteria were causing decay** – not being caused by decay.
- In 1865 he was called in to help the silk industry because a disease was killing the silkworms. He proved that the disease was being **spread by germs in the air**. This was the first time it was proved that germs were causing disease in **animals**.
- In 1865 Pasteur's young daughter's death and a cholera outbreak led him to investigate **human diseases**. He took samples of air from a cholera ward in a hospital but under his microscope he could only see a mass of bacteria. He could not discover which one was causing cholera.

Source 2

THEORY	EXPERIMENT
The air contains living micro–organisms	He took sterile flasks out into the streets of Paris, opened them briefly, then sealed them again. Bacteria grew in them.
Microbes are not evenly distributed in the air	He repeated the experiment in various places around France including high mountains. The number of bacteria varied.
Microbes in the air cause decay	He filled two flasks: one with stale air and the other with ordinary air. In the first there was no decay; in the second decay proceeded as normal.
Microbes can be killed by heating	He heated a material in a flask to make it sterile. He drove the air out, then sealed the flask. It remained sterile even 100 years later.

▲ Pasteur's theories and the experiments that proved them correct.

Robert Koch (1843–1910): biography

Born in Germany, Koch was a doctor who became interested in Pasteur's work and began to study bacteria himself. He was just as ambitious as Pasteur and just as brilliant at detailed, painstaking work in his laboratory and at working with a team of assistants. They saw each other as rivals, especially after the war between France and Germany in 1870–71, which was won by Germany. Both men wanted to be successful to glorify their countries.

2 Robert Koch – his work from 1873 to 1880

- Koch investigated anthrax, a disease affecting animals and people, and discovered the specific bacterium that causes anthrax. This was the first time the specific germ that caused an individual disease had been identified and it was the final proof of Pasteur's germ theory.
- Koch then developed a method of proving which particular bacterium was causing a disease, which could then be used by other scientists.
- Koch improved methods of studying bacteria. He developed ways of staining bacteria so they could be photographed using a new high-quality photographic lens and studied in detail. He also discovered how to grow bacteria on potatoes, which made them easier to study than in a liquid.

3 Louis Pasteur – his work from 1879 to 1881

- Pasteur was determined to match Koch's discoveries and so built up a research team to make faster progress. The team started work trying to help the farming industry because an epidemic of chicken cholera was killing many thousands of chickens. Pasteur quickly found the bacterium causing chicken cholera, something that was impossible before Koch's work just a few years earlier. In summer 1880 Pasteur left one of his team, Charles Chamberland, to inoculate a batch of chickens with the germs but Chamberland forgot and then the laboratory closed for the summer. When Chamberland came back he finally inoculated the chickens, expecting them to die from cholera. What happened next? You can see in the drawing below.

  Pasteur solved the riddle of the chickens that didn't die! He realised that the germs left over the summer had weakened and were not strong enough to kill the chickens but that, just like cowpox and smallpox, they then protected the chickens from a strong dose of cholera. Pasteur had studied Jenner's work in detail and made the link. When people said it had been a lucky discovery he replied 'No! Chance only favours prepared minds.'
- Now that he knew exactly how Jenner's vaccine had worked, Pasteur could create other vaccines. At first he continued to work on animals, producing a vaccine against anthrax. He tested this successfully in a public experiment and the news spread rapidly round Europe.

▼ How an effective vaccine against chicken cholera was discovered by Pasteur and his team.

Source 3

4 Robert Koch – his work from 1881 to 1882

Koch was angry when he heard of Pasteur's development of the anthrax vaccine. He thought Pasteur had stolen some of his research on anthrax. He decided to get ahead by becoming the first man to discover the specific germ that causes a human disease. He investigated tuberculosis and found a way of staining the bacterium causing the disease that made it stand out from other bacteria and human tissue – it was so small that it had been missed by other scientists.

This was the major breakthrough he had been searching for. His research team was able to use his methods to discover the specific bacterium that causes cholera. Other scientists joined in the hunt, finding the bacteria for the diseases in this list.

1882	Typhoid	**1883**	Cholera
1884	Tetanus	**1886**	Pneumonia
1887	Meningitis	**1894**	Plague
1898	Dysentery		

Source 4

◀ A cartoon from around 1880 showing Koch slaying the bacterium that causes tuberculosis.

5 Louis Pasteur – his work from 1881 to 1885

After his success with vaccines against animal diseases, Pasteur turned to human diseases. He investigated rabies, testing his vaccine successfully on dogs, but did not know if it would work on people. The chance to find out came in 1885 when he tested his vaccine on Joseph Meister, a boy who had been bitten by a rabid dog. If the vaccine did not work the boy would die. Pasteur gave Joseph thirteen injections over a two-week period. Joseph survived. Now other scientists set to work to follow Pasteur and find vaccines that could prevent other human diseases. Their successes included:

1896	Typhoid
1906	Tuberculosis
1913	Diphtheria
1927	Tetanus

Case study 2: How was penicillin discovered and developed?

Activities

We guided you carefully through Case study 1 on Pasteur and Koch but this time we'll give you more freedom. You have two tasks:

1. Create a diagram like the diagram on page 128 to tell the story of the development of penicillin. Use the headings on this page to structure the diagram.
2. Create a concept map like the map on pages 102–103.

a. Identify from this page all the factors that played a part in the development of penicillin.

b. Choose the factor or factors that you think played the most important part in the development of penicillin and explain your choice. Make a concept map to show how they are related to each other.

Stage 1: A false start

There are many examples in medicine of false starts, and penicillin is one of them. In 1872 a doctor called Joseph Lister (you'll find out more about him later) noticed that mould of bacteria called penicillin killed other bacteria. Years later, in 1884, he used this mould to treat a nurse who had an infected wound. But Lister did not use it again. A miracle cure lay waiting for someone else to rediscover it.

Information

Antibiotic
A drug made from bacteria that kill other bacteria and so cure an infection or illness.

Stage 2: 1928 – Fleming's discovery of penicillin – another false start?

During the First World War a scientist called Alexander Fleming was sent to France to study soldiers' wounds infected with streptococci and staphylococci bacteria. These wounds were not healed by chemical antiseptics, and many soldiers died from them. Back home Fleming worked on finding a way of dealing with these bacteria.

Ten years later, in 1928, Fleming found what he'd been seeking. He was working at St Mary's Hospital, London. Going on holiday he left a pile of Petri dishes containing bacteria on his laboratory bench. On his return he sorted out the dishes and noticed mould on one of them. Around the mould, as you can see in the picture, the staphylococci bacteria had disappeared.

Source 1

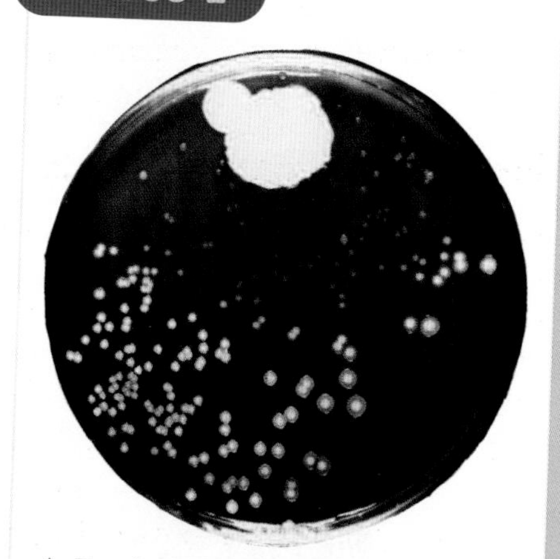

▲ Fleming's original dish. The mould is at the top. The bacteria originally around it have been killed but the bacteria further away have survived. The mould had probably been grown by another scientist in the room above Fleming's, and spores had floated out of the window, then downwards and in through Fleming's window before landing on the one place they could have an effect and then be noticed.

Fleming carried out experiments with the penicillin mould on living cells. He discovered that if it was diluted it killed bacteria without harming the cells. He made a list of the germs it killed and used it to treat another scientist's eye infection. However, it did not seem to work on deeper infections and in any case it was taking ages to create enough penicillin to use.

In 1929 Fleming wrote about penicillin in a medical journal but nobody thought his article was important. He had not used penicillin on animals to heal infections so had no evidence of it being useful.

Stage 3: 1938 – Florey and Chain's research and trials

In 1938 Florey and Chain were researching how germs could be killed. They read Fleming's article on penicillin and realised that it could be very effective so they tried to get funding from the government. They got £25. With a war about to start and no proof that penicillin could help people, the government had other things to spend its money on. Instead Florey asked for money from America and got enough to pay for five years' research.

Florey and Chain discovered that penicillin helped mice recover from infections but to treat one person they needed 3000 times as much penicillin! Even large drug companies could not afford to fund this quantity of work. So Florey and Chain began growing penicillin in whatever they could, using hundreds of hospital bedpans, even though bedpans were now in demand to make Spitfires!

By 1941 there was enough penicillin to test it on one person. The volunteer was Albert Alexander, a policeman who had developed septicaemia – a bacterial infection that attacks the whole body – from a tiny cut. Alexander was dying. Chemical drugs had not killed the infection. Florey and Chain requested permission to try their new 'purified' penicillin, and injections began. The penicillin worked and Alexander began to recover. However, the penicillin ran out after five days, even though Florey and Chain were extracting unused penicillin from the man's urine and reusing it in a desperate attempt to keep treating him. The poor policeman became ill again and died. Penicillin had shown that it worked and that it wasn't harmful to the patient – but how could they make enough of it?

▲ Left: Howard Florey, Australian doctor and Head of Pathology at Oxford University. Right: Ernst Chain, a Jewish German who escaped persecution in Nazi Germany to become a scientist at Oxford.

Stage 4: 1941 – Wartime need for penicillin

Florey and Chain needed help to mass produce penicillin but English factories were busy helping the war effort and couldn't be used. So Florey went to America – at just the right time. In 1941 America was attacked by the Japanese at Pearl Harbour and entered the war. The American government realised the potential of penicillin for treating wounded soldiers and made interest-free loans to US companies to buy the expensive equipment needed for making penicillin. Soon British firms were also mass producing penicillin, enough to treat the allied wounded on D-Day in 1944 – over 2.3 million doses.

Source 2

▲ Tanks used to produce penicillin. The quantity needed is difficult to comprehend: 2000 litres were needed to treat one case of infection. In June 1943, 425 million units of penicillin were being produced – enough for 170 cases.

Source 3

An account of the first use of penicillin in the British army in 1943, written by Lt Colonel Pulvertaft:

We had an enormous number of wounded with infections, terrible burn cases among the crews of armoured cars. The usual medicines had absolutely no effect. The last thing I tried was penicillin. The first man was a young man called Newton. He had been in bed for six months with fractures of both legs. His sheets were soaked with pus. Normally he would have died in a short time. I gave three injections of penicillin a day and studied the effects under a microscope. The thing seemed like a miracle. In ten days' time the leg was cured and in a month's time the young fellow was back on his feet. I had enough penicillin for ten cases. Nine were complete cures.

Review: Who and what deserves to be part of the 'Conquerors of Disease' statue?

Your statue can have more than one person on it – if you think more than one person deserves the credit for beating the killer diseases. And, as you have discovered, they did not make their discoveries completely independently. There were many links between them. This page helps you sort out those links and reach your decision – who was the most important person in the fight against the killer diseases.

Activities

1. Study the concept map on page 135. Write the speech bubbles for each of the other people in the concept map, summarising their greatest achievement. (Do not do this for 'Other scientists' – this person represents all the other scientists who built on the discoveries by the five main people.)
2. How many links can you find between the people on the concept map? We have drawn in two but there are others. Use the clues to identify the links and write cards to go on the linking string to explain them.
3. Look at your completed map with all the links showing. Who has the most links connecting him to other people? Why?
4. Now make your choice about which person or people should be on the statue. To help you, think about this question:
   'Was there one discovery that had to happen before any others could take place?'
5. Finally, complete the base of your statue using your work on the impact of factors in the case studies.

Clue 1

Koch used Pasteur's germ theory to identify the first ...

Clue 2

Pasteur had studied Jenner's work in detail, which helped him develop ...

Clue 3

The rivalry between these men spurred both on to new discoveries.

Clue 4

Ehrlich had learned a lot from Koch when ...

Clue 5

Without the germ theory these men would not have been able to make their discoveries.

Clue 6

Pasteur used Koch's new methods of studying bacteria when he developed ...

Clue 7

Other scientists developed vaccines against diseases such as typhoid, diphtheria and tuberculosis, building on ...

Clue 8

Other scientists discovered the bacteria causing individual diseases using the methods developed by ...

I discovered that vaccinating people with cowpox stopped them from getting smallpox. This was the first successful vaccination.
Jenner
Pasteur
WHO DESERVES TO BE PART OF THE STATUE COMMEMORATING THE DEFEAT OF THE KILLER DISEASES?
Other scientists
Ehrlich
Koch
Fleming, Florey and Chain

Improve your time planning on Development Study questions

You have already looked at the three main types of question you answer on your Development Study:

- **'describe'** (page 49)
- **'explain'** (pages 74–75)
- **'evaluate a statement'** (pages 100–101).

Question 2 tests how well you can tackle these three types of question. Twenty marks are available and you have 35–40 minutes to answer the three questions. It is **vital** that you **practise writing to time**. Running out of time is probably the main reason why good students do not get the grades they are capable of. Allow yourself 40 minutes to answer the three questions below. Use this time plan and advice to help you.

2 The second half of the nineteenth century and the first half of the twentieth century saw many important breakthroughs in the fight against disease.

(a) Briefly describe how Louis Pasteur developed the germ theory of disease. [5]

(b) Explain why the work of Robert Koch was so important. [7]

(c) 'In the fight against disease, Pasteur's work was more important than any other individual.' Explain how far you agree with this statement. [8]

Watch the clock – Stick to a time plan

The time plan gives you a **rough guide** to approaching Question 2 on Paper 1. Pupils often spend too long writing answers containing information that is not relevant to the question. It is better to spend less time writing and more time planning your approach to each question. This should ensure that your answer focuses on the question.

1 De-code and plan your approach to all three questions **(approx. 5 minutes)**.

Read each question a couple of times. Highlight:

- **Date boundaries** – the time period to cover
- **Content focus** – the topic the examiner wants you to focus on.
- **Question type** – different question types require different approaches.
- **Marks available** – a guide to how much you are expected to write.

Quickly jot down a rough plan of how you intend to approach each question. This is crucial – make sure your answer is focused on the question. Each answer should be different!

2 Answer part (a) (approx. 4–5 minutes).

This carries only 5 marks – one paragraph only.

3 Answer part (b) (approx. 10 minutes).

You need to **prove** that Koch's work was important. You are not describing what Koch did. You are **explaining** why what he did was so important, so use connectives to tie your answer together. Link the discoveries Koch made to later discoveries and developments. What did his work lead to? What impact did it have in the short and long term?

4 Answer part (c) (approx. 12 minutes).

This is an **iceberg question**. Use the advice opposite to help you.

5 Check your work (approx. 5 minutes).

Quickly scan your work to make sure that you have expressed yourself clearly.

- Check the spelling of key historical words, names and discoveries.
- In questions (b) and (c) make sure you used paragraphs to structure your answer and that your conclusion is clear. Does it focus on the question? Is there a clear line of argument?

Tackling iceberg questions

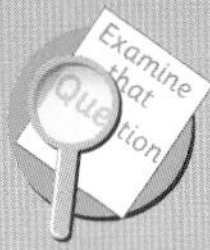

(c) 'In the fight against disease, Pasteur's work was more important than any other individual.' Explain how far you agree with this statement. [8]

What is an iceberg doing in a History book? It's here to warn you of hidden dangers beneath the surface of all kinds of historical enquiries. This exam question is a good example. Many students read it and see only 'Pasteur' – the top of the iceberg – so they only write about Pasteur. They don't see the iceberg below the surface – where the question asks them to compare the importance of Pasteur and other individuals. So always think 'ICEBERG'. Don't leap into the obvious answer – look for hidden dangers!

WARNING
WATCH OUT FOR THE HIDDEN PART OF THE QUESTION
Step 1: Deal with the part of the question that is above the surface.
• Explain why Pasteur's work was so important.
• Prove that he was important. Link his work to other discoveries and developments.
Step 2: Deal with the part of the question that lurks beneath the surface.
This is where you evaluate the importance of other individuals.
• Explain that other individuals played an important role in the fight to explain, prevent and cure disease. You could explore the importance of the work of Jenner, Koch, Ehrlich and Fleming in this paragraph.
• Try and show how the work of different individuals was linked. Use the concept map you produced on page 135 to help you.
Step 3: Write your conclusion.
Do not sit on the fence! Reach an overall judgement.
Was Pasteur the key individual or was there someone else who made a more important contribution?

Improve your time planning for your Source Investigation exam:
Topic – Penicillin

It is important to have a clear time plan for your Historical Source Investigation exam. These pages give you the chance to practise answering source-based questions to time.

In your **Historical Source Investigation** exam you have one hour and 30 minutes to answer questions based on a collection of sources.

Activities

Here is a sample Historical Source Investigation paper.

1. Time planning: you have 90 minutes. How would you divide it up? Do your own time plan before you look at our advice on page 140.
2. Now have a go at the practice paper.

Penicillin: Should Alexander Fleming get most of the credit?

Background information

Alexander Fleming was working at St Mary's Hospital, London, when he discovered that the mould on some of the dishes he had left in his laboratory seemed to prevent the spread of germs. In 1929 Fleming wrote about penicillin in a medical journal. However, he did not know how to turn the mould into a pure drug that could be used to treat large numbers of people. This was first done by Howard Florey and Ernst Chain.

Fleming, Chain and Florey were awarded the Nobel Prize in 1945, but more of the fame went to Fleming. He became a national hero in Britain and was honoured all over the world. Some scientists have argued that this was unfair and that Fleming has received too much credit for the development of penicillin. Why do people disagree about who deserves the credit for the development of penicillin and just how important was Fleming's contribution?

1. Study Source A.
   What impression of Fleming does this source give? Use the source and your own knowledge to explain your answer. [6]
2. Study Sources B and C.
   How far do these sources give different impressions about the importance of Fleming's work? Use the sources and your own knowledge to explain your answer. [8]
3. Study Sources B and C.
   Why do you think these sources say such different things about the work of Fleming? Use the sources and your own knowledge to explain your answer. [9]
4. Study Source D.
   How useful is this source to an historian studying why Fleming received so much of the credit for the development of penicillin? Use the source and your own knowledge to explain your answer. [8]
5. Study Source E.
   Does this source prove that Fleming's role in the development of penicillin has been exaggerated? Use the source and your own knowledge to explain your answer. [9]
6. Study all the sources.
   'Alexander Fleming received too much credit for his role in the development of penicillin.' How far do the sources on this paper support this view? Use the sources and your own knowledge to explain your answer. Remember to identify the sources you use. [10]

Source A

This stained glass window shows Fleming at work in his laboratory. It is in St. James' Church, Paddington, close to St Mary's hospital where Fleming worked for most of his career.

Source B

'Sir, in the leading article on penicillin yesterday, you refrained from putting the laurel wreath for discovery round anybody's brow. It should be given to Professor Alexander Fleming of this research laboratory. For he is the discoverer of penicillin and was the author also of the original suggestion that the substance might prove to have important applications in medicine.'

An extract from a letter written to The Times newspaper in August 1942 by Almroth Wright, the head of the inoculation department at St Mary's hospital.

Source C

'We would have started a research programme into anti-bacterial substances even if Fleming's paper had never been published. Even if we had not done so, someone else in the world would have taken on the research. As a result, some very interesting anti-bacterial substances, including penicillin, would have been discovered. The development of antibiotics might have been delayed a few years, but it would have inevitably taken place with the same final result as we have now.'

An extract from an article written by Ernst Chain in 1971.

Source D

'My policy here has been never to interview the press or allow them to get any information from us by telephone. This has been rigidly adhered to in spite of protests from some of my colleagues (especially Chain). In contrast Fleming has been interviewed apparently without cease, photographed, etc. (we have ample evidence of this here) with the upshot he is put across as the discoverer of penicillin (which is true), with the implication that he did all the work leading to the discovery of its properties (which is not true). Many of my colleagues feel things are going much too far, and are naturally restive at seeing so much of their own work going to glorify or even financially enrich someone else.'

An extract from a letter from Florey to the Secretary of the Medical Research Council, January 1944.

Source E

'Fleming told me often that he didn't deserve the Nobel Prize, and I had to bite my teeth not to agree with him. He wasn't putting on an act – at least around 1945/6. At the same time he would tell me that he couldn't help enjoying all the undeserved fame and I liked him for that. With me and others of his scientific colleagues he had the sense to know that none of us were more impressed by him than he was himself.'

An extract from a letter from Dr W. E. van Heuningen to Dr G. McFarlane, 3 August 1980 (from Alexander Fleming, the Man and the Myth, 1984).

Historical Source Investigation time plan

10 minutes – **Read the background information.**

Highlight key points. Then **read the sources and the questions to see how they relate to each other. Decode the questions**, highlighting date boundaries, content focus, question type and marks available.

10 minutes – **Question 1**

Do not spend too long on this question. It is only worth 6 marks; 10 minutes is plenty. This is an '**inference**' question. Use the advice on page 78.

12 minutes – **Question 2**

A '**cross-referencing question**'. You need to do more than simply describe what each sources says, you need to make direct comparisons between the sources. (Use the advice on page 79.)

12 minutes – **Question 3**

Here you are being asked to use the same sources but for a different purpose. You need to **explain why the two sources give a different impression** of Fleming. Use the key questions opposite to tackle this question effectively.

12 minutes – **Question 4**

This question is asking you to evaluate **how useful** the source is. We looked at this style of question on page 105.

12 minutes – **Question 5**

Make sure you look at both sides of the argument. The doctor met Fleming and discussed the development of penicillin with him. It suggests that Fleming and fellow scientists thought that he had received too much credit. However, this account is from just one doctor. How reliable is he? What is his motive for saying this? Cross-reference this source with other sources. Do they support what the doctor is saying?

15 minutes – **Question 6**

We looked at how to approach this type of question as part of the Jenner Source Investigation on page 117. Look again at the advice on how to approach this type of question.

7 minutes – **Check your answer paper.**

Remember to check your spelling of key words and that you come to a clear conclusion. It is crucial that you use the sources to support your answer. Make sure that you have referred to the source that you are using by letter so that the examiner can see which sources you are using to support your answer.

Question 3: Explaining why two sources disagree

- Aim to explore **at least two reasons** why the sources give a different impression. Your main focus will usually be on who wrote the source and why it was written.
- **Consider the provenance of each source.** Finish the table below and use it to make direct comparisons between the two sources.
- Remember to **refer directly to the sources**. You could also include a couple of quotations to support your answer.

Key questions	Source B	Source C
Who wrote or produced the source?	*Source B was written by Almroth Wright, who is the head of the inoculation department at St Mary's hospital. This is where Fleming worked. He would therefore be keen to present Fleming in a favourable light. He mentions that Fleming is 'of this research laboratory'. Wright may feel that both he and the hospital can share some of Fleming's glory.*	*In contrast, Source C is written by:* *Chain was part of the research team that...* *He would want to...*
What type of source is it? **Why** was it produced? What was the **purpose** of the source? Is the author trying to persuade the audience to take a certain viewpoint about a person or an event?	*Source B is a letter to a national newspaper. Wright is aiming to...* *Wright claims that '...* *This has been written in order to...*	*Source C is an extract from... Chain claims that without Fleming's work 'The development of antibiotics might have been delayed a few years, but it would have inevitably taken place with the same final result as we have now.'* *Chain is aiming to show that...*

Question 5:

Remember to:

- **plan your approach to the question**
  It is not simply a case of saying whether you agree or disagree with the statement. Ten marks are available, so the examiner will expect you to explore both sides of the argument.
- **use the sources**
  You will not achieve a good grade if you ignore the sources and simply write an answer to this question based on your own knowledge. Make sure you refer to the source that you are using by letter so that the examiner can see which sources you are using to support your answer.

Question 6: How to gain extra marks

You can gain extra marks on questions that ask you to evaluate a statement using the sources and your own knowledge by demonstrating to the examiner that you have **considered the reliability of the sources in reaching your conclusion**.

If you argue that Fleming did receive too much credit you might want to add an extra paragraph in which you **highlight weaknesses in the sources that do not support this point of view** (sources that claim that Fleming does deserve most of the credit for the development of penicillin).

Look at the answer on the right. It shows the examiner that the candidate has considered the reliability of the sources when reaching an overall judgement about the statement.

Some of the Sources suggest that Fleming got the credit he deserved for the development of penicillin and that his role was not exaggerated. For example, Source B states that the credit 'should be given to Professor Alexander Fleming' because 'he is the discoverer of penicillin and was the author also of the original suggestion that the substance might prove to have important applications in medicine.' However, this source was written by someone who worked at the same hospital and the same research laboratory as Fleming. Wright might want to exaggerate Fleming's importance so that both he and the hospital gain from the credit being given to one of their own.

Section 7: Public health after 1800: When did it finally improve – and why?

7.1 How bad was public health in the early 1800s?

The Industrial Revolution was a time of huge change, transforming people's lives, mostly for the better. But its immediate effects were terrible with people living and working in worse conditions than they had in the Middle Ages. So how bad was life in the early 1800s – and when did it get better and why?

My name is Edwin Chadwick. In 1842 I completed my 'Report on the Sanitary Conditions of the Labouring Population'. My conclusion is that the public health conditions of working people are worse than they have ever been.

Source 1

	Liverpool	Rutland
Gentry or Professionals	35	52
Tradesmen	22	41
Labourers or artisans	15	38

▲ This shows the differences in average age at death among different groups of people in 1840. Chadwick collected these statistics for his report. Liverpool was chosen as an example of a large, rapidly growing town. Rutland was chosen as a country area.

Source 2

Death rates in cholera epidemics in Britain

1831–2	26,101 deaths
1848–9	53,293 deaths
1853–4	20,079 deaths
1865	14,378 deaths

Source 3

A traveller's description of Leeds, reported in *The Morning Chronicle*, 1848: (Scavengers were employed to take away refuse and empty the privies.)

The east and north-east districts of Leeds are, perhaps, the worst, a perfect wilderness of foulness.

Conceive acre on acre of little streets, run up without attention to plan or health, acre on acre of closely-built and thickly-peopled ground, without a paving stone on the surface, or an inch of sewer beneath, deep trodden-churned sloughs of mud forming the only thoroughfares, privies often ruinous, all most horribly foul. Conceive streets and courts and yards which a scavenger never appears to have entered since King John's time and which gives the idea of a town built on a slimy bog. Conceive such a surface drenched with the liquid slops which each family flings out daily and nightly. Pigs seem to be the natural inhabitants, more common in some parts of Leeds than dogs and cats.

Activities

1. List the details in Sources 1–3 that show that public health conditions were very poor.
2. Which evidence do you think is the strongest argument against going back in time to live in the first half of the 1800s?
3. Why were conditions so bad? List as many reasons as you can find on the page opposite. (You will find out more on later pages.)

Source 4

◀ *Coalbrookdale at Night*, painted by Philippe Jacques de Loutherbourg in 1801. Coalbrookdale in Shropshire was the home of the iron industry. The great orange light comes from the fires in the furnaces where the iron was made. Artists flocked to paint scenes like this, which had never existed before. They also painted pictures of large textile factories, another new arrival in the landscape. However, for the people working in these industries the scenes were not so picturesque. Ten- or twelve-hour working days were common in hot and dirty conditions, surrounded by dangerous machinery.

Source 5

▲ *Over London by Rail*, an engraving of London housing by Gustave Doré in 1872. Houses in the towns were crammed together in the centre because people had to walk to work until the later 1800s. As towns grew fast between 1750 and 1850 there were no laws forcing local councils to provide sewers, fresh water or toilets in homes. Water came from pipes in the streets.

Source 6

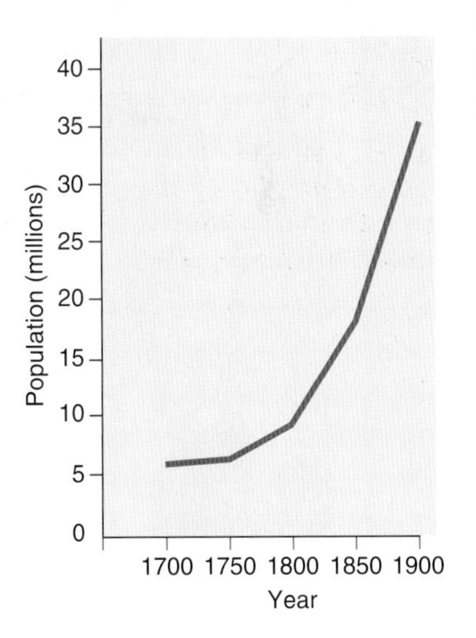

▲ The growth of the population of England and Wales 1700–1900.

Practise your skills at using sources:
Topic – Nineteenth-Century Public Health

Edwin Chadwick's report (see page 142) gives a very bad impression of the public health conditions.

In your exams you may well be asked to use a collection of sources to test a statement. Look at the question:

> How far do Sources A, B and C prove that there were major public health problems in towns across Britain during Chadwick's time?

Step 1: Use your inference skills

To answer such questions you need to use your inference skills to see if the impression given in the sources supports the statement. Remember: the cartoonist is aiming to get across a message. Each feature of the cartoon can give you a clue about this message.

- You should annotate the source. Highlight the main things that the cartoonist has included to get the message across. Use the space around the cartoon to jot what impression the artist may be trying to create.
- Look at how the student has used the obvious clues in Source A to work out the key messages of the cartoon. Then do the same for the cartoons on pages 146 and 147.

The street is overcrowded – would also cause disease to spread.

A coffin is being carried through the street – the cartoonist could be suggesting that death is very common.

Source A

A cartoon called 'A Court For King Cholera'. It is a drawing of London published in 1852.

Large pile of rubbish left in the street – gives the impression that the streets are rarely cleaned and that diseases would spread.

The children look very dirty and are playing with the rubbish – the overall impression is that people do not care about cleanliness and hygiene.

Step 2: Link the inferences you have made to the question

To gain high marks on this question you must do more than point out the key messages in the source. **You must explain how the inferences you have made either prove or disprove the statement**. Do the sources suggest that 'there were major public health problems in towns across Britain during Chadwick's time'?

In your first paragraph show how the sources could be used to support the statement. Refer to all three sources. For example:

Source A does seem to suggest that there were major public health problems.
In the cartoon we see ...... and ......
This gives the impression that ...
The cartoonist has also drawn ... This suggests ...
Source B gives a similar impression. For example, we see ...
This indicates that ...

The sentence starters for inferences are in red. They are the strong way to connect your inference to the question.

Step 3: Explore the limitations of the sources

In your second paragraph you should point out the limitations of using the sources. Ask yourself:

- Is there any evidence in the sources that challenges the statement?
- Consider the provenance of each source. What type of source is it? Who produced it and why? How does this affect how much we can trust what the source tells us? Remember cartoonists are often trying to put across a strong message, sometimes they exaggerate things to make their point.
- Think about how typical the sources are. The question asks about public health problems across Britain. These sources are all from London. How typical would they be of all towns across the country?

Step 4: Reach an overall judgement

Don't forget a conclusion! In your final paragraph, come to an overall judgement. Focus on how far the sources prove that there were major problems. Do the sources prove to a large extent or only a small extent that there were major problems? Why is this?

Extra sample questions!

You can use any of the sources on pages 142–147 to practise evaluating how useful a source or collection of sources is for an historical enquiry. Design your own practice questions. For example:

Study Source 3 on Page 142.
How useful is this source to an historian studying public health provision in towns during the first half of the nineteenth century?

Activities

Discuss in pairs:
Which Source on pages 142–147 do you think is most useful to a historian studying public health in Britain during the first half of the nineteenth century?

Activities

Annotate your own copy of Source B. Highlight the main things that the cartoonist has included to get the message across. Use the space around the cartoon to jot what impression the artist may be trying to create.

Source B

A cartoon published in 1831. It is commenting on where the Southwark Water Company in London got its water from.

Activities

Annotate your own copy of Source C. Highlight the main things that the cartoonist has included to get the message across. Use the space around the cartoon to jot what impression the artist may be trying to create.

Source C

THE WATER THAT JOHN DRINKS.

This is the water that John drinks.

This is the Thames with its cento of stink,
That supplies the water that John drinks.

These are the fish that float in the ink-
-y stream of the Thames with its cento of stink,
That supplies the water that John drinks.

This is the sewer, from cesspool and sink,
That feeds the fish that float in the ink-
-y stream of the Thames with its cento of stink,
That supplies the water that John drinks.

These are vested int'rests, that fill to the brink,
The network of sewers from cesspool and sink,
That feed the fish that float in the ink-
-y stream of the Thames, with its cento of stink,
That supplies the water that John drinks.

This is the price that we pay to wink
At the vested int'rests that fill to the brink,
The network of sewers from cesspool and sink,
That feed the fish that float in the ink-
-y stream of the Thames with its cento of stink,
That supplies the water that John drinks.

'The Water that John drinks', a cartoon from Punch *magazine, October 1849.*

7.2 Why wasn't anything done to protect people's health in the early 1800s?

You have already met the iceberg warning – look out for dangers below the surface! This iceberg is warning you to go beyond the obvious explanation. It's easy to assume that the only reason why public health was poor was because of vested interests – the selfish reasons of the rich who refused to pay for improvements. But what are the other reasons on the iceberg, hidden below the surface of the water?

Source 1

From 'Report on the Condition of the Town of Leeds' by James Smith, 1844:

'A proposal was made for the complete sewerage of the streets. I was present for nearly six hours of this debate. The chief theme of the speakers in opposition related to saving the pockets of the ratepayers and had very little regard to the sanitary results.'

Source 2

Extracts from a letter in *The Times* newspaper, 1 August 1854:

'We prefer to take our chance with cholera than be bullied into health ...'

'There is nothing a man hates so much as being cleaned against his will, having his floors swept, his walls whitewashed, his pet dung heaps cleared away.'

Activities

Complete your own copy of this iceberg illustration to explain fully why public health was so poor.

1. Read Sources 1 and 2. What exactly were the vested interests that were against improving public health? Add short notes to the bullet points at the top of the iceberg to summarise them.
2. What should go in the rest of the iceberg? Use the clues on the page opposite to write a series of short headings summing up the other reasons. Use the factors from page 9 to help you.
3. Now think about which reasons were most important. Review the reasons on your own iceberg drawing. How would you re-draw it to show which reasons were most important?
4. What was most needed to improve public health? Make three suggestions before you turn over and find out what happened.

Clue A

Pasteur's germ theory was not published and accepted by scientists and doctors until the 1860s. Pasteur's discovery of the value of boiling milk (pasteurisation) did not become common until the 1880s because many people believed that boiling killed the goodness.

Clue B

Towns had grown very fast. Landlords made profits from renting out houses so wanted them built quickly.

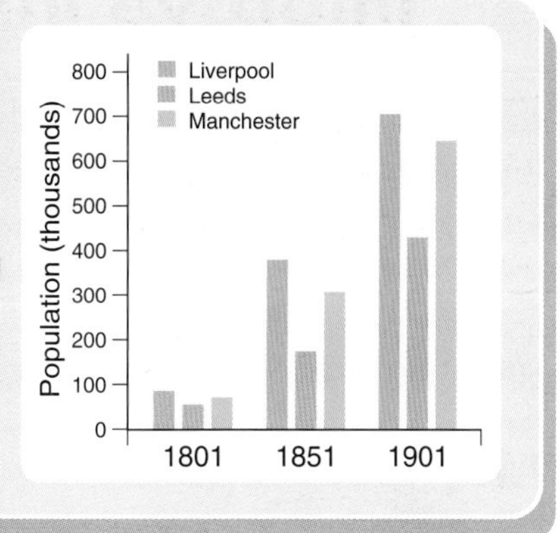

Clue C

Railways were not built to take people in and out of town centres in large numbers until the 1850s and later. Workers therefore had to live close to their places of work.

Clue D

There was a strong belief that people should help themselves to live better, healthier and more comfortable lives. People objected to local and national governments 'interfering' in their lives. The protests against compulsory smallpox vaccinations, which you read about in Section 5, are a good example.

Clue E

Governments were still not expected to play a major part in improving the living and working conditions of the people. There were no pensions or help for the sick and unemployed from governments. The first income tax was collected in 1798 and stayed low in the 1800s.

Clue F

Doctors were not paid by the government so had to charge fees to their patients. Therefore the poor could not afford to go to a doctor.

Clue G

Fresh food was difficult to get in many towns because it had to be brought in by horse and cart and was expensive. Food was often adulterated – mixed with other things (chalk in bread, sand in sugar, sawdust in flour) – by shopkeepers to increase its weight and so make more money from sales.

Clue H

Working conditions were at least as bad as home conditions. Workers in mines, workshops and factories had long hours and only very short breaks. Their toilet and washing facilities were very poor, with many people sharing one privy and only a pipe to wash at. Many people also fell ill from the work itself, swallowing coal and textile dust, which caused lung diseases.

7.3 Why did public health eventually improve in the later 1800s?

This page gives you an interpretation of why public health improved. Your task is to test this interpretation and then reach your own conclusions about why public health improved. Use pages 152–158 to help you. Pay special attention to the Meet the examiner pages 152–153 as this will help to structure your investigation.

My name is Edwin Chadwick. I can tell you exactly why public health improved. It was all my doing! Let me explain how I did it.

1 My great report

In 1842 I wrote my 'Report on the Sanitary Conditions of the Labouring Population'. Here's what my report shows:

1. The poor live in dirty, overcrowded conditions.

2. This causes a huge amount of illness.

3. Many people are too sick to work and so become poorer still.

4. Therefore other people have to pay higher taxes to help the poor.

My solution was simple:

We can cut taxes and save money in the long run by:

1. improving drainage and sewers

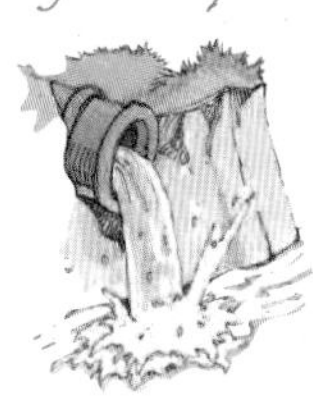

2. removing refuse from streets and houses

3. providing clean water supplies

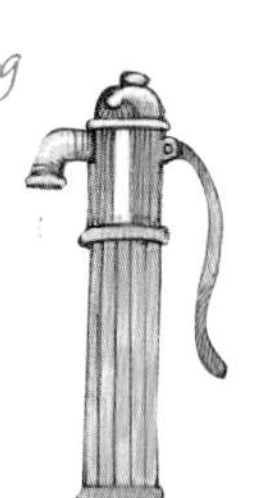

4. appointing medical officers in each area to check these reforms.

2 The Public Health Act 1848

Of course there was opposition. Many local tax-payers did not want to pay for improvements even though it meant lower taxes in the long run. The government was not happy either. It knew that local councils did not want the national government interfering in local matters. However, my ideas won, helped by another outbreak of cholera in 1848. The government, pushed by me, introduced the Public Health Act.

1 A national Board of Health was set up.
2 In towns where the death-rate was very high, the government could force the local council to make public health improvements to water supply and sewerage and appoint a Medical Officer of Health.
3 Local councils were encouraged to collect taxes (called rates) for public health improvements if they had the support of local rate-payers.
4 Councils were allowed to appoint Medical Officers of Health to oversee public health.

3 The Public Health Act of 1875

Of course I had wanted the government to do more. I wanted them to force all local councils to make changes. Some towns did make changes. Most did nothing. More outbreaks of cholera in 1853 and 1865 showed I was right. In 1875 the government finally did what I wanted and passed a proper Public Health Act. It said:

Local councils forced to provide clean water, public toilets and proper drains and sewers.

Councils forced to appoint a Medical Officer of Health.

More changes followed – a law against polluting rivers, a law to improve the quality of food sold in shops, a law to ensure new houses are built to clean, healthy standards.

4 The result of all my work

By 1900 people were living healthier, longer lives. Life expectancy for men had risen to 46, for women to 50. Towns were cleaner and safer. Yet for all my efforts they didn't give me a knighthood until I was 89, the year before I died. How ungrateful! But I died happy. **All those improvements came about because of my great report and hard work.**

Activities

1 Summarise Chadwick's explanation in two or three sentences. Include:
   a why public health improved
   b the major stages in that improvement.

2 Now look closely at the detail and think carefully about the Public Health Acts.
   a What were the limitations of the 1848 Public Health Act?
   b Why was the 1875 Public Health Act a major improvement?
   c How much involvement did Chadwick have with the 1875 Act?

3 **a** What seem to be the weaknesses of Chadwick's argument?
   b What other factors would you expect to play a part in improving public health?

Edwin Chadwick (1800–1890): biography

Chadwick was a civil servant who worked for the poor law commission in the 1830s and 1840s. In 1848 he became a member of the National Board of Health but it was disbanded in 1854 because it was unpopular. Chadwick retired in 1854 and played no part in advising governments after this. He had made too many enemies. His main weakness was that he did not know how to get other people on his side. He was argumentative, arrogant and rude as well as extremely hard-working.

Until his death, Chadwick continued to believe that disease was caused by miasmas, or 'bad air'. He did not accept Pasteur's germ theory.

Evaluating the significance of factors

'Edwin Chadwick's work was the most important factor in improving public health services in towns in the nineteenth century.' Explain how far you agree with this statement. [8]

By now you should be used to the iceberg warning – look out for hidden explanations! This is an even trickier iceberg question because the only clue about what's below the surface is in the words 'most important'. If you only see the top of the iceberg you will only write about Chadwick's work but if you remember the iceberg warning you will look below the surface and:

- evaluate the roles played by other individuals
- evaluate the roles played by other factors than individuals
- weigh up which factors did most to improve public health.

But first you need to investigate these other individuals and other factors. The page opposite helps you structure your investigation.

Step 1: Deal with the part of the question that is above the surface (evidence that supports the statement)
Paragraph 1 – Explain the importance of Chadwick's role
• Use the information on pages 150 and 154 to help you.
• Remember the importance of connectives to tie your answer together. Do more than simply describe what Chadwick did. Link what he did to changes that took place.
Step 2: Deal with the part of the question that lurks beneath the surface (evidence that challenges the statement)
Paragraph 2 – Explain the limitations of what Chadwick did
• Chadwick's argumentative and arrogant character meant that he found it difficult to get people on his side. Could Chadwick have achieved more? What were the limitations of what he did?
• Use the information on page 154 to help you.
Paragraph 3 – Evaluate the role played by other individuals
Other individuals played important roles in improving public health. Make sure you explain their importance. For example:
• William Farr (see page 154)
• John Snow (see page 155)
• Joseph Bazalgette (see page 158).
Paragraph 4 – Evaluate the role played by other factors
Other factors also played a very important role.
• The cards opposite provide you with other factors that played an important role in improving medicine. But which ones had a real influence on improving public health during the nineteenth century?
• As you study pages 154–159 find out which of these factors played a key role and explain their contribution.
Paragraph 5 – Conclusion
• Time to reach an overall judgement. Do you agree with the statement? Did Chadwick play the main role or were other factors more important?

Using card sorts to evaluate factors

It is important to **establish a clear line of argument** before you begin your answer to this type of question in the exam. As you can see from the cards below there are lots of factors that could have played a role in improving public health. You need to decide which factors were the most important before **you begin your answer**.

Activities

1. Make your own set of the cards below. As you read pages 154–158 you will find evidence that some of the factors played an important role in improving public health.
   Make notes explaining how these factors contributed on the back of the relevant factor card.
2. When you finish making notes organise the cards into a shape that shows how important you think each factor is.
   You can use one of the shapes below or use your own design.
   Remember that some factors did not contribute at all.

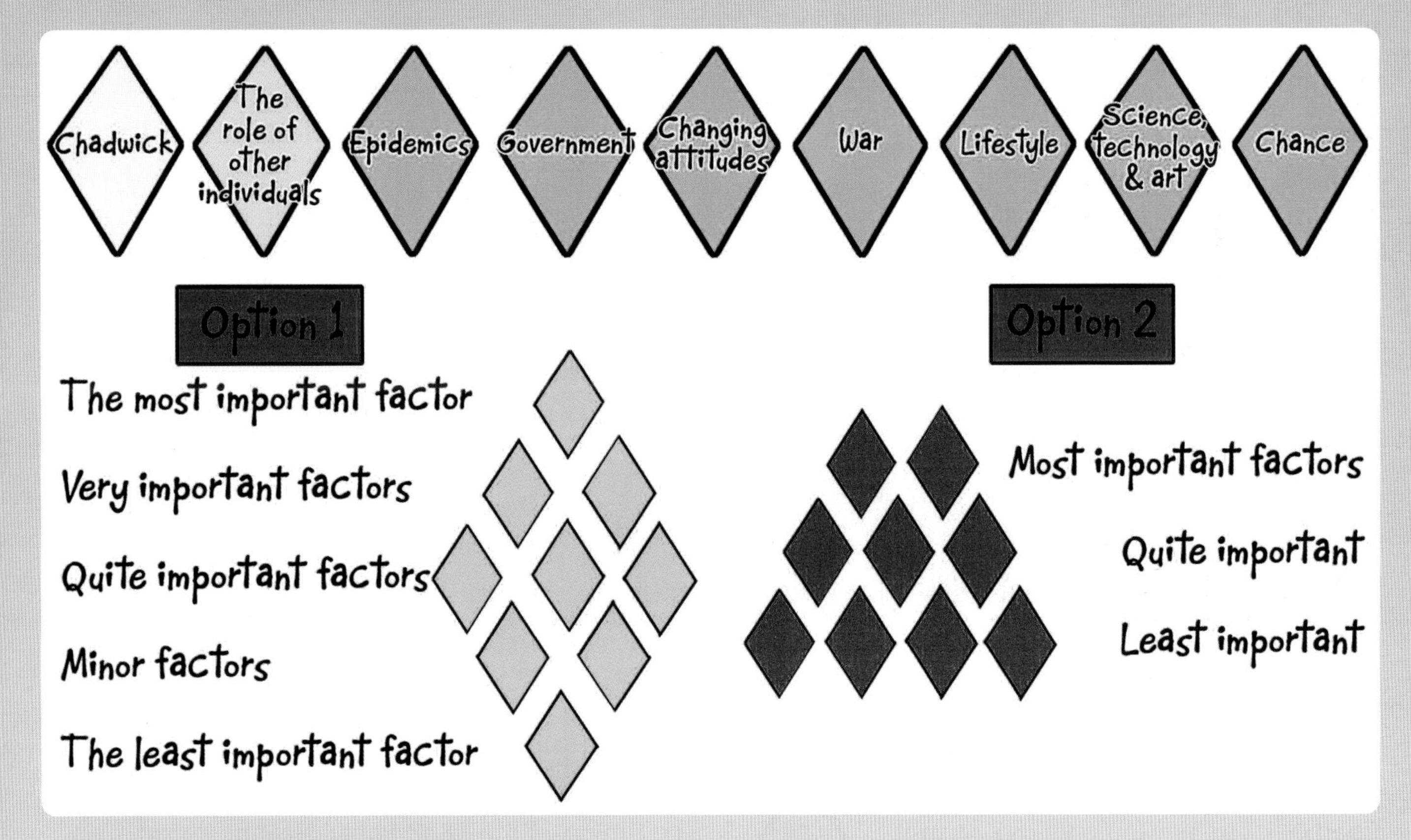

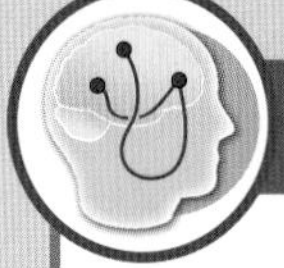

smarter revision

Why are card sorts useful?

Organising the cards in this way is really useful.

- It helps you to select what to include in your answer. After evaluating the role played by Chadwick and other individuals you will probably only have time to write about the role played by two or three other factors. The card sort should make sure that you include relevant and important factors in your answer.
- It helps you develop a clear line of argument. It is a lot easier to write a good answer that is focused on the question if you have a clear line of argument established in your head before you start to write. Students who are successful in the exam spend time thinking about their approach to the question before they start to write.

What was the most important factor in the improvement of public health?

Activities

1. What was Chadwick's major contribution to public health reform?
2. **a** Why was a Public Health Act passed in 1848?
   b Look back to page 55, Source 10. Do you think the Public Health Act had anything in common with King Edward's III's orders?
3. What was Snow's discovery?
4. **a** What is the message in Source 2?
   b Why do you think it was published?
5. Add evidence to your Diamond cards (see page 153) from the information on this page.

How important a part did Chadwick really play?

Chadwick's positive impact

- Hard-work produced a mass of evidence supporting public health reform.
- 1842 Report influenced the government and persuaded people that reform was needed.
- His report's recommendations were the basis for the 1848 Public Health Act.

Chadwick's negative impact

- 1842 Report did not lead to immediate reform. The Public Health Act came in 1848.
- The 1848 Act did not force councils to reform public health.
- His personality antagonised people and did not win support for his cause.
- His influence faded in the 1850s.

What role did William Farr play?

Chadwick was not the only civil servant who built up evidence of the links between poverty, dirt and ill-health. After 1837 all births, deaths and marriages had to be registered and William Farr used this information to build an accurate picture of where the death rate was highest and what people died of. This proved the link between high death-rate and unhealthy living conditions. His statistics shamed some towns into improving local public health conditions. Therefore Farr's evidence also put pressure on local and national government to make changes.

The impact of cholera

Epidemics

The timing of the 1848 Public Health Act was the result of the latest epidemic of cholera. As cholera spread across Europe in 1847 fear grew in Britain of many thousands of deaths to come. Therefore the government finally followed Chadwick's recommendations and passed the Public Health Act in the hope that this would reduce the impact of cholera. However, the 1848 Act was not compulsory. Only 103 towns set up local Boards of Health. Many more did not, and the National Board of Health, set up to oversee reforms, was abolished after only six years in 1854.

The work of John Snow

Snow was a pioneer in surgery as well as in public health, improving medical methods and using detailed evidence to challenge old theories. In 1849 he published a book saying that cholera spread through water, not in 'bad air', but his suggestion was mocked by many doctors. In 1854 another cholera outbreak gave him the chance to prove his theory that people caught cholera from water they used for washing and drinking.

Cholera killed over 500 people around Broad Street, near Snow's surgery, in just ten days. This led Snow to map out the deaths in detail and write a report detailing his evidence: 'On the Mode of Communication of Cholera'.

Snow's evidence was so strong that the handle of the Broad Street water pump was taken away, stopping people getting water from the pump. There were no more deaths. It was later discovered that a cesspool, only a metre away from the pump, was leaking into the drinking water.

Snow had proved that clean water was essential for preventing the spread of cholera but even this did not lead to a new Public Health Act enforcing change. Many scientists still clung to the 'bad air' theory (Pasteur had not yet published his germ theory).

▲ John Snow was born in Yorkshire in 1813, the son of a farm labourer. Aged 14 he was apprenticed to a surgeon and eventually became a fully-qualified doctor.

Source 1

From Snow's 'On the Mode of Communication of Cholera', 1854:

'On proceeding to the spot, I found that nearly all of the deaths had taken place within a short distance of the Broad Street water pump. There were only ten deaths in houses situated decidedly nearer to another street pump. In five of these cases, the families of the deceased persons informed me that they always used the pump in Broad Street as they preferred the water to that of the pump that was nearer.

There is a brewery in Broad Street. Perceiving that no brewer's men were registered as having died of cholera, I called on Mr Huggins, the owner. He informed that there were about 70 workmen employed in the brewery and that only two of them had been indisposed by cholera and then not seriously. The men are allowed to drink beer, and Mr Huggins believed that they do not drink water at all and never obtained water from the Broad Street pump.'

Source 2

▲ This cartoon is called Death's Dispensary. It was published in 1860.

Source 3

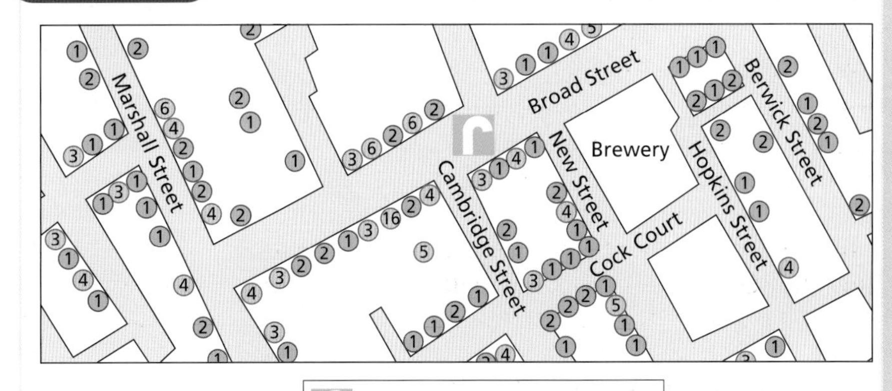

Pump
1 or 2 deaths from cholera
3 or more deaths from cholera

▲ A copy of part of Snow's map detailing deaths in the Broad Street area.

Activities

1. a What is the message in Source 1?
   b Why do you think it was published?
2. Why were there no more public health reforms in the 1850s?
3. Why was another Public Health Act passed in 1875?
4. Add more evidence to your Diamond cards (but you'll have to decide which ones to fill in yourselves from information on this page!).

The Great Stink

The summer of 1858 was hot, very hot. There was no rain to fill the rivers, and river levels fell, especially the Thames in London. As a result the smell from the river grew worse and worse and one of the very worst places was at the Houses of Parliament which are right on the river bank. The 'Great Stink' (as it was called) added to the evidence that more public reform was needed. In London itself an effective, modern sewer system was built but there was no new Public Health Act to enforce improvements throughout the country.

Source 1

Diphtheria.
Scrofula.
Cholera.
No government interference in my town!
FATHER THAMES INTRODUCING HIS OFFSPRING TO THE FAIR CITY OF LONDON.
(A Design for a Fresco in the New Houses of Parliament.)

◀ This cartoon was published in *The Times* newspaper 18 June 1858.

Why was there no compulsory Public Health reform in the 1850s?

Why should we pay taxes to protect other people's health?

Source 2

A letter in *The Times* newspaper, 1 August 1854:

'The Board of Health has fallen. We prefer to take our chance with cholera than be bullied into health. Everywhere the board's inspectors were bullying, insulting and expensive. They entered houses and factories insisting on changes revolting to the habits or pride of the masters and occupants. There is nothing a man hates so much as being cleaned against his will, having his floors swept, his walls whitewashed, his pet dung heaps cleared away, all at the command of a sort of sanitary bumbailiff. Mr. Chadwick set to work everywhere, washing and splashing, and Master John Bull was scrubbed and rubbed till the tears came to his eyes and his fists clenched themselves with worry and pain.'

So why was conservatism finally defeated?

Factor 1 The impact of Pasteur

In 1861 Pasteur published his germ theory. In 1864 he conducted a series of public experiments that convinced most scientists that diseases were caused by bacteria (germs) (see page 129). This finally provided the clear proof that was needed of the link between dirt and disease and showed that Chadwick, Farr and Snow had all been correct in their arguments.

Faced with this scientific proof, people were more willing to pay taxes to cover the costs of public health reforms – fresh water supplies, good sewers, public toilets – and more local towns began to make these reforms.

Factor 2 Government and political reform

For years governments had been unwilling to make public health reform compulsory. The only voters in general elections were wealthy land-owners and the well-off middle classes, the very people who would have to pay more if public health reforms became compulsory. Governments did not want to offend these men (they were all men – no women could vote) and risk losing their votes in an election.

All this changed in 1867 when working men in towns were given the right to vote for the first time. Suddenly the numbers of voters had doubled. It increased again in 1884 when many working men in country areas got the vote. Politics had changed dramatically even though all women and some men still could not vote.

Working men have got the vote at last.
Now MPs will have to listen to us.
They'll have to improve conditions in our towns or we won't vote for them.

If politicians wanted to win elections they had to promise laws to win the votes of working men, not just the wealthy and middle classes. The 1870s and 1880s saw many new laws passed designed to improve the lives of ordinary people. One of these was the Public Health Act of 1875.

The result The Great Clean-up

The Public Health Act (1875) made it compulsory for local councils to improve sewers and drainage, provide fresh water supplies and to appoint Medical Officers and sanitary inspectors to inspect public health facilities.

Other laws were passed that:

- improved the standards of housing
- stopped the pollution of rivers (from which people got water)
- shortened working hours in factories for women and children
- made it illegal to add ingredients that made food unhealthy
- made education compulsory.

How did technology make the Clean-up possible?

Sewers

Passing a law saying public health reform was compulsory was only the beginning. After that came the hard engineering work, building the new systems. This used engineering knowledge that had not been available a hundred years earlier but there had been great improvements in technology during the Industrial Revolution and the building of the railways (e.g. machinery powered by steam engines, methods of building pipelines and embankments). This knowledge was essential to make the laws effective.

Source 1

▲ Until the 1860s cities had open sewers like this one in London. This photograph, taken in 1900, shows how long it took for local councils to get rid of the many, many miles of open sewers.

Source 2

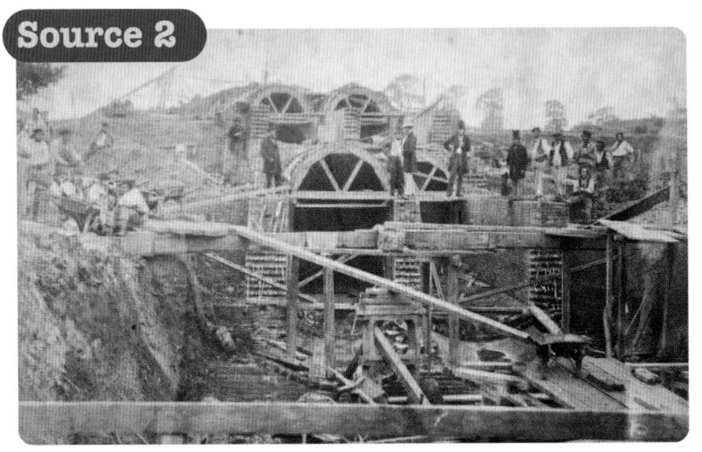

▲ Public health reform involved huge engineering projects to build sewers and water pipes under city streets. This photograph shows sewers being built.

Joseph Bazalgette (1819–1891): biography

Bazalgette was the engineer who designed and built London's sewer system after the Great Stink of 1858. He spent his early career in the railway industry, gaining experience of large engineering projects. After 1858 he planned and organised the building of London's sewer system, the same system that is still used today. This system included:

- 83 miles of main sewers, built underground from brick
- 1100 miles of sewers for each street and connecting to the main sewers
- a series of major pumping stations to drive the flow of sewage along the pipes.

The core of the work was completed by 1865 but it was such a huge project it took another ten years to complete. Fortunately, Bazalgette looked ahead and forecast the growth of population so made sure the system had a much higher capacity than was needed in the 1860s.

Lavatories

An invention that also made a difference was the flushing lavatory. Instead of privies needing to be emptied by hand and spade (and left rotting for days or weeks) the flushing system sent the waste instantly down into the sewer network. Of course at first such lavatories were only available to the rich but it was the beginning of a very important change.

Source 3

Soap

And there was soap! Today a bar of soap is a very ordinary thing but it was much rarer in the mid-1800s partly because it was taxed and so was too expensive for many people to buy. In 1853 the tax was taken off soap so many more people could afford it and so washing did more to kill germs even if they did not know it then.

How much had Public Health reforms really improved people's health?

By the 1900s towns were healthier with better public health facilities. As you can see from Source 1, people were starting to live longer but clean towns were only part of the solution. There was increasing evidence that poverty was causing a lot of ill-health.

Those who could not get help from friends and relatives had to give up homes and go into a workhouse, run by the local council. Two major reports were published at the end of the 1800s that highlighted the links between poverty and ill-health.

Charles Booth surveyed poverty in London, and Seebohm Rowntree carried out a similar study in York. Both showed that a third of families did not have enough money to pay for their housing, clothes and food. Many were working but earned only very low wages. The sick, unemployed and elderly received no help from the national government no matter how poor they were.

Source 1

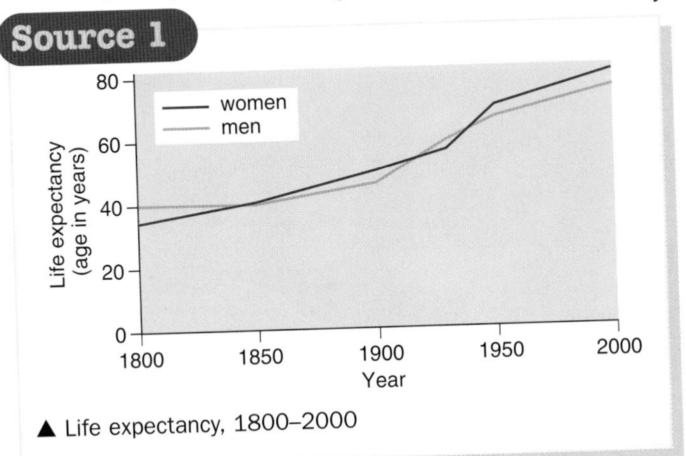

▲ Life expectancy, 1800–2000

Source 2

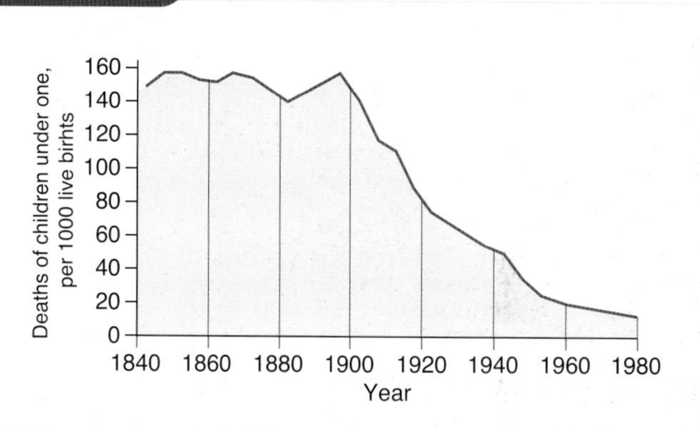

▲ The death-rate of children under one year old, 1800–1980

Source 3

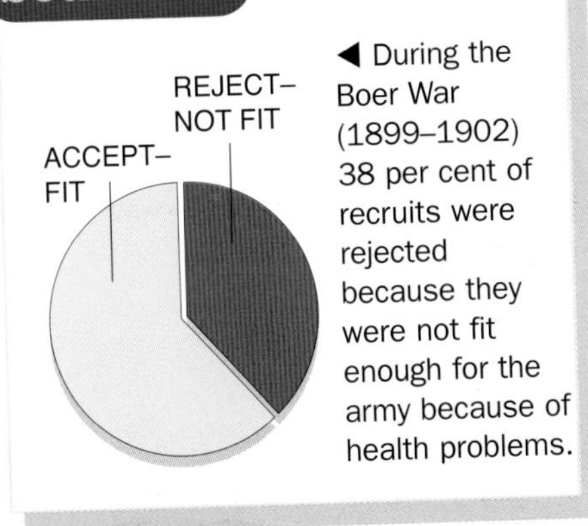

◀ During the Boer War (1899–1902) 38 per cent of recruits were rejected because they were not fit enough for the army because of health problems.

Source 4

Written by the Reverend Samuel Bartlett in 1889:

'The mother among the poor, in her joy that a son is born, cannot look forward to his life. What is it to her that science has proved stronger than disease? The rich man's family may grow up unbroken around the hearth but the children of the poor must die and their family circle is broken by death that carries off the weak. What is it to the poor that it has been proved that cleanliness is the secret of health? They cannot have the latest sanitary appliances. They cannot take baths or have constant changes of clothing. They cannot secure that the streets are swept or, as the wealthy inhabitant of Belgrave Square, protect themselves from the neighbourhood of the tallow factory.'

Source 5

From the memoirs of Mrs John Brown (1847–1935) describing a visit in the late 1800s:

In the bed was a young woman, wan and dazed. She was holding a week-old baby to her empty breast. It was so pitiful I did not know what to say. 'I thought there were two children.'
'There was three days ago,' the woman said. 'Show her, Jem.'
The man opened the bottom drawer of a rickety chest and there lay a little dead child of two. He said, 'We be waiting for the parish to come and bury her.' The mother said 'We couldn't put her upstairs, alone in the empty room.' I stood still, sobbing, but the parents shed no tears nor said a word, except when Jem closed the drawer.
'She were a nice little lass, she were,' he said.

Activities

1. Which of these statements do you most agree with? Explain your choice.
   - **a** By 1900 Public Health reforms had led to huge improvements in health.
   - **b** By 1900 Public Health reforms were beginning to improve people's health.
   - **c** By 1900 Public Health reforms had had no improvement in health.
2. What kinds of changes do you think were needed to produce more improvements in people's health?

7.4 Why did public health improve further in the twentieth century?

We guided you through the story of nineteenth-century public health. Now you have to plan your own investigation using pages 160–163 so that you can answer the examination question on the right.

Explain why public health improved in the twentieth century. [7]

Improvements in the early 1900s

In 1906 a new Liberal government was elected with a landslide majority of votes. Many people expected this government to make major reforms to improve everyday life. Here are some of the measures it took. They may seem unimportant nowadays but a hundred years ago they were revolutionary.

1902 – Training was made compulsory for midwives.

1906 – Meals provided free for schoolchildren in need.

1907 – All births had to be notified to the local Medical Officer of Health. A health visitor visited each mother to make sure she knew how to protect her baby's health.

1907 – Nurses or doctors had to carry out medical checks on children in schools.

1908 – People in need over the age of 70 were paid an old-age pension.

1909 – Back-to-back housing was banned. New regulations enforced higher standards of house building.

1912 – Clinics were held in schools to give children free medical treatment.

Source 1

▲ Schools for mothers first opened in 1907.
The schools taught:
- the importance of hygiene and the danger of diarrhoea for infants
- how flies spread disease from privies and rubbish in streets
- that breast-feeding was better than bottle-feeding
- that good mothering was a duty to be performed for King and Country!

A big step forward – the 1911 National Insurance Act

One of the greatest changes introduced by the Liberal government was the National Insurance Act of 1911. The aim was to give workers medical help and sick pay if they could not work through illness. Until then workers who fell ill had a choice – carry on working or get no pay, which meant they had no chance of affording medical help.

As Source 2 shows, the National Insurance scheme required the worker, his employer and the government to pay into a sickness fund. It was a major step forward but many people were left out of the scheme. It only included people in work, not their families. Most women and all children were excluded. So were the unemployed and elderly, and anyone who had a long-lasting illness.

Source 2

The 1911 National Insurance Act said that workers, employers and the government must all pay money into a sickness fund.

2d a week
Government
3d a week
Employer
4d a week
Worker
When a worker fell ill, he received ten shillings (50p) a week for up to 26 weeks and free medical care. This was paid out of the sickness fund.
SICKNESS FUND

Developments in the 1930s

In 1919, after the end of the First World War, a new Housing Act became law. The government had promised 'Homes fit for Heroes' for the returning soldiers, and this Act said that local councils had to provide good homes for working people to rent. A quarter of a million new homes were built. In the 1930s many old, unhealthy slum houses were cleared and another 700,000 new houses were built.

However, in other ways medical care was harder to find. In the 1930s unemployment rose to over 3 million, leaving all those unemployed outside the National Insurance Scheme. Even people in jobs could not afford to keep up their payments and so could not get free medical help (see Source 3). The system set up in 1911 was failing. The most worrying evidence came from towns where unemployment was high. In some towns the number of deaths among children under the age of one was rising again, as you can see in Source 4.

Source 3

From an interview with Kathleen Davys, one of a Birmingham family of thirteen children growing up in the 1920s and 1930s. The local doctor charged sixpence for each visit:

'Headaches, we had vinegar and brown paper; for whooping cough we had camphorated oil rubbed on our chests or goose fat. For mumps we had stockings round our throats and measles we had tea stewed in the teapot by the fire – all different kinds of home cures. They thought they were better than going to the doctor's. Well they couldn't afford the doctor.'

Source 4

Town	1928	1931	1933
Wigan	93	103	110
Liverpool	94	94	98
St Helens	98	88	116
Bath	47	39	52
Brighton	50	54	47
Oxford	38	44	32

▲ The changing death-rate of children aged less than one year in a variety of towns

The impact of the Second World War

The Second World War had a major impact on people's attitudes. It wasn't just the armed forces who were risking their lives. It was the first war in which all people felt they were 'in it together'. Many people at home died during bombing raids. The feeling grew that everyone should have the chance to good health care, not just the wealthy. In addition:

- Many children were evacuated from towns to the countryside and to better-off homes. Middle-class families were shocked at the condition of some of the children who were dirty, unhealthy and under-nourished.
- After all the sacrifices of the war, people wanted a better future. Better health care was an important part of this.
- During the war many people did get free health care to keep them fit for the war effort.

The Beveridge Report, 1942

The national coalition government asked a leading civil servant, Sir William Beveridge, to write a report on what should be done to improve people's lives. Among his recommendations were:

- Setting up a National Health Service, free to everyone and paid for from taxes. Doctors, nurses and other medical workers would become government employees instead of charging the sick to create their wages.
- Everyone in work would pay National Insurance out of their wages. This would pay benefits (sick-pay, old-age pensions, unemployment pay, etc.) to everyone whether they were working or not.

The impact of the National Health Service

The Beveridge Report was greeted with enthusiasm by many people. People queued outside shops to buy their own copy and 600,000 copies were sold. However, there was opposition (see below). The most important opposition came from the doctors themselves but their opposition ended when Aneurin Bevan, the Minister of Health, agreed that doctors could continue to treat patients privately and charge them fees as well as working for the National Health Service (NHS).

Source 5

Daily Mirror DEC 2

12,189 ONE PENNY
Registered at the G.P.O. as a Newspaper.

Beveridge tells how to

BANISH WANT

Cradle to grave plan | All pay—all benefit

SIR WILLIAM BEVERIDGE'S Report, aimed at abolishing Want in Britain, is published today.

He calls his Plan for Social Security a revolution under which "every citizen willing to serve according to his powers has at all times an income sufficient to meet his responsibilities."

Here are his chief proposals:

All social insurance—unemployment, health, pensions—lumped into one weekly contribution for all citizens without income limit—from duke to dustman.

These payments, in the case of employees, would be:

Men 4s. 3d. Employer 3s. 3d.
Women 3s. 6d. Employer 2s. 6d.

radle to the grave benefits for all, cluding:

ree medical, dental, eyesight and hospital treatment;

hildren's allowances of 8s. a week each, after the first child.

ncreases in unemployment benefit (40s. for a couple) and abolition of the means test; industrial pension in place of workmen's compensation.

A charter for housewives, including marriage grant up to £10; maternity grant of £4 (and 36s. for 13 weeks for a paid worker); widow's benefit; separation and divorce provision; free domestic help in time of sickness.

ld age pensions rising to 40s. for a married couple on retirement.

neral grants up to £20.

Allies separate Axis armies in Africa

AMERICAN and French forces were reported last night to have driven a wedge between the two Axis armies in North Africa—between Nehring, fighting to Bizerta and Tunis, and Rommel, at bay at El

Messages from North Africa and New York stated that the Allies have reached the Tunisian coast between

Govt. give hint of post-war planning

CHOOSING the eve of the publication of Sir William Beveridge's long-awaited report on Social Security, the Government yesterday gave the country its first indication of their own plans for post-war Britain.

These include the continuance of rationing for some time and control of industry (some industries being taken over as public corporations); the development of agriculture, forestry and public utilities like electricity.

The Government also announced the immediate setting up of a new Ministry of Town and Country Planning, and the ...ection of the Scott and Uthwatt Committees' proposals for placing main responsibility for planning in the hands of a permanent commission.

▲ The front page of the *Daily Mirror* for 2 December 1942, reporting the publication of the Beveridge Report.

Social Security
Here's to the brave new world!
O, rare and refreshing Beveridge!

Opposition to the NHS

- Doctors were afraid they would lose their freedom and be unable to treat private patients who paid fees.
- Some people still believed that the poor and sick were poor simply because of laziness. They did not think the poor should be helped.
- Some people thought that people would grow lazy because they were getting 'something for nothing' and this would make people less likely to bother working.
- Local councils and charities objected to the government taking over control of hospitals from them.

THE NEW

NATIONAL HEALTH SERVICE

Your new national Health Service begins on 5th July. What is it? How do you get it?

It will provide you with all medical;, dental, and nursing care. Everyone–rich or poor, man or woman or child–can use it or any part of it. There are no charges, except for a few special items. There are no insurance qualifications. But it is not a "charity". You are all paying for it, mainly as taxpayers, and it will relieve your money worries in time of illness.

In July 1948 the NHS was introduced. Now everyone could get free treatment. Until 1948 about 8 million people had never seen a doctor because they could not afford to do so. Source 6 shows the range of services provided by the NHS. Many hospitals were rebuilt. Doctors and nurses got new, improved equipment. The NHS played an important part in increasing people's life expectancy, particularly helping to reduce the numbers of women dying during, or shortly after, childbirth.

Source 6

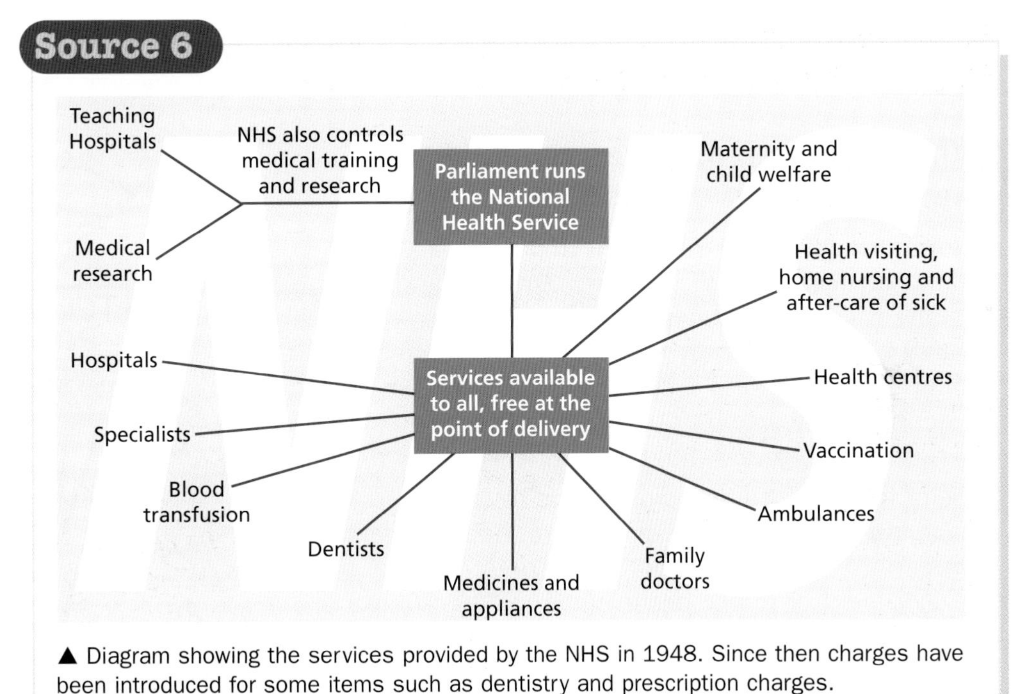

▲ Diagram showing the services provided by the NHS in 1948. Since then charges have been introduced for some items such as dentistry and prescription charges.

Source 7

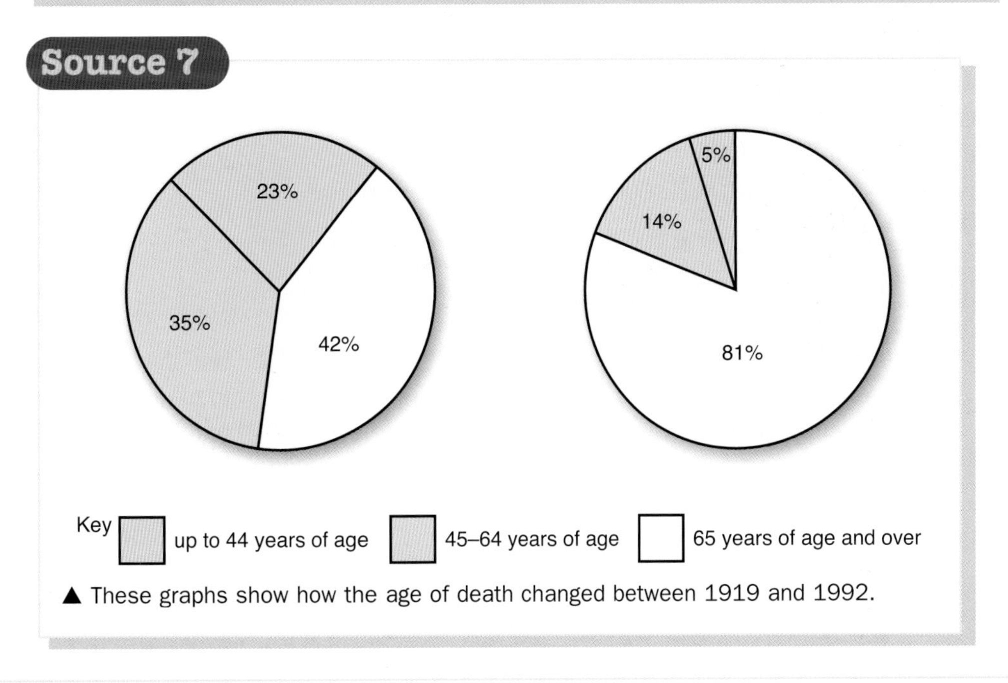

▲ These graphs show how the age of death changed between 1919 and 1992.

Source 8

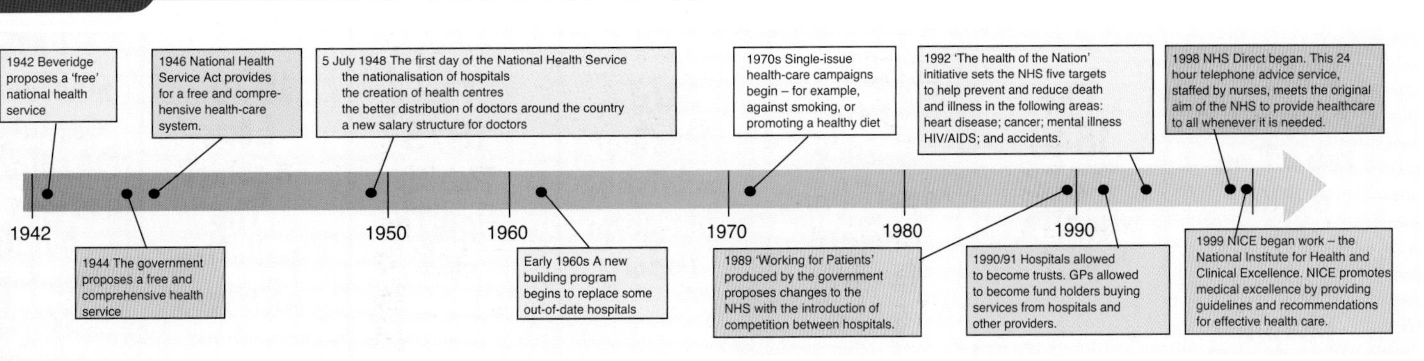

1942 Beveridge proposes a 'free' national health service
1946 National Health Service Act provides for a free and comprehensive health-care system.
5 July 1948 The first day of the National Health Service
the nationalisation of hospitals
the creation of health centres
the better distribution of doctors around the country
a new salary structure for doctors
1970s Single-issue health-care campaigns begin – for example, against smoking, or promoting a healthy diet
1992 'The health of the Nation' initiative sets the NHS five targets to help prevent and reduce death and illness in the following areas: heart disease; cancer; mental illness HIV/AIDS; and accidents.
1998 NHS Direct began. This 24 hour telephone advice service, staffed by nurses, meets the original aim of the NHS to provide healthcare to all whenever it is needed.
1942
1950
1960
1970
1980
1990
1944 The government proposes a free and comprehensive health service
Early 1960s A new building program begins to replace some out-of-date hospitals
1989 'Working for Patients' produced by the government proposes changes to the NHS with the introduction of competition between hospitals.
1990/91 Hospitals allowed to become trusts. GPs allowed to become fund holders buying services from hospitals and other providers.
1999 NICE began work – the National Institute for Health and Clinical Excellence. NICE promotes medical excellence by providing guidelines and recommendations for effective health care.

Evaluating the significance of events

Why are some changes more important than others?

Some changes are so important that they can be called '**turning points**' in history. Another kind of change is called a **catalyst** (which speeds up changes that are already taking place). A turning point is more important because it changes the direction of the way that things are going.

For many people the establishment of the NHS is one of the key turning points in the history of medicine. It changed the direction of health care in this country. Was it the key turning point in the development of public health since 1800 or were there other turning points that were more important?

Imagine that you are going on a car journey and you then decided to turn right off the road you had been travelling on and head in a different direction. That would be a turning point in your journey. If you then went down a steep hill, that would act as a catalyst. It would speed up your journey but it would not change the direction in which you were travelling.

Activities

1 Sort the events and developments below into three categories:
- Turning points
- Catalysts
- Events or developments that had little impact

2 Use this information and the examiner's advice to plan this exam question. Use the advice on pages 100 and 137 on evaluating statements.

'More important changes in public health provision happened in the nineteenth century than in the twentieth century.' Explain how far you agree with this statement. [8]

1842 – Chadwick's report on public health for working people	The 1848 Public Health Act	1854 – John Snow's report links cholera to dirty water	1861 – Pasteur publishes his germ theory	The 1875 Public Health Act	1876 – Laws against the pollution of rivers	Late nineteen[th] century Bazalge[tte] designs a[nd] builds London['s] sewer system

Look at the list of public health developments on the cards below. There are eight events or developments from the nineteenth century compared with six from the twentieth century. However, does this mean that the statement in the exam question on page 164 is correct and that more important changes took place in the nineteenth century?

You need to consider how important each change was. Imagine that you are putting each development on a set of scales – some will weigh more than others.

Develop your own weighing system to evaluate the changes that took place in each century. You could, for example, give turning points a weighting of 3, catalysts 2 and the less important developments a weighting of 1.

You could also develop a chart like the one on the right.

As well as evaluating specific developments you can also **use your knowledge of the big picture**. How much had public health been improved by the end of the nineteenth century? Had most of the major problems really been solved? If so, why was life expectancy still quite low?

Development	Weighting	Explanation

The nvention of the flushing avatory	1908 – Old-age pensions introduced	The 1911 National Insurance Act	1912 – Clinics set up in schools to give children free treatment	The 1919 Housing Act	1948 – The NHS is established	1970s – Health care campaigns begin – for example, against smoking

What was surgery like in 1800?

Surgery in the 1800s was very dangerous. Visual and written sources from the time contain lots of clues about the dangers facing patients. So, instead of us telling you what it was like, this section begins by asking you to use some sources. What can you work out from the sources about surgery in 1800?

Use your **source handling skills** to spot the dangers facing patients and answer the exam questions below.

1 Study Source A. What dangers faced patients during operations at the beginning of the nineteenth century? [5]
2 Study Sources B, C and D. How far do these sources support the impression given of surgery given in Source A? [5]

Source A

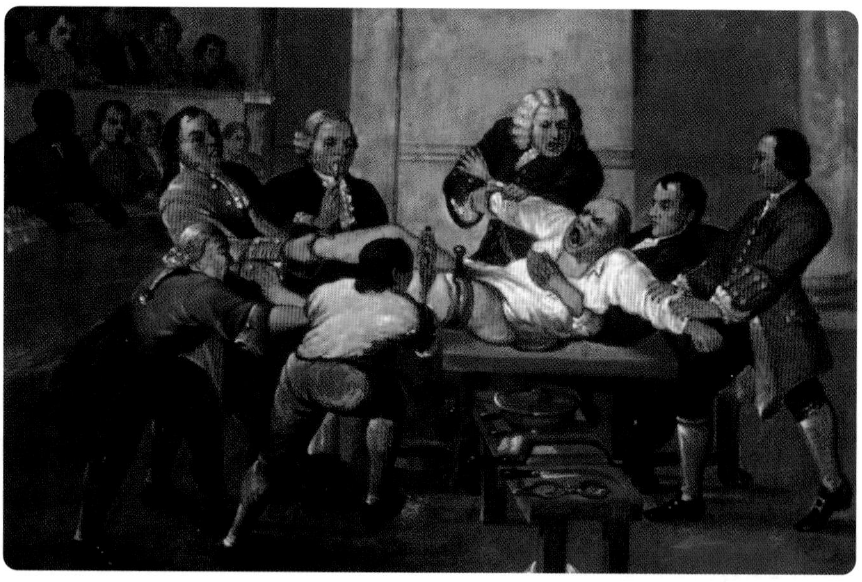

A painting of an operation dating from around 1800.

3 Do these Sources prove that by the beginning of the nineteenth century surgery had improved little since the time of Paré? Use the sources and your knowledge to explain your answer. [5]

A Use the advice on pages 78 and 144 to help with Question 1. Annotate the source, highlighting clues in the picture. Explain what they tell us about surgery at the time.

B Source A is very useful, containing lots of clues. However, it is just one painting. How typical is it of other operations that took place at the time? Use your **cross-referencing skills** to test the key messages contained in the source. Do not describe what each source tells us. Instead make direct comparisons as you go through your answer. For example, ' Source B says … which is directly supported by Source D which says …'

C Imagine Paré time-travelling to the early nineteenth century and witnessing surgical operations.

- Would he have been surprised by what he saw?
- Would he have seen methods that he was familiar with?
- Would he have seen any changes?

Practise your skills at using sources: Topic – Nineteenth-Century Surgery

Source B

A drawing of a surgical operation, published around 1800.

Source C

'… when the dreadful steel was plunged into the breast – cutting through veins, arteries, flesh, nerves – I began a scream that lasted during the whole time of the incision – I almost marvel that it does not ring in my ears still! So excruciating was the agony. When the wound was made, and the instrument was withdrawn, the pain seemed undiminished, for the air that suddenly rushed into those delicate parts felt like a mass of small but sharp and forked poignards [daggers], that were tearing at the edges of the wound.'

The novelist Fanny Burney's account of her mastectomy operation in 1811.

Source D

'I introduced a narrow knife about a foot long ... I cut along the bone. Finally I passed the knife around the head of the bone, cutting the remaining portion of the ligament, and this completed the operation, which certainly did not occupy at the most one minute. [My assistant] relaxed [the tourniquet so] that we might estimate the size and number of the bleeding vessels. It seemed at first sight as if the vessels which supplied so many jets of arterial blood could never be closed … a single instant was sufficient to convince us that the patient's safety required all our [speed], and in the course of a few minutes haemorrhage was effectively stopped by the application of twelve ligatures.'

An account by Professor James Syme of his amputation of a leg at the hip joint. Syme was a surgeon working in Edinburgh during the first half of the nineteenth century.

Activities

1. Discuss: which of the dangers facing patients during surgery do you think will be dealt with first during the nineteenth century?
2. How do you think people at the time would react to new inventions that might solve some of the problems that surgeons faced?

8.1 Opposition to changes in surgery: Did surgeons really want the sick to suffer?

In the early 1800s pain, infection and blood loss were still the three big problems in surgery, just as they had always been. In the 1800s surgeons found answers to two of these problems – pain and infection. Yet instead of applauding these changes many surgeons opposed them. Why? Did they really want the sick to suffer?

The struggle against pain and infection

The problem of blood loss was not tackled successfully until the twentieth century (see pages 180–181) but the timeline below shows the key breakthroughs in the struggle against pain and infection.

Activities

Study the timeline.

1. a Which development was the major breakthrough in fighting pain?
   b Which development was the major breakthrough in fighting infection?
2. Why do you think Pasteur's germ theory is included in the timeline?
3. Why is some information shown in blue and some in green in the timeline?

1845 Horace Wells used nitrous oxide as an anaesthetic.

1846 William Morton, an American dentist, used ether as an anaesthetic when removing teeth. It was also used during operations to remove tumours.

1847 Ignaz Semmelweiss called for doctors to wash their hands before entering the maternity wards in the General Hospital in Vienna.

James Simpson experimented with chloroform and established that it is an effective anaesthetic without some of the drawbacks of ether.

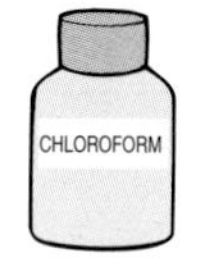

1853 Queen Victoria was given chloroform for the birth of her son Prince Leopold, by Dr John Snow, who was the leading anaesthetist of the time.

1861 Louis Pasteur published his germ theory.

1867 After reading Pasteur's germ theory, Joseph Lister, a Scottish surgeon, experimented with carbolic acid spray to produce the first antiseptic.

1878 Robert Koch, a bacteriologist, discovered the bacterium which caused septicaemia (blood poisoning). This boosted Lister's antiseptic ideas and was the start of aseptic surgery where operations were carried out in germ free environments.

1880 Lister used sterilised catgut for internal stitches.

1889 William Halstead, an American surgeon, introduced the wearing of sterilised rubber gloves and surgical masks to further prevent infection.

Answering 'Are you surprised by...?' questions

Study Sources 1, 2 and 3.
Are you surprised by what these sources say? Use the sources and your knowledge to explain your answer. [8]

Using sources effectively (placing sources in their historical context)

To answer this question effectively you need to combine details in the sources with your own knowledge of a period. It is important that you **consider the historical context**. To us today, it seems almost unbelievable that people in the nineteenth century opposed new inventions that would make surgery less painful and safer. To understand why there was so much opposition to the introduction of new anaesthetics and antiseptics you will need to explore nineteenth century surgery **and** the attitudes and beliefs of people living at the time in more depth.

Activities

You will be able to answer this question after have you have worked on pages 170–177. You can't do it yet!
But you can start thinking about the answer, using Sources 1–3 and your knowledge of opposition to medical changes in the past.

4 **a** Which new developments are Sources 1–3 opposed to?
b What are the reasons for opposition?

5 **a** Why had people previously opposed new medical ideas and methods (e.g. in the Middle Ages, Harvey, Jenner)?

6 Jot down a list of reasons why you would **not** be surprised by opposition to these new developments in surgery. You can check them and add to them as you read pages 170–177.

How did people react to these breakthroughs?

Source 1

Extract from a letter to the medical journal *The Lancet* in 1849 and 1853:

'The infliction [of pain] has been invented by the Almighty God. Pain may even be considered a blessing of the Gospel, and being blessed admits to being made either well or ill.'

Source 2

A notice to army doctors issued in 1855 by Dr John Hall, Chief of the Medical Staff in the British Army:

'Dr Hall takes this opportunity of warning medical officers against the use of chloroform in the severe shock of gunshot wounds, as he thinks few will survive if it is used. It is much better to hear a man bawl lustily than to see him sink silently into the grave. But Dr Hall knows that public opinion, based on mistaken kindness, is against him.'

Source 3

Memories of Lister by Watson Cheyne, one of his assistants, published in 1927:

'When Lister migrated to London (TEN years after his publication of the benefits of using carbolic to prevent infections) the number of London surgeons who were using his method could probably be counted on the fingers.

'Among other things it was very difficult to convince surgeons that tiny pieces of protoplasm one twenty-thousandth in diameter could be the cause of septic disease. The surgeons were interested in developing their anatomical knowledge and operating as rapidly as possible. Minute germs seemed very far removed from practical work.'

Why was there opposition to anaesthetics?

Activities

Pages 170–173 tell the story of anaesthetics in the nineteenth century. As you have discovered, there was a lot of opposition to new anaesthetics even though they were effective in saving patients from pain. Your task is to fill your 'Are you surprised?' basket with reasons why this opposition was **not** surprising. Look out for reasons when you see the basket!

Speed – the solution to pain in the early 1800s

Surgery in 1800 was little different from 2000 years earlier when the Roman author Celsus wrote: 'A surgeon should be filled with pity so that he wishes to cure the patient yet is not moved by his cries. He does everything just as if the cries of pain cause him no emotion.'

There were still no effective anaesthetics in the early 1800s. The patient was held down or tied down by the surgeon's assistants while the surgeon operated as quickly as possible. At the Battle of Borodino in 1812 Napoleon's surgeon, Dubois, amputated 200 limbs in 24 hours.

Because speed was the only way of reducing pain, surgeons were used to operating as speedily as possible. They prided themselves on their speed. Speed was one of the signs of a good surgeon. However, the development of effective anaesthetics from the 1840s onwards meant that speed was no longer so important and was a huge change for surgeons to get used to.

Information

The dangers of speed!
Some surgeons became famous for their speed, although speed could also cause problems. Robert Liston, a famous London surgeon, once amputated a leg in two-and-a-half minutes but worked so fast that he accidentally cut off his patient's testicles as well. During another high-speed operation Liston amputated the fingers of his assistant and slashed the coat of a spectator who, fearing that he had been stabbed, dropped dead with fright. Both the assistant and the patient then died of infection caught during the operation or in the hospital ward.

The pathway to effective anaesthetics

Step 1 'Laughing gas' (nitrous oxide)

Anaesthetics developed partly because of improved knowledge of chemistry. Scientists were finding that certain chemicals could have an effect on the human body. In 1799 Sir Humphry Davy discovered that 'laughing gas' (properly called nitrous oxide) reduced the sensation of pain. He suggested that it might be used in surgical operations and by dentists.

BUT

1 It did not make patients completely unconscious so was not a complete answer to the problem of pain.
2 An American dentist, Horace Wells, became convinced of the value of laughing gas after inhaling it at a fair. However, when he used it in a public demonstration his patient was in agony. This killed confidence in laughing gas as an anaesthetic.

Step 2 Ether

Source 1 describes the first successful operation using ether. A year later, in 1847, ether was used by J. R. Liston in London to anaesthetise a patient during a leg amputation.

BUT

Ether had severe drawbacks as an anaesthetic. It irritated the eyes and lungs, causing coughing and sickness. It could catch fire if close to a flame and had a vile, clinging smell that took ages to go away. Finally, ether came in a large, heavy bottle that was difficult to carry around.

Source 1

An account of an operation to remove a neck tumour using ether as an anaesthetic by John Collins Warren, senior surgeon at Massachusetts General Hospital in the USA, in1846:

'The patient was arranged for the operation in a sitting posture, and everything was made ready... The patient was then made to inhale a fluid from a tube with a glass globe. After four or five minutes he appeared to be asleep, and was thought by Dr Morton to be in a condition for the operation. I made an incision between two or three inches long in the direction of the tumour, and to my great surprise without any starting, crying, or other indication of pain.'

Step 3 Chloroform

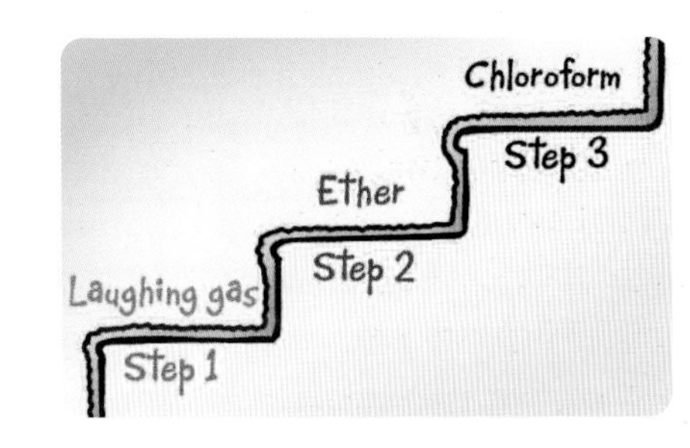

James Simpson was Professor of Midwifery at Edinburgh University. He had used ether but was searching for a better anaesthetic. One evening in 1847 he and several colleagues sat around a table experimenting with different chemicals to see what anaesthetic effects they had. Simpson wrote later, 'I poured some of the Chloroform fluid into tumblers in front of my assistants, Dr Keith and Dr Duncan, and myself. Before sitting down to supper we all inhaled the fluid, and were all "under the table" in a minute or two, to my wife's consternation and alarm.' Simpson realised that in chloroform he had discovered a very effective anaesthetic. Within days he started using it to help women in childbirth and other operations. He wrote articles about his discovery and other surgeons started to use it in their operations.

Chloroform was the most effective anaesthetic yet discovered, but that didn't mean it was problem-free, as Source 3 shows.

Source 2

◀ Simpson and friends recovering from the effects of chloroform. A drawing made in 1857.

Source 3

Written by Margaret Matthewson of Shetland. In 1877 she went to Edinburgh for a shoulder operation. The surgeon, needing more time, gave her an extra large dose of chloroform. Afterwards she took seventy minutes to regain consciousness.

'I was conscious of no more until I awoke in a bed in a strange ward. My first thought was "My arm! Is it off or not?" I at once sat up to feel for it. I found it bandaged to my waist and breathed a sigh of thankfulness.

'I felt very sick and kept on vomiting ... at intervals for several hours ... I doubt it will be sometime ere I get over this horrid chloroform taste and its effects.'

Opposition to chloroform

Do you remember opposition to earlier medical developments?

- In 1800 Jenner's use of vaccination had been strongly criticised.
- In the 1600s many doctors had refused to accept Harvey's theory of the circulation of the blood because it challenged Galen's ideas.
- In the Middle Ages the Church had discouraged the whole idea of enquiry and new thinking.

So it is not surprising that even something that seems today to be such a good development met opposition when it was first tried.

Activities

1 Look at the reasons for opposition to the use of chloroform given below. What categories could you organise them into?

Reason 1

Chloroform was a new and untested gas. No one knew for sure if there would be long-term side effects on the bodies or minds of patients. They did not know what dose to give to different patients.

Reason 2

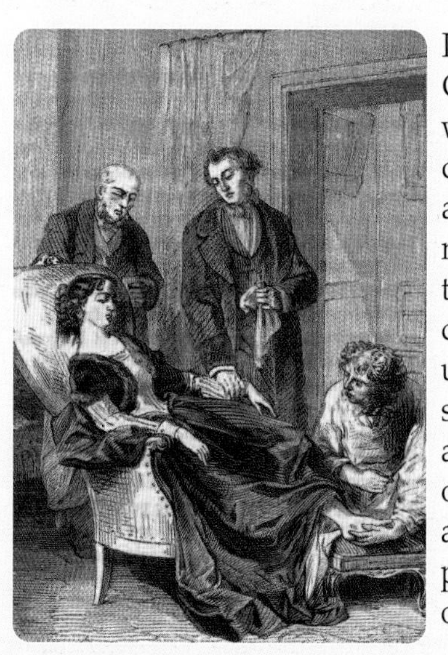

In 1848 Hannah Greener died while being given chloroform during an operation to remove her toenail. This first death from the use of chloroform scared surgeons and gave opponents of anaesthetics powerful evidence of their danger.

Reason 3

Anaesthetics did not necessarily make surgery safer. With a patient asleep, doctors attempted more complex operations, thus carrying infections deeper into the body and causing more loss of blood. The number of people dying from surgery may have increased after the discovery of anaesthetics. In the 1870s some surgeons stopped using chloroform as they were concerned about the high death rate (1 in 2500 operations) and returned to using ether mixed with nitrous oxide.

Reason 4

Letter to the medical journal *The Lancet* in 1849:

'The infliction [of pain] has been invented by the Almighty God. Pain may even be considered a blessing of the Gospel, and being blessed admits to being made either well or ill.'

Reason 5

Some people were particularly opposed to the idea of easing the pain of childbirth – believing that this would be unnatural. Letter to the medical journal *The Lancet* in 1853:

'It is a most unnatural practice. The pain and sorrow of labour exert a most powerful and useful influence upon the religious and moral character of women and upon all their future relations in life.'

Reason 6

A quotation from Army Chief of Medical Staff, 1854:

'... the smart use of the knife is a powerful stimulant and it is much better to hear a man bawl lustily than to see him sink silently into the grave.'

Why was opposition to chloroform overcome?

Activities

2 List the reasons why anaesthetics became commonly used.
3 Which of these reasons do you think were most important?

The struggle continued for ten years, with anaesthetics gradually winning wider acceptance. James Simpson continued to play a leading role, presenting a powerful case for the use of chloroform as an anaesthetic. He brought the example of Ambroise Paré to his defence.

The final breakthrough came when Queen Victoria accepted the use of chloroform during the delivery of her eighth child in 1857. She publicly praised 'that blessed chloroform'. The support of the queen meant opposition to anaesthetics was doomed.

However, all problems were not solved (see Reason 3 opposite). Over time the use of anaesthetics improved. Other chemicals were used which relaxed muscles as well as simply putting patients to sleep. New chemicals also had fewer side-effects than chloroform. Local anaesthetics were developed as well as general anaesthetics. This took time – but Simpson's use of chloroform had been the key turning point.

Source 1

James Simpson speaking to a meeting of doctors in Edinburgh in 1847:

'Before the sixteenth century surgeons had no way of stemming the flow of blood after amputation of a limb other than by scorching with a red hot iron or boiling pitch. The great suggestion of Ambroise Paré, to shut up the bleeding vessels by tying them, was a vast improvement. It saved the sufferings of the patient while adding to their safety. But the practice was new, and like all innovations in medical practice, it was at first and for long, bitterly decried … attacked … suppressed.

'We look back with sorrow on the opponents of Paré. Our successors in years to come will look back with similar feelings. They will marvel at the idea of humane men confessing that they prefer operating on their patients in a waking instead of an anaesthetic state, and that the fearful agonies that they inflict should be endured quietly. All pain is destructive and even fatal in its effects.'

Source 2

◀ What is the message in this cartoon about the use of anaesthetics? When do you think it was published and why? Use the evidence on page 172 to help you.

Why was there opposition to antiseptics?

Infection – the biggest danger in surgery

The idea of operations without anaesthetics is dramatic and horrible. Such operations did kill patients because the shock of the incision could kill. However, many more patients survived the operation but then died from something much less dramatic – infection. Doctors had used liquids such as wine and vinegar to keep wounds clean for centuries but, before Pasteur's germ theory, no-one knew what was causing infection in open wounds. That was why surgeons did things that seem obviously dangerous today. They reused bandages, spreading gangrene and skin infections from patient to patient. They did not wash their hands before an operation, nor did they sterilise their equipment, and some operated wearing old pus-stained clothes. This was how they had carried out operations for years. It was what they were used to.

A false start – the 'crazy' ideas of Ignaz Semmelweiss

The notice in Source 1 was placed by Dr Semmelweiss at the entrance to the maternity ward in the General Hospital in Vienna in 1847. It was so unusual that other doctors called him a crank and a fanatic and said that he was mentally unstable. Semmelweiss put up the notice because he was worried by the deaths of healthy women after childbirth. Most doctors regarded this as inevitable but Semmelweiss realised that women whose babies were delivered by midwives were much less likely to die from infection than women whose babies were delivered by medical students. He believed the reason was that medical students came straight to the delivery rooms from dissecting dead bodies. If they simply washed their hands, he thought, they would reduce the risk of infection to women. Semmelweiss pursued his crusade with great passion, calling doctors who did not wash their hands 'murderers'. Unfortunately he had little support and no-one built on his ideas.

Source 1

From today, 15 May 1847, any doctor or student coming from the postmortem room must, before entering the maternity wards, wash his hands thoroughly in the basin of chlorinated water placed at the entrance. This order applies to everyone, without exception.

Joseph Lister and the wonders of carbolic acid

Source 2

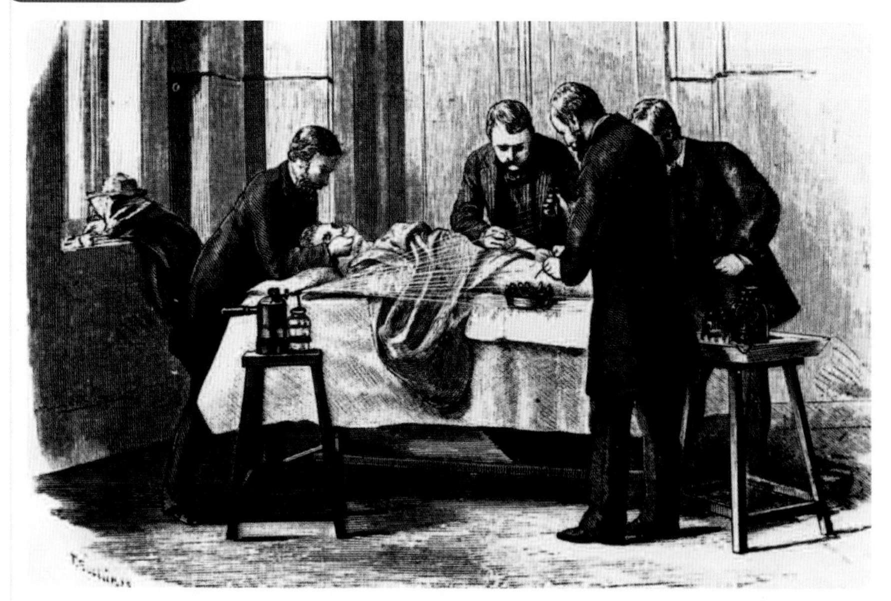

▲ An operation taking place while a carbolic spray disinfects the area. One assistant is using chloroform to anaesthetise the patient, another is mopping up blood with a sponge.

Activities

1 Pages 174–177 tell the story of the use of antiseptics in the nineteenth century to kill infections. Twenty years after Simpson discovered the value of chloroform there was just as much opposition to the first antiseptics. Your task is to fill your 'Are you surprised?' basket with reasons why this opposition was not surprising.

Where did his idea of **stopping infection** come from?

Joseph Lister's use of carbolic acid to prevent infection was as important a turning point as Simpson's use of chloroform. Lister was one of the outstanding surgeons of the nineteenth century. He had researched gangrene and infection, and had a keen interest in the application of science to medicine. That was why he knew all about Pasteur's work on germ theory, which helped to spark the idea for his own discovery.

There are bacteria in the air which cause rotting and infections such as gangrene.
Then these bacteria must be causing infections in open wounds. I can save patients if I find a way of stopping these bacteria getting into operation wounds.
Pasteur
Lister

▲ This meeting and conversation never happened but this drawing shows you how their ideas were linked.

Where did the idea of using **carbolic** come from?

The answer is sewage, as Lister described (see Source 3). He experimented with using carbolic in treating people who had compound fractures where the bone breaks through the skin. Infection often developed in these open wounds. Lister applied carbolic acid to the wound and used bandages soaked in carbolic. He found that the wounds healed and did not develop gangrene.

Source 3

Lister's description of how the idea of using carbolic developed:

'In 1864 I was struck by an account of the remarkable effects of using carbolic acid upon the sewage of Carlisle. It prevented all odour from the lands covered by the sewage and destroyed the parasites that usually infest cattle feeding on such land. The idea of using carbolic acid for the treatment of open fractures naturally occurred to me.'

Source 4

Joseph Lister, *On the New Method of Treating Compound Fracture*, 1867:

'James, aged 11 years, was admitted to the Glasgow Infirmary on August 2, 1865, with compound fracture of the left leg caused by the wheel of an empty cart passing over the limb a little below the middle. The wound, an inch and a half long and three quarters of an inch broad, was over the line of the fracture.

'A piece of lint dipped in carbolic acid was laid on the wound, and splints padded with cotton wool were applied. It was left undisturbed for four days and, when examined, it showed no sign of suppuration. For the next four days the wound was dressed with lint soaked with a solution of water and carbolic acid and olive oil which further prevented irritation to the skin. No pus was present, there seemed no danger of infection, and at the end of six weeks I found the bones united, and I discarded the splints. The sore was entirely healed.'

Source 5

From Lister's own record of amputations:

	Total amputations	Died	Percentage who died
1864–66 (without antiseptics)	35	16	45.7
1867–70 (with antiseptics)	40	6	15.0

Activities

2 Before you turn the page, using all you have found out about opposition to medical developments list possible reasons you expect surgeons might oppose Lister's use of carbolic spray during operations.

Opposition to Lister's use of carbolic

In 1867 Lister published his results, showing the value of using carbolic acid. He also worked at improving his method:

Improvement 1
Handwashing with carbolic before operations to avoid infections getting into wounds.
Improvement 2
A carbolic spray to kill germs in the air around the operating table.
Improvement 3
An antiseptic ligature to tie up blood vessels and prevent blood loss.

Activities

1. Look at the reasons for opposition below. What categories could you organise them into?
2. Can you see any differences between the reasons for oppositions to the use of chloroform (see page 172) and the opposition to the use of carbolic?

Reason 1

Lister's carbolic spray, which soaked the operating theatre, seemed very extreme. It cracked the surgeon's skin and made everything smell. The new precautions caused extra work, and made operations more expensive and less pleasant for the surgeons. One doctor wrote:

'The whole scene of an operation was covered in carbolic spray which dispersed its globules into every nook and cranny of the wound. Our faces and coat-sleeves often dripped with it. It was a relief to us all when the spray was abandoned. It was costly and cumbersome and often broke down.'

Reason 2

Despite anaesthetics, surgeons were still convinced that speed was essential in an operation – often because of the problem of bleeding. It seemed that Lister's antiseptic methods just slowed operations down.

Reason 3

When some surgeons did try copying Lister's methods they did not achieve the same results. This was usually because they were less systematic, but that didn't stop them criticising Lister. Others argued that antiseptics actually prevented the body's own defence mechanisms from operating effectively.

Reason 4

Pasteur's ideas had spread very slowly. Even trained surgeons found it difficult to accept that there were tiny micro-organisms all around which could cause disease.

One surgeon regularly joked with his assistants that they should shut the door of the operating theatre in case one of Mr Lister's microbes flew in.

Reason 5

For many centuries surgeons had lived with the idea that many of their patients would die. When Lister said he achieved good results, their first reaction was disbelief. For many the next reaction was to feel defensive, that Lister was criticising them for letting patients down.

Reason 6

Lister was not a showman like Pasteur. He did not give impressive public displays. Indeed, he appeared to be cold, arrogant and aloof and was sometimes critical of other surgeons. Many surgeons regarded him as a fanatic.

Reason 7

Lister was always changing his techniques. He did this because he wanted to find a substance that would work equally as well as carbolic spray, but without the corrosion that it caused. His critics simply said he was changing his methods because they did not work.

How did Lister help to change surgery?

Despite opposition, Lister's methods marked a turning point in surgery. In 1877 he moved to London to train young surgeons. Then came a link to another great name in medical history. In 1878 Robert Koch discovered the bacterium which caused septicaemia (blood poisoning). This gave a great boost to Lister's ideas.

This just shows how many medical discoveries are interconnected.
Lister
Koch

▲ In 1892 Lister and Pasteur were together given an award at the Sorbonne University in Paris for their contribution to the fight against disease.

Aseptic surgery

By the late 1890s Lister's antiseptic methods (which killed germs on the wound) developed into aseptic surgery, which meant removing all possible germs from the operating theatre. To ensure absolute cleanliness:

- Operating theatres and hospitals were rigorously cleaned.
- From 1887 all instruments were steam-sterilised.
- Surgeons abandoned operating in their ordinary clothes and wore surgical gowns and face masks.
- In 1894, sterilised rubber gloves were used for the first time. For, however well surgeons' hands were scrubbed, they could still hold bacteria in the folds of skin and under the nails.

More ambitious operations

With two of the basic problems of surgery now solved, surgeons attempted more ambitious operations.

- The first successful operation to remove an infected appendix came in the 1880s.
- The first heart operation was carried out in 1896 when surgeons repaired a heart damaged by a stab wound.

Simpson and Lister had made a major contribution. Their achievements helped make such operations possible.

Activities

3. On pages 170–177 we have mostly focused on the reasons for opposition to new ideas. But why did these developments happen? Which factors helped in the development of anaesthetics and antiseptics in the nineteenth century? (Can you find examples of science and technology, communications, chance, individual insights and attitudes?)
4. 'Role of the individual' chart: complete charts for Simpson and Lister.

And there's a love story linked to that last bullet point!

In 1889 Caroline Hampton, an operating theatre nurse in America, developed a skin infection from the chemicals used to disinfect hands before operations. She showed her hands to the chief surgeon, William Halsted, and he arranged for the Goodyear Rubber Company to make a pair of thin rubber gloves to protect Caroline's hands. Within a year the nurse and the surgeon were married – and Halsted spread the idea of wearing rubber gloves during operations. He went on to become one of America's most famous surgeons, responsible for many new developments.

8.2 Why has surgery improved so much since 1900?

By 1900 doctors had gone a long way to solving the problems of pain and infection, two of the three major problems facing surgeons. The major problem remaining was bleeding – how to stop heavy blood loss. This problem was solved in the early 1900s, and many other surgical developments followed. This enquiry returns to the factor hunt and considers why surgery has changed so dramatically.

Which team should win this tug-of-war? The Science and Technology team or the War team? Your task is to use the information on pages 180–181 to decide which developments in surgery belong on which team and who is pulling harder.

But before you start – think back over the history of surgery. Which factor has had the bigger impact on surgery in the past?

War has had by far the biggest impact on surgery since 1900. Wars have given surgeons far more opportunity to work together, practising new techniques and developing new equipment. And war makes governments and industries provide more equipment.
WAR

Activities

Step 1: Evidence collection

On pages 180–181 you can find out about eight developments in surgery since 1900. Each one could be on the War team or the Science and Technology team. Your first job is to decide which team each development is on.

Step 2: How powerful are the teams?

Not everyone on a team is as skilled or as heavy as everyone else – so which of the developments do you think were most important in the development of surgery? Give the ones that you think were most important a double-strength pull.

Step 3: Look for other factors

Were war and science and technology the only factors helping the development of surgery since 1900? Did you spot any more?

Step 4: Debate the result

Decide which team you think has won the tug-of-war and write a speech explaining your choice and the evidence for your choice. Make sure you include at least one point that shows the weakness in the opposition argument.

Now debate the result with your class. Debates are very helpful for revision because you have to know the topic well enough to talk about it. If ideas and information stay in your mind it can be a bit of a jumble but a debate forces you to sort it out clearly – talking about a topic gets you more than half-way to writing about it effectively in an examination.

Developments in surgery since 1900

Information

Development 1: X-rays

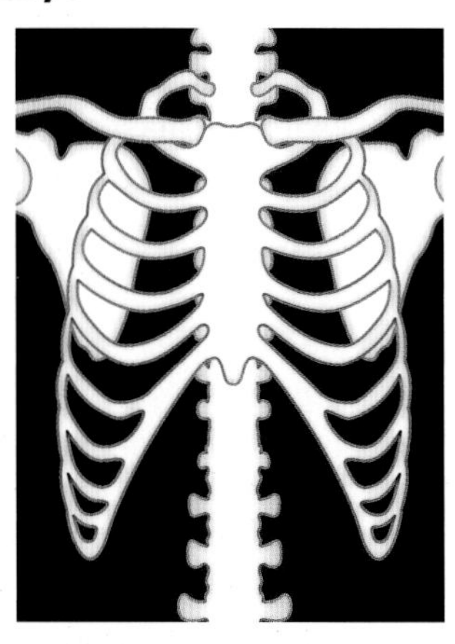

A German scientist, Wilhelm Rontgen, was carrying out experiments in 1895 when he realised that rays of light in a covered tube were lighting up a far wall. They could pass through black paper, wood and flesh. He did not know what they were so he called them X-rays.

Within months of Rontgen publishing his discovery the first X-ray machines were being used in hospitals. The First World War had a major impact on the common use of X-rays. Surgeons needed to locate bullets and shrapnel lodged deep within wounded men and X-rays provided the answer. Governments ordered the making of many more X-ray machines and they were installed in all major hospitals on the Western Front.

Information

Development 2: Blood transfusions

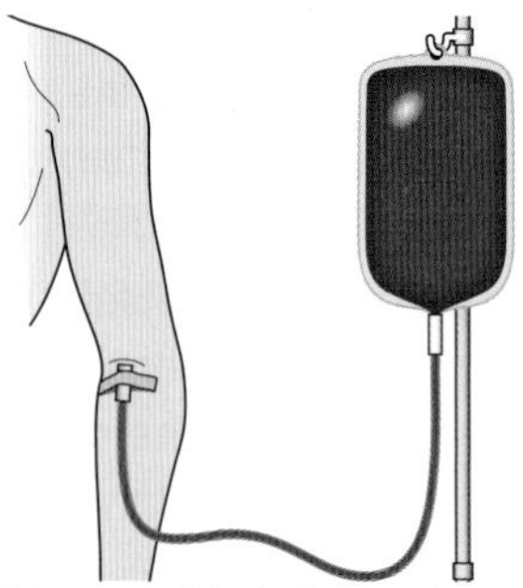

Blood transfusions were often attempted in the 1800s. Sometimes they worked. Mostly they did not. Nobody knew why. Then in 1901 Karl Landsteiner discovered the existence of blood groups. After this, blood transfusions became possible, provided the patient and the donor were in the same place.

When doctors tried to store blood it clotted and could not be used for transfusions.

The problem of storing blood was solved during the First World War. There was a huge need for blood, and many soldiers bled to death because there was no store of blood to use. Two breakthroughs solved this problem. Firstly sodium citrate was added to blood to prevent it clotting. Later in the war scientists discovered how to separate and store the crucial blood cells and keep them in bottles for future use. This made possible the huge blood banks that supply blood today.

Information

Development 3: Fighting infection

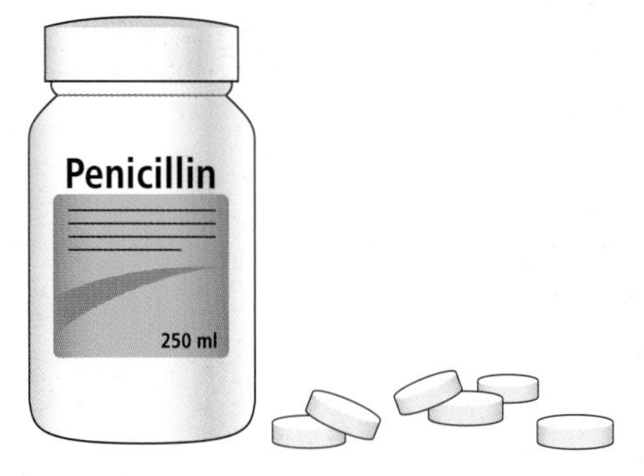

Lister had begun the fight against infection but wartime wounds caused problems that needed new solutions. Many wounds were very deep and bullets carried fragments of clothing carrying bacteria deep inside the body. This caused very deep infections. Gradually, through practice and trying out new methods on thousands of cases, surgeons learned to cut away the infected tissue and protect it with a saline solution. However, the development of penicillin in the Second World War (see page 132) was the real breakthrough in fighting infection successfully.

Information

Development 4: Radiotherapy

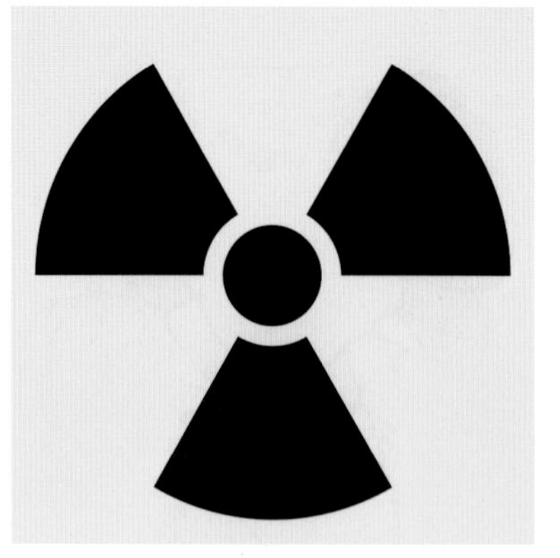

Marie Curie, together with her husband, Pierre, developed Rontgen's research on X-rays. In the process they discovered radium, which has been used ever since to diagnose cancers, and in radiotherapy to treat cancers. Their research was the beginning of modern treatment of cancers. As the research continued it became so complex that they built up a team of research scientists to share ideas. Marie Curie is the only woman to have won two Nobel Prizes, for her work on X-rays and on radium.

Information

Development 5: Plastic surgery

Plastic surgery had been carried out in India centuries earlier but was always limited by pain and the danger of infection. The terrible injuries of both World Wars led to a rapid improvement in techniques, especially the use of skin grafts. In World War One the injuries were mostly from bullet and shell damage. Surgeons carried out over 11,000 plastic surgery operations, increasing their experience and learning from each other. In World War Two there were many more burns cases in tanks and aeroplanes. Archibald McIndoe alone carried out 4000 operations on burns cases.

Information

Development 6: Transplant surgery

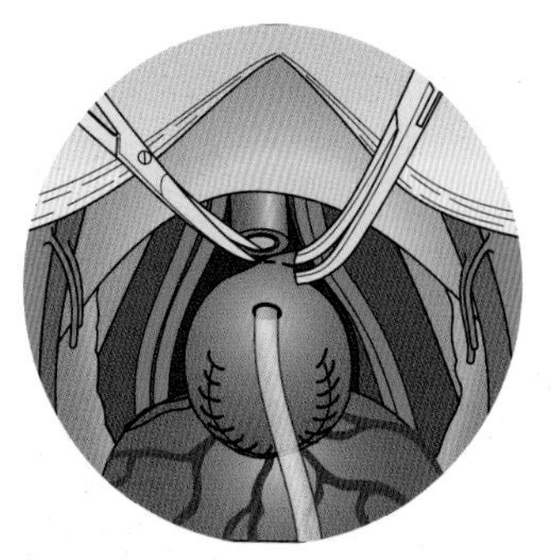

The first heart transplant was carried out in South Africa in 1967. The lead surgeon was Dr Christiaan Barnard, who became world famous, but in reality he headed a team of highly skilled and experienced doctors, nurses and scientists. Other organs had been transplanted before then (kidneys in 1954 and liver in 1963) and since then even more ambitious transplants have been carried out including the first marrow transplant in 1980 and first heart and lung transplant in 1982. All depend on high levels of technical and scientific expertise. So many transplants have been carried out that a transplant Olympics is now held at regular intervals.

Information

Development 7: Improved anaesthetics

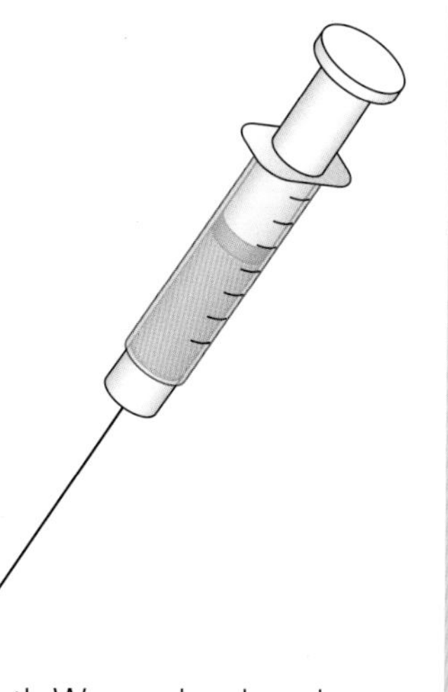

Anaesthetics in the later 1800s had to be inhaled through nose and mouth. This made it difficult to control the dosage. Surgeons had to err on the side of caution for fear of killing a patient, so still tended to operate as fast as they could. In the 1930s Helmuth Wesse developed anaesthetics that could be injected into the blood stream, allowing more precise control of doses, therefore greater safety, and enabling longer operations. Nowadays local anaesthetics are so effective that patients can even have major operations such as hip replacements under local anaesthetic and without going to sleep at all (see page 204).

Information

Development 8: Keyhole and micro-surgery

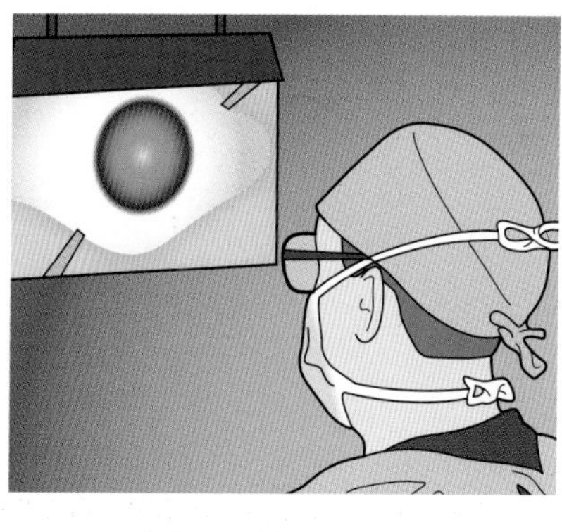

Once upon a time major surgery required surgeons to make large cuts into the body. Nowadays such large incisions are avoided as often as possible and in some universities there are 'Departments of minimally-invasive surgery', meaning that surgeons cut into the body through as small a hole as possible. All the tools needed are inside an instrument called an endoscope controlled by the surgeon using miniature cameras, fibre-optic cables and computers. Micro-surgery has also developed because of improvements in technology. Surgeons can now rejoin blood vessels and nerves, restoring the use of damaged and even severed limbs.

Improve that answer!

By now you should feel like an expert on surgery and feel confident that you know how to approach the different types of exam questions. This 'Meet the examiner' page is different. You will not get advice from the examiner ... you are the examiner! You give the advice.

Activities

1. How would you advise students to tackle Questions 1 and 2?
   - **a** Write some key 'Do's and Don'ts' on answering 'Describe' and 'Explain' style questions. Use pages 49 and 74 to help you.
   - **b** What should the students include in their answer? You could record your advice on tape to help with revision.
2. Look at the answer to Question 3. The strengths of the answer have been highlighted. But what are the weaknesses? Advise the student on how to improve the answer.

1 Briefly describe the work of Paré. [5]

2 Explain why there was so much opposition to the introduction of anaesthetics and antiseptics during the nineteenth century. [7]

3 'The twentieth century saw many improvements in surgery. War was more important than science and technology as a factor that led to change.' Explain how far you agree with this statement. [8]

The First World War led to many improvements in surgery. During the war X-rays became widely used for the first time. They were used to find bullets deep in the body. The war also created a need for better ways to carry out blood transfusions. Before the war these were carried out with on the spot donors because doctors had no way of storing blood properly. During the First World War large amounts of blood were needed and this method was not practical. This led to new methods of storing blood being developed. Doctors discovered that tiny cells in the blood could be bottled, ~~packed in~~ ice and stored where needed.

The war also created a need to develop new methods to prevent infection during surgery. By trial and error, surgeons developed new techniques. They cut away infected tissue and soaked the wound with a saline solution. During the First World War surgeons were faced with hundreds of thousands of casualties. This meant that they had to learn fast and had the opportunity to practise new techniques. For example, surgeons developed new ~~techniques~~ for repairing broken bones. They also improved methods of grafting skin which led to the development of plastic surgery. The Second World War also led to improvements in surgery. During the twentieth century there have been big improvements in surgery. War was the key factor that led to change.

The student **proves** that changes took place during the war – by briefly referring to the situation before the war.

The student **explains** that the war provided the need for change.

The student **links** things that happened during the war to changes in surgery.

The student provides **specific examples** to support their points.

Smarter Revision: Freeze-framed photos

On page 37 we looked at how you can use a camera to help you remember the key features of a period or the work of an individual. You can also use this technique to explore change and continuity across a period. These students have produced freeze frames that sum up how surgery changed during the nineteenth century. They have collected or made their own props. These 'before and after' shots show the key changes that took place.

Activities

1. Can you spot the key changes that took place in surgery during the nineteenth century? On your own copy label the bottom photo to show what has changed.
2. Can you think of any changes or continuities that the students have missed? You may want to try to produce a better freeze frame.
3. Choose a different area of medicine, for example, public health or treatments. Produce two photos that show change and continuity across a period of your choice.

▼ BEFORE (Surgery at the start of the nineteenth century)

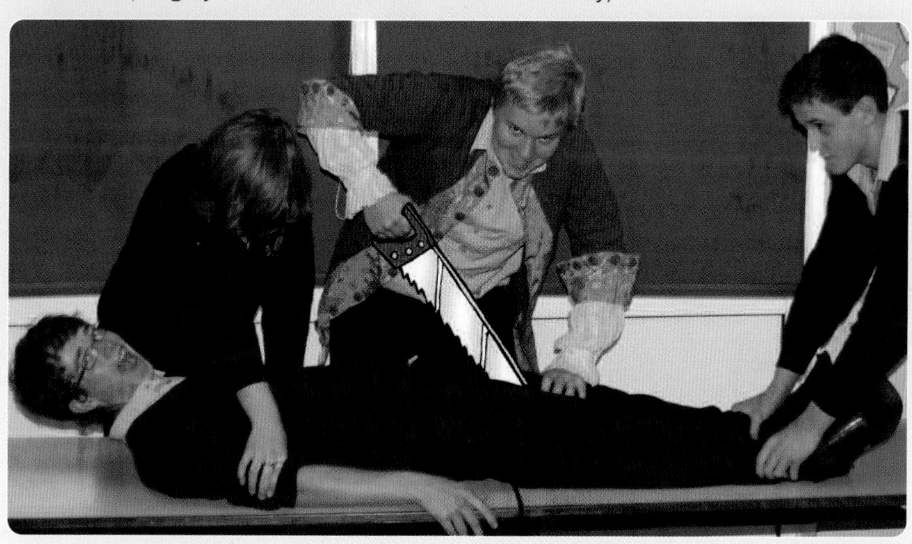

▼ AFTER (Surgery at the end of the nineteenth century)

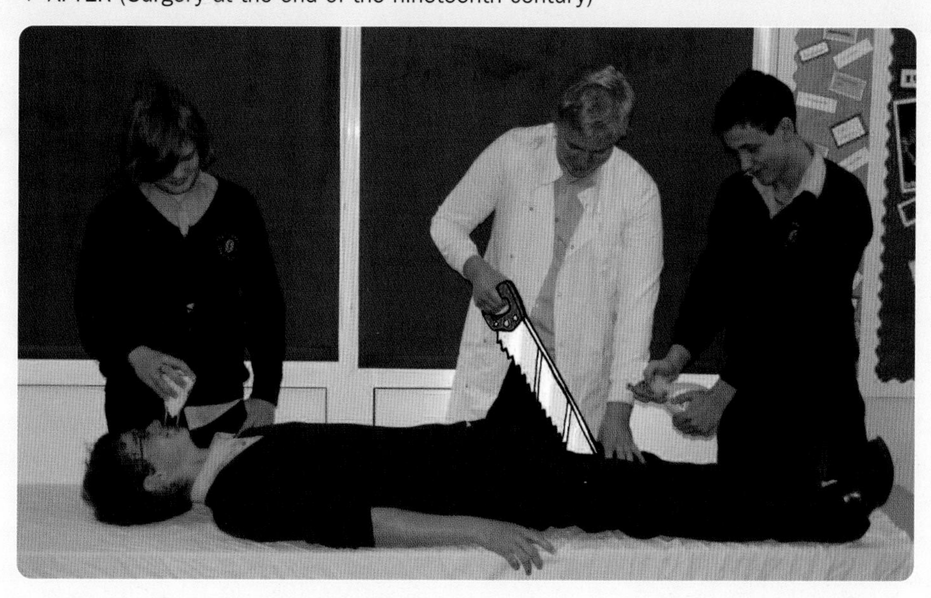

Section 9: Did Florence Nightingale revolutionise hospitals single-handed?

You probably noticed that women have all but disappeared from the story of medicine in the last three sections. After centuries of trying to keep women out of medicine, men seemed to have succeeded completely by the early 1800s but it was a short-lived success. One woman in particular from this period is very famous – Florence Nightingale. Your task is to decide whether she really did change nursing and hospitals single-handed.

Source 1

Thomas Huxley, a leading scientist, in 1851:

'In every excellent characteristic, whether mental or physical, the average woman is inferior to the average man.'

How difficult was it for women to make an impact on medicine?

Source 2

'An ideal woman' as described by the novelist W.M. Thackeray in the 1850s:

'An exquisite slave: a humble, flattering, tea-making, pianoforte-playing being who laughs at our jokes, however old they may be.'

Source 3

A statement by students (all male) at Middlesex Hospital, London, protesting against Elizabeth Garrett attending lectures in 1861:

'We consider that the mix of the sexes in the same class is likely to lead to results of an unpleasant nature. Lecturers are likely to feel some restraint through the presence of females in giving that explicit enunciation of some facts which is necessary. The presence of young females as spectators in the operating theatre is an outrage on our natural instincts and feelings.'

▲ Elizabeth Garrett, the first woman to qualify as a doctor in Britain.

Sources 1–3 sum up the attitudes women had to fight against. Women had always provided the bulk of medical care and were often very knowledgeable about, for example, herbal remedies but a new law in 1852 required all doctors to belong to one of the Colleges of Surgeons, Physicians or Apothecaries. All were closed to women.

Despite this, a handful of women fought to become doctors. Elizabeth Blackwell, the first woman to qualify as doctor in the USA in 1849, was an inspiration, travelling to England in 1859 when she met Elizabeth Garrett. Garrett was the first women to qualify as a doctor in Britain but had to overcome huge obstacles to do so.

1. Boxes A–D tell the story of women's fight to become doctors. Boxes E–H explain the different ways in which men tried to block women's progress. Match up the boxes in pairs, showing how men tried to push back each advance by women.
2. What attitudes did women have to overcome to become doctors?

Box A
During the 1860s Elizabeth Garrett worked as a nurse and then attended lectures at the Middlesex Hospital.

Box B
Elizabeth Garrett passed all the exams to qualify as a doctor. The final step before she could work as a doctor was to become a member of one of the Colleges of Surgeons, Physicians or Apothecaries.

Box C
In 1874 six women, led by Sophia Jex-Blake, completed the medical course at Edinburgh University.

Box D
In 1876 a law was passed opening all medical qualifications to women.

Box E
The Colleges of Surgeons and Physicians refused to allow women members, which therefore stopped Garrett working as a doctor. She had to take the College of Apothecaries to court before it accepted her as a member. After that it too changed its rules so that women could not become members.

What were hospitals like in the early 1800s?

Source 4

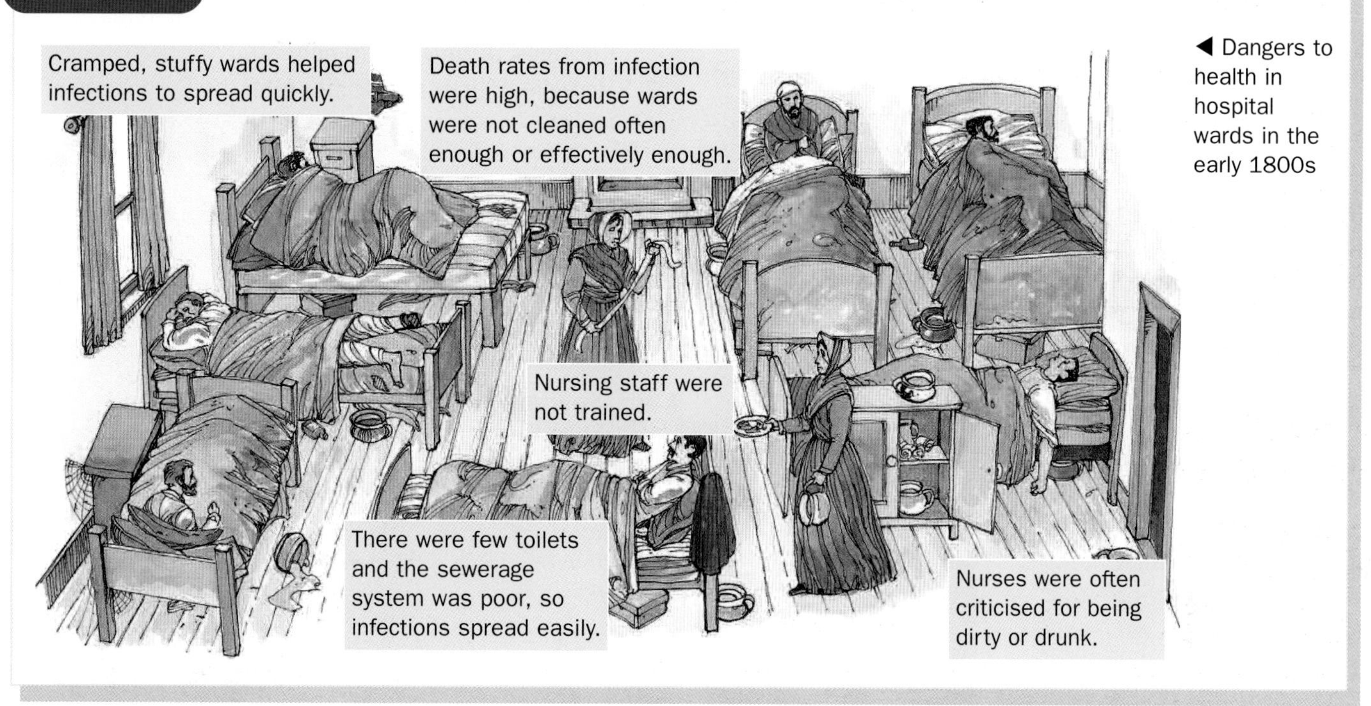

Cramped, stuffy wards helped infections to spread quickly.
Death rates from infection were high, because wards were not cleaned often enough or effectively enough.
Nursing staff were not trained.
There were few toilets and the sewerage system was poor, so infections spread easily.
Nurses were often criticised for being dirty or drunk.

◀ Dangers to health in hospital wards in the early 1800s

This is what hospitals were like in the days before Pasteur, Lister – and Nightingale. For many people, hospitals were the places they went to die – if not from the disease they had when they went in, then from another disease they caught on the wards. Anyone who had the money paid for nurses and doctors to visit them at home. Even operations were carried out at home because home seemed a healthier place than a hospital ward.

Source 5

An extract from *Martin Chuzzlewit*, a novel by Charles Dickens, published in 1844. In this extract, the nurse, Betsy Prig, is handing her patient over to the care of another nurse, Sarah Gamp. Dickens wrote in his introduction to this novel that 'Mrs Betsy Prig is an accurate description of a hospital nurse':

'How are we?' asked Mrs Gamp. Mrs Prig said, 'He's as cross as two sticks. He wouldn't have washed if he'd had his own way.'

'She put soap in my mouth,' said the unfortunate patient, feebly.

'Couldn't you keep it shut then?' said Mrs Prig.

Mrs Prig seized the patient by the chin and began to scrape his unhappy head with the hair brush. The brush was the hardest possible instrument and his eye-lids were red with the pain.

Then Mrs Gamp and Mrs Prig put on his coat.

'I don't think it's quite right' said the poor invalid. 'There's a bottle in my pocket. Why have you made me sit on a bottle?'

'Oh' cried Mrs Gamp, 'he's got my gin bottle. I put it in his coat when it hung behind the door.'

Activities

Box F
Male students at the Middlesex Hospital protested that Elizabeth Garrett should not be allowed to attend lectures.

Box G
For five years after 1876 the Royal College of Surgeons refused to allow anyone to take exams in midwifery as a way of preventing women from learning alongside men.

Box H
Edinburgh University said it could only give medical degrees to men.
The women had to complete their degrees in Dublin or Switzerland.

Activities

3 Using Sources 4 and 5 make a list of the reforms that were needed to improve hospitals and nursing.

4 Which developments in Sections 6, 7 and 8 do you think do most to improve hospital wards?

5 Use what you learned on the opposite page. How difficult would it be for any woman to play a major part in changing conditions in hospitals?

Two medical heroines

The story of changes in hospitals and nursing begins far away from Britain. In 1854 the Crimean War broke out between Britain and France on one side and Russia on the other. British and French troops, invading the Crimea, found themselves fighting in mud and freezing temperatures. For the first time people back in Britain received rapid news of the conditions and the fighting, thanks to reports sent back by W.H. Russell, the first war correspondent. His reports helped to prompt the work of two women who became nationally famous during the Crimean War.

Activities

1. Why was each woman a national heroine in the 1850s **during** the Crimean War?
2. How did their careers differ **after** the Crimean War?

Florence Nightingale 1820–1910

Before the Crimean War Born into a wealthy family, Florence horrified them by wanting to be a nurse. She trained in Germany, returning to work as a nurse and becoming Superintendent of Nurses in a London hospital.

When she heard reports of the terrible conditions in the Crimea she talked to the Minister for War, Sidney Herbert, who was a family friend. He arranged for her to take 38 nurses to the Crimea.

In the Crimea Arriving at the army hospital at Scutari, Florence was appalled by the dirty conditions. She concentrated on cleaning the hospital and patients. She wrote back to the British government:

'It appears that in these [army] hospitals the washing of linen and of the men are considered a minor detail. No washing has been performed for the men or the beds – except by ourselves. When we came here there was neither basin, towel nor soap in the wards. The consequences of this are fever, cholera, gangrene, lice, bugs, fleas.'

The death-rate in the hospital fell from 40 per cent of wounded to 2 per cent. Florence and her nurses worked at the hospital rather than visiting the frontline of fighting.

After the Crimean War Florence returned to Britain a national heroine and this helped her raise money to set up her first nursing school.

Training focused on hygiene and cleanliness to prevent infections and diseases spreading in hospitals.

In 1859 she wrote her book *Notes on Nursing* and in 1863 *Notes on Hospitals*. Both books were very influential all over the world, providing the basis for training nurses and hospital design. As in the Crimea, her work concentrated on cleanliness and providing fresh air.

Mary Seacole 1805–1881

Before the Crimean War Born in Jamaica, the daughter of a local healer, Mary became a very knowledgeable healer and midwife.

She gained more experience in Panama where she showed people how to deal with an outbreak of cholera, isolating patients and cleaning out dirt. She also treated gunshot wounds.

In 1854 she travelled to Britain and volunteered her services to the army but nobody would see her. She paid her own way to the Crimea.

In the Crimea Mary set up her 'British Hotel' providing food and drinks to the soldiers. She also treated sickness and tended the wounded on the battlefield.

Her bravery in helping the wounded while fighting continued made her hugely popular and highly respected among the soldiers.

After the Crimean War Mary returned to Britain without money. Ex-soldiers and *The Times* newspaper tried to raise funds to help her but this failed when the organising company went bankrupt.

After publishing her memoirs she was better-off but nobody in Britain tried to use or learn from her medical skills.

An extract from a poem published about Mary Seacole in *Punch* magazine, 1856, after Mary returned to Britain:

She gave her aid to all in need
To hungry, sick and cold
Open hand and heart, ready to give
Kind words, and acts, and gold
And now the good soul is 'in a hole'
What soldier in all – the land
To set her on her feet again
Won't give a helping hand?

Practise for your Historical Source Investigation exam:
Topic – Hospitals

How important was the work of Florence Nightingale and Mary Seacole during the Crimean War?

Study the Background Information and the sources carefully. You are advised to spend at least ten minutes doing this and then answer all the questions. In answering the questions, you will need to use your knowledge of the topic to interpret and evaluate the sources. When you are asked to use specific sources you must do so, but you can also use any of the other sources if they are relevant.

1. Study Sources A and B.
   How far do these sources give different impressions of Scutari Hospital before Nightingale arrived? Use the sources and your knowledge to explain your answer. [6]

2. Study Source C.
   Does this source prove that conditions in Scutari Hospital improved after Nightingale's arrival? Use the sources and your knowledge to explain your answer. [8]

3. Study Sources D and E.
   Why do these sources give different impressions of Florence Nightingale's work in the Crimea? Use the sources and your knowledge to explain your answer. [9]

4. Study Sources F, G and H.
   How useful is Source F to an historian trying to find out about Mary Seacole's work in the Crimea? Use the source and your knowledge to explain your answer. [9]

5. Study Source I.
   After her death Mary Seacole was forgotten by most people. In contrast, Florence Nightingale has become one of the most well-known people in the history of medicine. Are you surprised by this? Use the source and your knowledge to explain your answer. [8]

6. Study all the sources.
   'Mary Seacole played just as important role as Florence Nightingale during the Crimean War.'
   How far do the sources on this paper support this view?
   Explain your answer. Remember to identify the sources you use. [10]

Background information

During the Crimean War, newspaper reporters sent regular reports back to Britain about the terrible conditions in the army hospitals. Many soldiers were dying because of dirt and a lack of good nursing. Florence Nightingale was asked by the government to lead a group of trained nurses to the Crimea to try and improve conditions in the army hospitals. Within six months Nightingale and her team were able to reduce death rates at Scutari Hospital from 40 per cent to 2 per cent. The newspapers in Britain reported her work and she became famous as 'The Lady with the Lamp'. By the time she returned to Britain she was a national heroine.

Nightingale and her team were not the only nurses who worked in the Crimea. Mary Seacole was born in Jamaica where she worked as a midwife and treated the sick. When the British government ignored her offers of help she went to the Crimea at her own expense. Seacole supplied soldiers with food and drink and dealt with a range of wounds and diseases. Did Mary Seacole make just as important contribution in the Crimea as Florence Nightingale?

Source A

'I have much satisfaction in being able to inform you that the hospital in Scutari is now in a highly satisfactory state and that nothing is lacking.'

From a letter written by Dr John Hall, Chief of the Medical Staff in the Crimea, to his boss in London. The letter was written in October 1854, which was before Florence Nightingale arrived in the Crimea.

Source B

(i) 25 November 1854

'When we came here, there was no soap or basins or towels in the wards. The consequences of all this are fever, cholera, gangrene, lice … Two or three hundred arm-slings, stump-pillows and other medical appliances are being weekly manufactured and given out by us. No arrangement seems to have been made to do this before.'

(ii) 10 December 1854

'What we have achieved:

- A great deal more cleaning of wards – mops, scrubbing brushes given out by ourselves
- The supervision and stirring up of the whole organisation generally
- Repair of the wards for 800 wounded.'

Extracts from two letters from Florence Nightingale in Scutari to Sidney Herbert, Secretary of State at War.

Source C

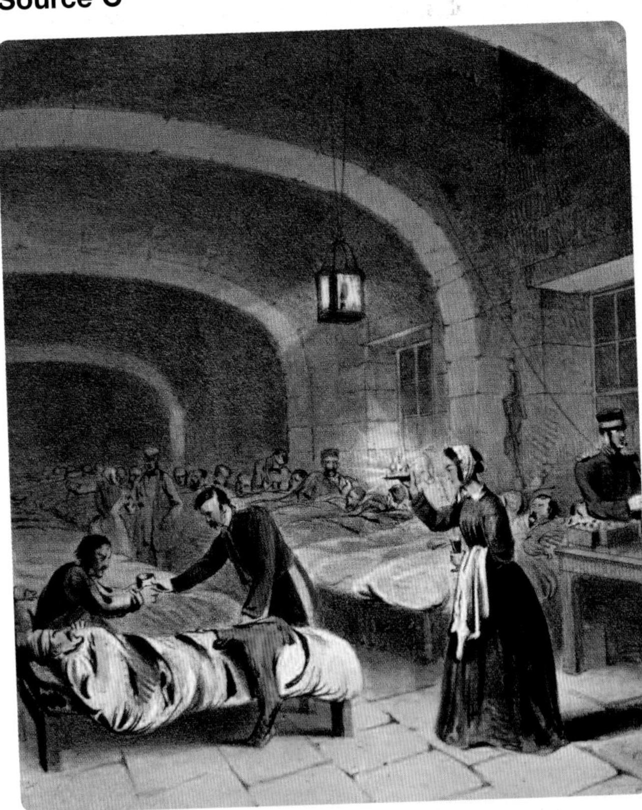

A painting from 1855 which shows Florence Nightingale in Scutari Hospital. Newspapers began to call her 'the lady with the lamp' because it was claimed that she walked the wards at night making sure wounded soldiers were comfortable.

Source D

'On Wednesday Mr Bracebridge gave a lecture in Coventry describing his experiences of British hospitals in the Crimea. He described the difficulties Miss Nightingale and her party faced when they arrived in the Crimea. When they arrived in Scutari, there was no kitchen, coal or candles. They soon set to work, however, to make the place comfortable. In two days they had made a great change to the look of the inside of the building. At first they were despised by the doctors for their lack of medical knowledge. But two or three days later, after 600 wounded were brought down, they dressed the wounds of 300 of them. The doctors began to think they might be of some use. Without *The Times* fund, so many things which were needed urgently would never have been obtained. (Cheers from the audience)'

An extract from The Times newspaper, 16 October 1855. Mr Bracebridge was Florence Nightingale's friend and went to the Crimea to work with her. He returned to England in 1855.

Source E

'Such nonsense was uttered by Mr. Bracebridge and reported with approval in *The Times*. He talked about Miss Nightingale putting hospitals containing three or four thousand patients in order in a couple of days helped by *The Times* Fund. I despise the man for such exaggerations and I pity the ignorant multitude who are taken in by these fairy tales.'

From a letter written November 1855 by Dr John Hall to the Director of the Army Medical Service. Dr Hall was Chief of the Medical Staff in the Crimea.

Source F

'I was generally up and busy by daybreak, sometimes earlier. By 7 o'clock the morning coffee would be ready. From that time until 9 o'clock, officers on duty in the neighbourhood, or passing by, would look in for breakfast. About half past nine my sick patients began to show themselves. In the following hour they came thickly, and sometimes it was past 12 noon before I had got through the duty. That over, there was the hospital to visit across the way.'

An extract from Mary Seacole's own life story, The Wonderful Adventures of Mrs Seacole in Many Lands, 1857. In this extract Seacole describes a typical day for her during the Crimean war.

Source G

'In the hour of their illness, these men have found a kind and successful physician, a Mrs Seacole. She is from Kingston (Jamaica) and she doctors and cures all manner of men with extra-ordinary success. She is always in attendance near the battlefield to aid the wounded, and has earned many a poor fellow's blessing.'

This article was published in The Times newspaper in September 1855. It is written by William Howard Russell who sent regular reports to the newspaper from the Crimea.

Source H

'Here I met a celebrated person. A coloured woman, Mrs Seacole. Out of the goodness of her heart and at her own expense she supplied hot tea to the poor sufferers while they waited to be lifted into the boats (that took them to the hospital). She did not spare herself if she could do any good to the suffering soldiers. In rain and snow, day after day, she was at her post. With her stove and kettle, in any shelter she could find, she brewed tea for all who wanted it – and there were many.'

An extract from a letter written by Dr Reid to his family in 1855. Dr Reid was a surgeon serving in the British army during the war.

Source I

'It is now emerging that the "Lady with the Lamp" was not really the best-loved nurse of the Crimean War. That honour belongs to Mary Seacole. It was she whom soldiers considered the true "Mother of the Army". While Miss Nightingale worked at the official hospital far from the fighting, Mrs Seacole set up her own supply store and medical unit just five miles from the fighting. While Miss Nightingale dismayed wounded officers by walking past their beds without even a word, Mrs Seacole went into the war zone armed with bandages and medicines, to look after the wounded.'

From an article in The Times, 4 September 2000.

What really changed hospitals and nursing?

Activities

1 These cards can be organised into a pattern to explain why hospitals and nursing changed a great deal in the sixty years after the Crimean War. Your task is to create that pattern, using the text opposite, the information on page 187 and the following hints as a guide:
   a Begin by thinking about which cards might start and finish the sequence.
   b Look for links to those start and finish cards.
   c Build up links – draw in lines on your own copy and annotate the lines, explaining why you have made the links.
2 Which of the developments on the cards do you think were most important in changing **a** hospitals and **b** nursing?

Florence Nightingale's work in the Crimea

The discovery that bacteria cause diseases

Increased public awareness of the need for clean hospitals and qualified nurses

Money raised for Nightingale fund

Developments in surgery such as anaesthetics and antiseptics

Mary Seacole's work in the Crimea

Improvements in engineering and public health

Better hospitals and better-qualified nurses.

A wider range of operations and treatments carried out so the demand for good nurses increased.

Florence Nightingale's books influenced training and the design of hospitals.

Florence Nightingale set up training schools for nurses. These nurses showed their value, increasing respect for nurses and leading to more women becoming nurses.

Source 1

	1861	1921
Number of patients	About 65,000	228,500
Hospital beds per thousand people	3.2	6.1

▲ The number of patients and hospital beds 1861 and 1921

Source 2

Problems in 1860	Solutions in 1920
Unhygienic surgery dressings	Aseptic surgery and and dressings
Untrained nurses	Trained nurses
Cramped, stuffy wards	Spacious, light, well-ventilated wards
Poor sanitation and sewerage	Good sanitation, toilets
Lack of cleanliness	Cleanliness

▲ A summary of changes in hospitals between 1860 and 1920

The impact of Mary Seacole

Both Florence Nightingale and Mary Seacole played important roles in the Crimea but those roles and their impact after the war were very different. Mary Seacole's skills were ignored and her fame was brief, apart from among the many soldiers she had helped, who always remembered her with affection. It is only recently that her work has received the acclaim it deserves.

The impact of Florence Nightingale

Florence Nightingale's work had far greater impact in the long run. She was not a hands-on nurse but a great organiser, convinced that her life's work was to improve conditions in hospitals and training of nurses for the good of the patients. Those skills and beliefs were visible in the Crimea where she concentrated on improving hygiene and cleanliness. She continued to focus on these aspects of care throughout her life.

One surprising thing about her was that she paid little attention to Pasteur's germ theory when it appeared in the decade after the Crimean War. Like Chadwick, she had been brought up in the early 1800s when miasma (bad air) was the main theory about what caused disease. She continued to associate disease with dirt and this is why she concentrated on improving:

- sanitation in hospitals – clean water supplies, good drains and sewers, toilet facilities, total cleanliness
- ventilation in hospitals to make sure patients got fresh, clean air to breathe
- food supplies, clothing and washing facilities for patients.

As a result her nursing schools concentrated on training nurses in very practical skills. She did not let doctors teach nurses about germ theory because she felt that such ideas would simply get in the way of nurses' more important task – keeping patients and wards clean.

The impact of other factors

Although Florence Nightingale's nurses were not taught about some of the major medical breakthroughs these did affect their careers and the development of hospitals.

The improvements in hospital buildings and sanitation could not have come about without improved engineering techniques and the new ideas about public health you read about in Section 8. Changes in surgery increased the numbers of complex operations and so surgeons required better-trained nurses to assist them. And, despite Nightingale's relegation of germ theory, it had a very significant impact on all aspects of medicine, including surgery, and so in turn affected the ways that nurses carried out their work.

This final section helps you look back across your whole course and make sense of the overall pictures of the history of medicine and health. The activities will help you revise effectively. But first let's go back to the very first question we asked and returned to on page 122 – why do we live much healthier and longer lives than in the past?

10.1 What do we owe our lives to?

'History is not the story of strangers, aliens from another universe; it is the story of us had we been born a little earlier.'

This is a wonderful quotation. It reminds us that we aren't any different from people who lived many years ago – after all, they were our ancestors. Way back in time, in the 1800s, 1400s, the Roman Empire, there were people with our DNA, people who looked like us, had the same colour hair or eye-colour, the same way of walking, the same energy or laziness!

But what if you'd been born in their time?

You now know that there is one very important way in which we are different from our ancestors. On average we live much longer, healthier lives. Let's take the example of one real family – John and Margaret Pepys and their children from the 1600s. John was an ordinary working man, a tailor who worked in London. They had eleven children, born between 1627 and 1641, shown below at their time of death.

Why do we live so much longer nowadays?

Activities

On page 122 we used the cards shown below to introduce the question why we live much longer, healthier lives than people in earlier centuries such as the Pepys family. Now it's time to come up with an answer.

1. Create your own set of cards, then fill in the bullet points by listing the most important developments in each topic.
2. Draw the pattern of cards below onto a large sheet of paper, then mark in links between the topics, such as how the work of Pasteur and Lister was linked. Jot down a few words explaining each link you draw.
3. Do you agree with this pattern, suggesting that the development of germ theory, followed closely by public health, is the most important reason why we live longer, healthier lives nowadays?

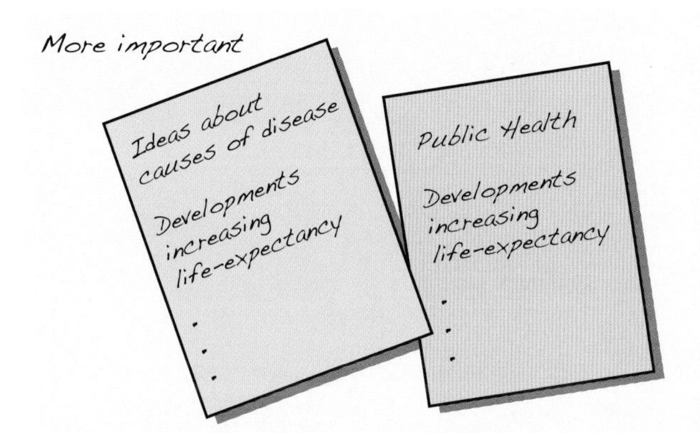

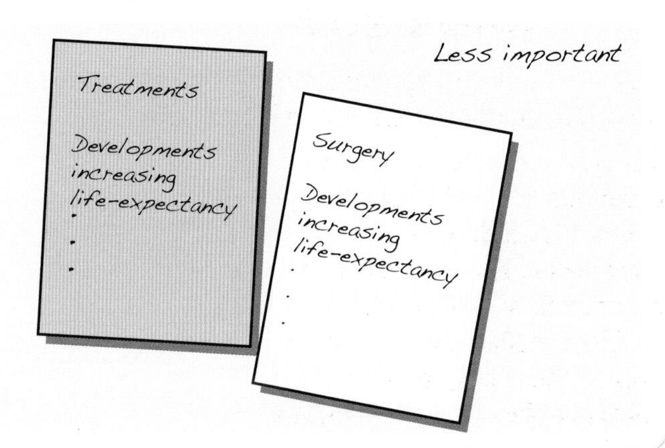

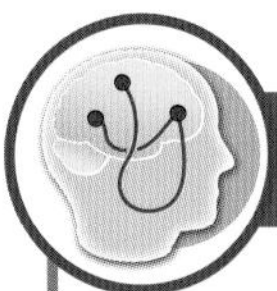

smarter revision reminder

In Section 1 we introduced you to a number of methods of building up the information you need to revise from. It was important to do this from the beginning so that you've done it steadily, in small chunks. Imagine if you were starting now from scratch on your revision notes! But you may have gaps or you may not have completed all the activities for the most recent periods of medical history – and you will need them to help with the activities on the next few pages! So make sure you are up to date with:

Living graphs summarising the development of major themes over time. See pages 6–7.

Memory maps recording the chief features of medicine in each period of history. See pages 14–15.

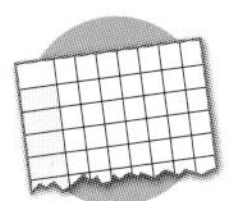

Factors charts recording the impact of factors that helped or hindered the development of medicine. See pages 44–45.

'Role of the individual' charts summarising the work of an individual and his or her impact. See pages 26–27.

10.2 The road to Bacteria-ville – using road maps to revise key themes

Creating a road map is an excellent way of summarising developments across a long period of time. We have created this example for you as a guide. Can you use your living graphs to help complete road maps for other important themes?

Activities

1. This road map summarises the story of changing ideas about the causes of disease across time. Work with a partner or in a small group. You will have one minute to tell the story of this theme aloud to the rest of the class. Use the map to help you plan and tell the story.
2. Create your own road map for at least one of these themes across time:
   - **a** surgery
   - **b** public health
   - **c** treatments.

   Think about how your map shows changes and continuities, pace of change, connections between topics, important people, reasons for change and continuity, ideas that got nowhere and any other parts of the story.

GODS AND SNEEZES SPREAD DISEASES
ONE PRAYER WILL STOP THE BLACK DEATH
RELIGION ROW
BACTERIA-VILLE
PEOPLE HERE SEEM TO LIVE A LOT LONGER
PASTEUR MANSION
KOCH HALL
SPONTANEOUS GENERATION VILLAS
I'M ALMOST THERE BUT I CAN'T GET IN YET
ROAD CLOSED UNTIL 1860
LANCET
I'VE TRIED ALL THE SIDE ROADS BUT I DON'T SEEM TO BE GETTING ANYWHERE
THIS COULD GET VERY TALL INDEED
BUT I BUILT IT UP AND MADE SURE ALL THESE PEOPLE CAME TO LIVE HERE
GALEN DRIVE
CHURCH SUPPORT ROAD
AD 1100
AD 200
DNA TOWERS
BLOOD STREET
PHLEGM STREET
AD 500
AD 1300
THOSE ANCIENT CHAPS WHO BUILT THIS ROAD GOT EVERYTHING RIGHT WHY WOULD YOU WANT TO LIVE ANYWHERE ELSE?

10.3 What was so special about each period of medical history?

Now it's time to think about each period of medical history. What made each period special and can you sum up each period by identifying its key features in just FIVE words or phrases? Dig out those memory maps and make sure you can remember the key developments in each period.

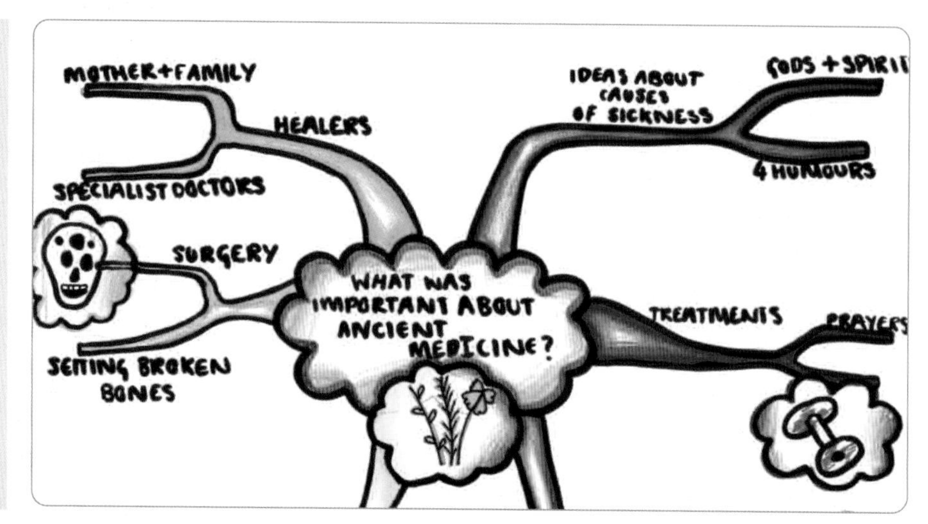

Activities

The period cards opposite sum up medical knowledge and methods in each period.

1. Create a new Word file or start a sheet of A4 paper for each of the five periods.
2. Put down the period name and the four headings below. Then note down the major features of medicine in the period under each heading, adding your own examples and details to support the outline on the cards.
   - Understanding of the cause of disease and the body
   - Public Health
   - Surgery
   - Treatments
3. At the foot of each page write down the names of key individuals from this period.
4. Across the top of the page write down up to five single words, names or short phrases that sum up medicine in the period. To choose your words, names or phrases think about:
   - **a** what makes this period different from others
   - **b** whether this was a time of continuity or change (if change, how rapid was it?)
   - **c** the overall significance of the period in the history of medicine.
5. Compare your five words, names or phrases with those chosen by the rest of the class. For each period pick out the best five words, names or phrases from the ideas put forward by the class.

1

Prehistoric and ancient medicine

Some important, long-lasting aspects of medicine began in the Prehistoric Period. These included the idea that gods and spirits caused diseases, simple surgery and the use of herbal remedies. While most people continued to pray to the gods to help them recover from illness, Egyptian and Greek specialist doctors believed that sickness had natural causes. Hippocrates developed the Theory of the Four Humours, which was further developed by Galen. Treatments included herbal remedies, prayer, bleeding and purging, and rest, exercise and diet. Most people had to look after their own health and hygiene but the Romans made a major effort to improve public health in military forts and towns by building aqueducts, sewers and public baths.

Medieval medicine

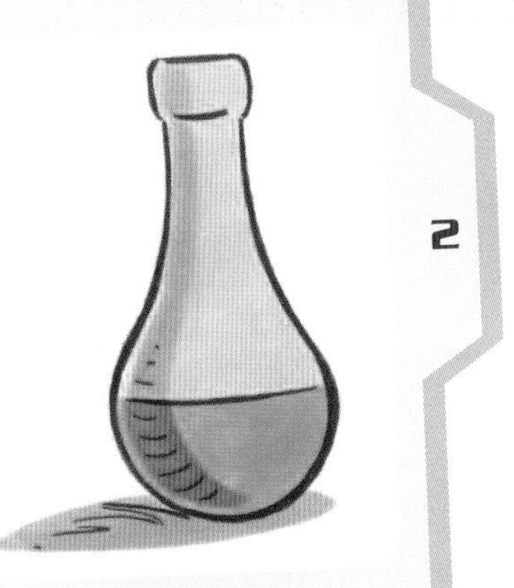

The destruction of the Roman Empire led to the collapse of Roman public health systems and the destruction of many books containing medical knowledge. However, everyday medicine for ordinary people continued unchanged, based on prayers and herbal remedies. In the 1200s universities were set up and physicians were trained, reading the works of Galen and Arab doctors such as Ibn Sina. Their methods were based on Greek and Roman ideas and so they believed that illness was caused when the humours were out of balance. Some attempts were made to clean up towns, especially after the Black Death in 1348. There were minor improvements in surgery as surgeons gained a lot of practice in war but, overall, new ideas were discouraged by the Christian Church.

2

Renaissance medicine

The Renaissance saw a battle between old and new ideas. There were some important new discoveries – Vesalius improved knowledge of anatomy, Harvey discovered that the blood circulates round the body and Paré improved surgical techniques. These discoveries (and the invention of the microscope) provided the basis for later developments but did not make people healthier. Many doctors were still hostile to new ideas and people still believed that God or bad air caused diseases. Governments still did not think it was their responsibility to improve public health. However, the idea of science being based on experiments and challenging old ideas was growing, providing the essential background for later breakthroughs.

3

Medicine in the 1800s

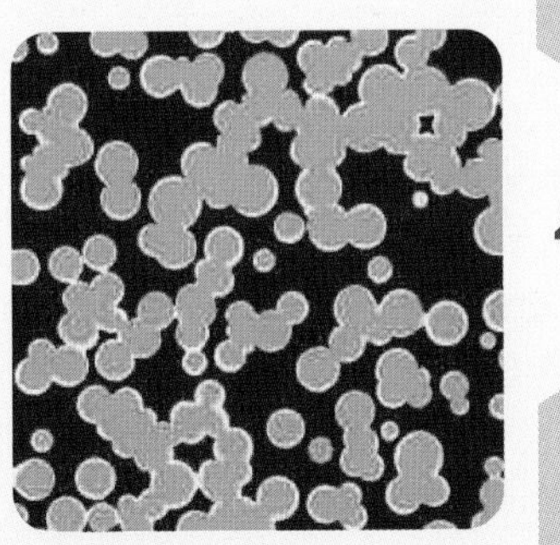

The major breakthroughs began. First came the use of vaccination against smallpox, which showed that opposition to new ideas was still strong but could be beaten. Epidemics of diseases such as cholera in the filthy, over-populated industrial towns forced governments to begin to improve public health. Then came Pasteur's germ theory, which at last explained the true cause of disease. From this came more vaccines to prevent diseases and major improvements in public health, which also benefited from improved engineering methods. Surgery was also revolutionised with the first effective anaesthetics and antiseptics. Hospitals became places to go to get well instead of places to go to die. By 1900 life expectancy was finally beginning to increase but there was still a huge gap between the health of rich and poor, and very high infant mortality.

4

Medicine since 1900

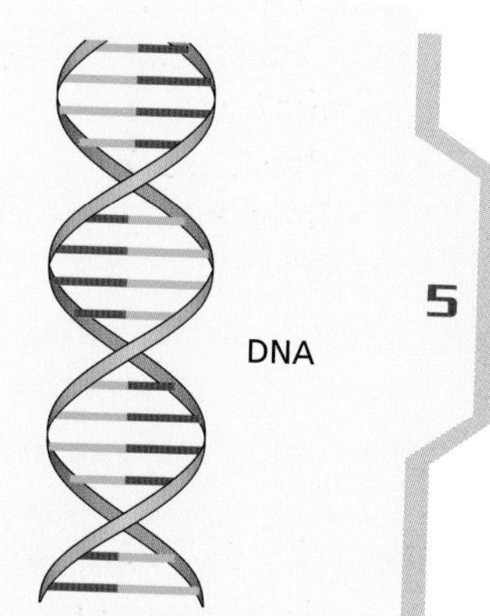

The 1900s continued the stories begun in the 1800s. Developments in science and technology continued to improve surgery and to help find the first chemical and antibiotic cures for illnesses and infections.

Wars also forced governments to invest more in these developments and to improve public health. They introduced better education, housing and public health provision, leading to the Beveridge Report in 1942 and the foundation of the National Health Service providing free medical care. In the 1950s scientists discovered the existence of DNA, the 'building bricks' of the human body, paving the way in the twenty-first century for the possibility of preventing inherited diseases – possibly an even bigger breakthrough than Pasteur's germ theory.

5

10.4 How did the factors affect the development of medicine?

You have done a lot of work on factors – the reasons why medicine developed – or didn't – in each period. Pages 198–201 give you the chance to weigh up the overall impact of these factors and revise for factors questions in your exam.

Factor chart

1 Factor	2 Evidence of factor helping development	3 Evidence of factor hindering development	4 Assessment – did this factor do more to help or hinder development?
War	*Battlefield surgery*		
Government		*It's not the Pharaoh's job to keep people healthy.*	
Religion			

Activities

... above. Use the examples below to complete your chart.

Evaluating the importance of factors over time

Medicine has often been helped or hindered by factors such as religion, war or chance. There are often questions in the exam about these factors. Sometimes you might be asked to evaluate whether a factor has done more to help or hinder the overall development of medicine. Look at the exam question below:

'Religion has hindered, rather than helped, medical progress.' Explain how far you agree with this statement. [8]

You should be expert by now at tackling questions that ask you to evaluate a statement. The key things to remember are to:

- Explore **both sides** of the argument – include two or three examples of religion helping and hindering medical progress.
- Use **specific examples** to support your answer.
- Do not list examples. **Explain how** the examples you have chosen hindered or helped medicine.
- Finally, in your conclusion, make sure you reach an **overall judgement**. How far do you agree with the statement? Overall, has religion hindered medical progress?

Evaluating the importance of factors over time

Helped
Egyptians took out body organs because they believed they needed to be preserved for the next life. This led to them learning a little more about the body
Egyptian religious belief stopped them from dissecting the body. This meant that they could not learn about the body in detail
Hindered

In many periods of history, people's religious beliefs have had a big influence on their ideas about medicine. Throughout history there are lots of examples of religion holding back medicine. However, religion has also led to important advances being made. Look at the 'Hinder or Help' Washing Line above. It shows how in Egyptian times some religious beliefs both helped and hindered medicine.

Activities

1. Add examples from periods to your 'washing line' of history. Use the table below to help you.
   Think carefully where you place each example on your washing line. If an example played a major role in holding back medical improvements place it a long way to the left. If it played a less important role in hindering medical progress, place to the left but closer to the middle.
2. Use your 'washing line' to help you answer exam question 3.
   Do not try to include everything. Select the examples that you feel most confident writing about.

	Helped or hindered rating	Explanation
Prehistoric gods p. 19		
Egyptian hygiene p. 24		
Asclepia pp. 32–33		
Roman gods p. 34		
Medieval ideas about causes and prevention of disease pp. 54–55		
Impact of Islam and Christianity pp. 60–61		
Medieval hospitals p. 64		
Monasteries p. 73		
Opposition to Renaissance discoveries pp. 88–91		
Opposition to vaccination p. 115		
Opposition to use of chloroform p. 172		

Sample questions

1. Briefly describe the impact of religion on medicine in the Middle Ages.
2. Explain ways in which governments have had an impact on the development of medicine since 1800.
3. 'Since Roman times, War has hindered, rather than helped, medical progress.' Explain how far you agree with this statement.

10.5 Which factors were most influential?

On the last page you learned how to analyse the impact of a single factor. Now you can debate which factors had the most impact on the history of medicine. This will not only help you revise but develop that very important skill – working as a team. It's amazing how a group of people working together can spark a whole host of good ideas that a person working by him or herself would have missed.

Activities

Your whole class is going to work as a team to reach a verdict on which factors were most important in helping and hindering the development of medicine.

Stage 1

Divide into pairs or small groups. Each group take one of the factors opposite and complete a washing line (like the one on page 199) for the factor. Use the details opposite and the factor charts you have compiled through the course to help your research. (Leave out religion – you have already researched that factor.)

Stage 2

Decide where the factor should go on the chart below. You need to weigh up the impact of the factor overall. Most of them will have examples at both ends of the washing line so you have to think about their overall impact.

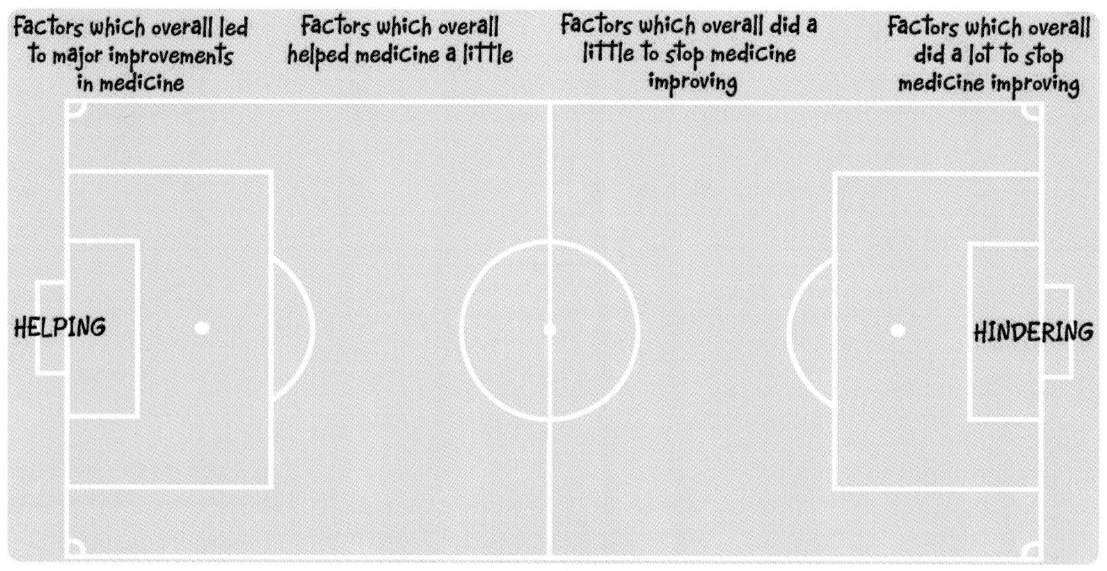

Stage 3

Repeat Stages 1 and 2 for one other factor.
Then compare your conclusion about the factor with the group who researched the factor in Stage 1. Between your groups reach a final decision on where the factor goes on the pitch.

Stage 4

a As a class decide where religion goes, based on pages 198–199.

b Report back to the whole class on where your factor goes on the pitch. Your teacher will build up this plan on the board.

c Now debate which of the factors in the Helping penalty area did most to help medicine develop. Each group that researched these factors in Stage 1 has a minute to argue in its favour and 30 seconds to argue against its opponents. Then take a class vote on the winner.

d Repeat the debate for the factors in the other penalty area.

Get busy! What about the Romans and their Empire, Paré, Pasteur and Koch's rivalry, and blood transfusions? And the Boer War and the Second World War, penicillin and plastic surgery, the NHS?
WAR
PORTABLE X-RAY MACHINE
The Romans and their army, kings and the Black Death, making vaccination compulsory, Public Health Acts, Liberal government reforms, funding research (or not!).
GOVERNMENT
BEVERIDGE REPORT
You researched my impact on page 198–199. Which part of the field do I go in?
RELIGION
Think about opposition to Harvey, Jenner, Simpson and Lister – and those good people who opposed Public Health reform. Long live vested interests!
ATTITUDES
CONSERVATISM
THE CHURCH SAYS OLD IDEAS RULE!
ENQUIRY
NEW IDEAS ARE BEST ASK WILLIAM HARVEY
What about the people who bravely tried new ideas – Vesalius, Snow, Pasteur and all those people you listed who fought against those selfish vested interests?
Pasteur said germs cause disease. So that means I can …
INDIVIDUAL GENIUS
GALEN VESALIUS JENNER PASTEUR KOCH CURIE NIGHTINGALE
COMMUNICATIONS
Who began keeping medical records? How did ideas spread in the Renaissance and in the nineteenth and twentieth centuries? But what happened after the Roman Empire?
Check up on Pasteur and chicken cholera and how Fleming discovered penicillin.
CHANCE
SURGERY BY PARE
WAY OF LIFE
These industrial towns are filthy.
Check up on prehistoric lifestyles, what the Egyptians learned from farming and all those horrible dirty towns.
SCIENCE TECHNOLOGY AND ART
Lots to research here – Greek philosophy, Roman engineering, Renaissance inventions, Pasteur's industrial research, stopping the Great Stink, chemicals, X-rays and all kinds of modern developments.
TEAMWORK
PENICILLIN
PENICILLIN
PENICILLIN
Pasteur's research … and Koch's team … and chemical cures like Salvarsan … and radium

10.6 Which individuals were most significant?

One of the key factors has been the work of individuals so let's complete these revision tasks by deciding on the greatest medical pioneer of them all. And make yourself a set of Top Trumps cards to help revision while you're awarding the gold, silver and bronze medals.

Activities

Below you can see the some of the candidates for the awards ceremony at the Medical Olympics. Your task is to decide which of these medical pioneers get the medals. This is how you do it.

1. Work in a small group to create a Top Trumps card for key individuals in the history of medicine. Use your 'Role of the Individual' charts to help you.

   a. Decide which people to have in your list. Use the group below to set you thinking but look for some famous names who are missing.

   b. Decide what score each person gets for each of the criteria opposite and reach a decision about their overall score.

   c. Make your cards.

▲ GCSE students present the candidates for the 'Most Significant Individuals' award.

Use your criteria carefully!

What do the criteria on the Top Trumps card mean?

Originality – the highest marks go to people who did or thought something that nobody had ever done or thought of before. Lower marks for building on someone else's idea even if it was a great success.

Impact – how many people were helped or hindered by this individual's work? High marks for a world-wide impact, lower marks for a local impact.

ORIGINALITY %
CHANGE %
IMPACT %
LONGEVITY %
CORRECTNESS %
SIGNIFICANCE 1 2 3 4 5
MEDICINE TOP TRUMPS

Correctness – the highest marks go to ideas that were not only correct but people understood why they were correct. Good marks for correct ideas or methods when the individual knew it worked but didn't know how. And low marks for ideas that turned out to be wrong even if they lasted a long time!

Overall significance – use half marks if you wish – it might help separate all these star performers?

Longevity – how long did someone's impact last? The idea might be wrong but a wrong idea that lasted a long time was still very influential. What about a modern discovery that's not been around long? Do you think it will last? If so, then give it a high mark.

Activities

2 **a** Add up the class totals for each individual and see who is the winner.

b Write short acceptance speeches for the top three, explaining why they won their medals.

10.7 Into the future?

It's the last page! This isn't revision. It may even be out of date by the time you use this book! It's here to get you thinking (yes, again!) but not about the history of medicine or even the future of medicine. It's about how history helps us understand the things happening around us.

What do we learn from history?

There are all sorts of answers to this question.

Some people think history is just a lot of facts to remember – dates and 'who did what?' and 'when?'

Other people think we study history to avoid repeating the mistakes that were made in the past – but that doesn't work. No problem or event is ever exactly the same as a previous problem or event. Things change in the meantime.

My answer is that knowing and understanding history helps us understand why things are happening today and places them 'in perspective'. What does that last bit mean?

- It means that we understand whether something is really important or different or whether it's only slightly different from what's gone before – in other words what's really worth getting excited about!
- It means that we can compare our lives with our grandfathers' lives and their grandfathers' lives and so on – and realise that, compared with people in the past, we're very lucky in many ways.
- It means that we have a sense of how quickly things are changing nowadays and therefore why it's difficult to get everything right straightaway. People couldn't do that when the world was less hectic.
- It means we understand how those changes are linked to changes in the past, for example how so much of medicine today stems from the work of Pasteur 150 years ago. We can be grateful to all those people who lived before us who created our world.

So – just to get you thinking – here are some of the issues that are around today, 14 January 2009, when I wrote this page.

- How does history help you understand them?
- Which issues about medicine and health are in the news when you complete your course and how does History help you put them in perspective?

Issue 1 Medical advances – anaesthetics

Recently a friend of mine had a big operation. Here's her account of what happened – because she stayed awake throughout!

'The two-hour operation to replace the ball & socket of my left hip took place without a general anaesthetic. I had had a local anaesthetic in my lower back so I could feel nothing. I lay on my right side with a strap to stop me rolling over. Throughout the operation I was able to watch my heart rate on a machine near my head. There was a sheet between me and the surgeon but throughout the operation the surgeon told me what he was about to do next. For example, "Now I will saw through your femur" and I heard the electric saw cutting through me. I saw the nurses carry in my new ball and socket, and I felt my body being stretched when the consultant asked people to help with the traction. One advantage of not having a full anaesthetic was that I did not have the danger of an adverse reaction to the anaesthetic and I was able to recover much more quickly because the effects of anaesthetic can remain in one's system for weeks and even months.'

Perspective

1. How might Simpson have reacted to this development?
2. Think back to the development of anaesthetics. How quickly has this development come about? What does it tell us about the pace of change in medicine?

Issue 2 Medical advances – inherited illnesses

Last weekend there was an article in our newspaper explaining that scientists working on human DNA had discovered how to identify whether a person's genes carry the risk of suffering from breast cancer. This means that in the future it may be possible to screen people for this gene and reduce the chances of people getting breast cancer. However, it could also mean choosing which embryos develop into babies and which do not. The same kind of research is being applied to many other genetically inherited illnesses for which there is no cure but which may in the future be avoidable.

Perspective

3 What does this tell us about the pace of change in medicine?
4 Think back to what you have learned about attitudes to medical changes. What different kinds of reactions do you expect to such research?

Issue 3 Differing life expectancies

This book has been almost entirely concerned with medicine in Britain and Europe. One of its key questions has been 'why do we live so much longer nowadays?' But not everyone does live longer than in the past. Look at these statistics from 2007.

Country	Male life expectancy	Female life expectancy	Infant mortality – deaths per 1,000 births
United Kingdom	76.1	81.1	5.1
USA	75.0	80.8	6.4
China	70.9	74.5	23.1
Israel	77.3	81.7	6.9
Kenya	49.8	48.1	59.3
Liberia	38.0	41.4	155.8
Nigeria	46.5	47.7	97.1
Rwanda	46.3	48.4	89.6

Perspective

5 How does your knowledge of the history of medicine help you understand the differences in life expectancy between:
a countries
b sexes
c ages?
6 What is probably needed to improve life expectancy in third world countries?

Issue 4 The value of vaccinations

When I was growing up in the 1950s measles was common. It was a serious illness. Occasionally children died from measles. It also caused other problems. My mother had measles when she was three, back in 1928, and lost the hearing in one ear as a result. Seventy years later she lost the hearing in her other ear (for a different reason) and so spent her last ten years completely deaf. That outbreak of measles at age three caused her a lot of misery. Another disease in the 1950s was polio. I remember vividly hearing on the news that Jeff Hall, a Birmingham City footballer, had died of polio. Can you imagine what kind of story that would be today if a Premier League footballer died of a disease like polio?

Vaccines put an end to both polio and measles, but recently there has been a rapid increase in the number of measles cases in Britain. Some people have stopped using the vaccine for fear – now disproved by research – that the vaccine led to other medical problems.

Perspective

7 Is it unusual for helpful medical ideas to meet opposition? Why does it happen?
8 How might knowledge of the development of vaccination against smallpox in the 1800s affect attitudes to vaccinations today?
9 Would knowledge of the history of medicine, particularly the impact of epidemic diseases, help to persuade people to use vaccines?

Medical terms

ailment an illness that is not serious
amputation the removal of a limb by surgery
amulet a charm that the wearer believes gives protection from disease
anaesthetic a drug or drugs given to produce unconsciousness before and during surgery
anatomy the science of understanding the structure and make-up of the body
antibiotics a group of drugs used to treat infections caused by bacteria, e.g. penicillin
antisepsis the prevention of infection by stopping the growth of bacteria through the use of antiseptics
antiseptics chemicals used to destroy bacteria and prevent infection
apothecary a pharmacist or chemist
arteries blood vessels that carry blood away from the heart
arthritis the painful swelling of joints
Asclepion temple of the Greek god of healing Asclepius (or Asklepios)
astrology the study of the planets and how they might influence the lives of people

bacterium (pl. bacteria) see germ
bezoar stone a ball of indigestible material found in goats' stomachs
biochemist a scientist who studies the make-up of living things
Black Death a phrase used in the Middle Ages to describe bubonic plague. (The 'blackness' was caused by bleeding under the skin. Over 50 per cent of all cases were fatal.)
bleed/bleeding the treatment of opening a vein or applying leeches to draw blood from the patient. Also means the loss of blood caused by damage to the blood vessels
buboes black swellings in armpits and groin that were symptoms of the Black Death

cauterise using a hot iron to burn body tissue. This seals a wound and stops bleeding
cell the basic unit of life which makes up the bodies of plants, animals and humans. Billions of cells are contained in the human body
cesspool/cesspit a place for collecting and storing sewage
charlatans people pretending to have a skill or knowledge that they don't really have
chilblains painful swellings on feet and hands caused by exposure to cold and wet
chirurgery/chirurgeons surgery/surgeons
chloroform a liquid whose vapour acts as an anaesthetic and produces unconsciousness
chromosomes thread-like structures in the cells of the body that contain genetic information
consumption/consumptive fever tuberculosis which was observed as the wasting away of the body
contagion the passing of disease from one person to another
contaminated/contamination something that is infected
court an enclosed area of housing, often with little daylight and heavily over-populated
culture/culturing the growth of micro-organisms in the laboratory

diarrhoea a symptom of a disease; frequent, fluid bowel movements
dissection the cutting up and examination of a body
DNA Deoxyribonucleic acid, the molecule that genes are made of. See gene
dysentery a severe infection causing frequent, fluid bowel movements

effluvia/effluvial unpleasant smells from waste matter. Blamed for disease in the eighteenth and nineteenth centuries
embalm the treatment of a dead body to preserve it
endoscope an instrument used to view inside the body

faeces waste material from the stomach and digestive system

gangrene (gas gangrene) the infection of dead tissue causing, in the case of gas gangrene, foul smelling gas
gene part of a cell that determines how our bodies look and work. Genes are passed from parents to children
genetic engineering the investigation of genes and how they can be used to change how the body works
germ a micro-organism that causes disease
germ theory the theory that germs cause disease, often by infection through the air

Health Authority the people controlling NHS health care in the regions
herbal remedy a medicine made up from a mixture of plants, often containing beneficial ingredients
high-tech surgery surgery using the most modern techniques, including computers, new skills and new drugs
Hippocratic Oath the principles by which doctors work, for the best health of the patient and to do no harm, named after Hippocrates who wrote it
Humours the Ancient Greeks believed the body contained four humours or liquids – blood, phlegm, black bile and yellow bile

immune protected against a disease
immunise the process of giving protection from disease through the body's own immune system
immunity protection against disease through the body's own defences or immune system
incision a cut made with a knife during surgery
infection the formation of disease causing germs or micro-organisms
infirmary a place where the sick are treated, a hospital
inoculation putting a low dose of a disease into the body to help it fight against a more serious attack of the disease

King's Evil see scrofula

laissez-faire belief that governments should not interfere in people's lives. It prevented public health schemes getting underway in the nineteenth century
leeches blood-sucking worms used to drain blood from a wound
leper someone suffering from leprosy, an infection that causes damage to the nerves and skin
ligament tough elastic tissue that holds joints of the body together
ligatures a thread used to tie a blood vessel during an operation
lunatic an old-fashioned word for someone who is insane

malady see ailment
maternity concerning motherhood and looking after children
medical officer a person appointed to look after the public health of an area
melancholy part of the theory of four humours, brought on by excess of gloominess
miasma smells from decomposing material that were believed to cause disease
microbe another name for a micro-organism
micro-organism a tiny single-celled living organism too small to be seen by the naked eye. Disease-causing micro-organisms are called bacteria

osteoarthritis see arthritis

papyrus early 'paper' made from the papyrus plant
penicillin the first antibiotic drug produced from the mould penicillium to treat infections
physic a medicine or the skill of healing
physician a doctor of medicine who trained at university
physiology the study of how the body works
plague a serious infectious disease spread to humans by fleas from rats and mice
pneumonia the inflammation of the lungs due to an infection
Poor Law Commission three commissioners who controlled the work of parishes which provided help for the poor. They were influential in public health reforms
poultice a warm dressing made of layers of fabric and moist paste
prognosis medical judgement about the probable course and result of a disease
public health refers to the well being of the whole community
pus a pale yellow or green fluid found where there is an infection in the body
putrid decomposing

quack a person who falsely claims to have medical ability or qualifications
quinine the drug treatment for malaria

remedy a drug or treatment that cures or controls the symptoms of a disease
rheumatism a term describing stiffness in muscles or joints
rickets a disease caused by a poor diet resulting in a misshapen skeleton

sanatorium a place where people who are chronically (very) ill can be cared for
scrofula sometimes known as the King's Evil. It is tuberculosis of a gland in the neck. At one time it was believed that being touched by the king could cure the disease
septicaemia blood poisoning caused by the spread of bacteria from an infected area
sinew a tendon or fibrous cord that joins a muscle to a bone
spontaneous generation the theory that decaying matter turns into germs
staphylococci bacteria found on the skin that can cause infection if the bacteria become trapped
sterilise to destroy all living micro-organisms from surfaces and surgical instruments, e.g. on a scalpel before an operation
stye a small pus-filled abscess near the eyelashes caused by infection
sulphonamide an antibacterial drug used to treat bronchitis and pneumonia
supernatural something that cannot be given an ordinary explanation
superstition an unreasonable belief based on ignorance and sometimes fear
suppuration the formation and/or discharge of pus
suture the closing of a cut or wound by the use of stitches (sutures)
syphilis a sexually-transmitted disease that was common from the late fifteenth century until the introduction of penicillin

thalidomide a drug to help morning sickness that was withdrawn in 1961 after it was found to cause limb deformities in babies born to women who had taken it
therapy the treatment of either a physical or mental disease
transfusion the use of blood given by one person to another when a patient has suffered severe blood loss
trephining the drilling of a hole in the skull (also called trepanning)
tumour a swelling caused by cells reproducing at an increased rate. An abnormal growth of cells which may or may not be cancerous

ulcer an open sore on the skin
unpasteurised food or drink that has not been pasteurised. Pasteurisation is a process of heating which destroys harmful bacteria
uroscopy diagnosing illness by examining the patient's urine

vaccination the injection into the body of killed or weakened organisms to give the body resistance against disease
virus a tiny micro-organism, smaller than bacteria, responsible for infections such as colds, flu, polio and chicken pox

wise woman a person believed to be skilled in magic or local customs
witch/witchcraft a person who practises magic and is believed to have dealings with evil spirits
worms an infestation where worms live as parasites in the human body

Index